The Metal-benders

John Hasted

The Metal-benders

Routledge & Kegan Paul
London, Boston and Henley

First published in 1981
by Routledge & Kegan Paul Ltd
39 Store Street,
London WC1E 7DD,
9 Park Street,
Boston, Mass. 02108, USA and
Broadway House,
Newtown Road,
Henley-on-Thames,
Oxon RG9 1EN
Set in 10/12 pt Press Roman by
Hope Services, Abingdon, Oxon
and printed in Great Britain by
Lowe & Brydone Printers Ltd
Thetford, Norfolk

British Library Cataloguing in Publication Data

Hasted, John Barrett
The metal-benders.
1. Psychical research
I. Title
133   BF1031   80-41469

ISBN 0 7100 0597 0

Contents

Illustrations

Figures

Introductory verses

'A book about those twisted forks!
What could be more absurd?
No matter how the Professor talks,
'Twas trickery, on my word!

'Twas but a quiz; a clever hoax,
Played by some lad, or lass;
Or both, perhaps; and wiser folks
Will let the matter pass.'

Thus, peradventure, some may prate.
Reader, with courteous grace,
Ere thou shall give thy judgment, wait
Till thou hast read the case.

Facts, simple facts alone we state.
We've studied them in vain,
And having stated them, we wait
Till you their cause explain.

'A book about those Bealings Bells', wrote the Suffolk poet Bernard
Barton in 1841, when his friend Major Edward Moor, FRS begged of
him a prelude to the book[1] he had written about the haunting of the
great house at Bealings; something 'preternatural' had been ringing the
domestic bells. We can now conjecture that the bursts of ringing could
have been bursts of metal-bending action on the bell springs; indeed,
the author (who is Major Moor's great-great-great-nephew) obtained

near a metal-bender similar spring movements, made visible by means of a galvanometer mirror and laser beam. Realizing later that poor Major Moor may have entertained a metal-bender unawares, he mutilated the two sets of verses for your edification.

Apologia

Psychic research is an underrated branch of science; it is likely to lead to a depth of understanding of reality greater than that which we already have; and the social consequences of such an understanding could be very great. Yet the number of serious scientists willing to devote time to it is at present small. And this has usually been the case throughout modern history; but there have nevertheless been times when the most far-sighted and competent scientists have seen fit to devote serious effort to it – one is reminded of Boyle, Faraday, Wallace, Weber, Crookes, Rayleigh, Langevin and others. There have been certain periods when interest has been aroused, usually as a result of publicity given to a psychic subject of remarkable power. In a matter of years the interest subsided, only to revive when another set of social circumstances arose. Yet although many observations have been made and some valuable knowledge obtained about the patterns of psychic behaviour, there is next to nothing which could be described as physical theory by which the phenomena might be interpreted. The lack of such a theory has led to the observations themselves being discredited, and indeed there are various social and psychological pressures which reinforce this discredit. It is an interesting example of the thesis that scientific observations are often judged by social criteria.

The subtlety and elusiveness of the psychic phenomena are very great, as great as any in the history of science. Unfortunately, the polarization of opinions not only among the population at large, but among scientists themselves, is also great. It would be presumptuous to claim that these chapters will set all this to rights. But they may spread some seed of influence, from which theoretical advance could come; before many years our outlook on these phenomena will probably have changed beyond recognition.

It is from the standpoint of an experimental physicist that this book is written. Always to some extent dissatisfied with existing physical theory, I became interested in psychic research when the young Uri Geller visited England to demonstrate paranormal metal-bending on television. Once I became committed by my own observations to recognizing that these peculiar physical phenomena really took place, I started to spend time on observations, in the belief that the phenomena demanded a new approach in physics in order to explain them. The study has therefore a rather different aim from the usual parapsychological studies descended from the pioneer work of Rhine. I am more concerned here with physical than with mental phenomena. Very probably the two types of study are different sides of the same coin; but it is more befitting that the physicist should concentrate on investigations in which he has most experience and expertise.

Physical scientists are on the whole ignorant of the concepts used by psychologists, and the neurological bases for these concepts are very far from being understood. I shall find it necessary to distinguish between mind and brain, without claiming that the mind is necessarily non-material. In interpreting psychic and parapsychological phenomena, I shall claim that mind is unlike the rest of matter in having characteristics which are apparently trans-spatial and trans-temporal. The importance of these phenomena lies partly in their evidence for what has been called a dualistic mind-matter interaction.

Validation of psychic phenomena − that is, the observational proof of their reality by many instrumentalists in agreement − is an important part of psychic research. Orthodox techniques of physics provide the basis for this validation.

The backbone of the study is the detailed instrumental observation of 'the metal-bending phenomenon'. But having described this, I feel entitled to speculate about its interpretation. And immediately I am confronted by the most serious implications for physical theory. What is needed is a minimum hypothesis required for the interpretation of physical psychic phenomena. I rashly attempt to explore one such hypothesis, and comment on other possibilities. This is my apologia for writing what might be claimed to be a book containing not only reports of observation, but speculation.

There remains the possibility that my own observations have been grossly in error, or alternatively that I have personally indulged in scientific fraud, of the kind occasionally described in the novels of C.P. Snow.[2] The second alternative has been to a large extent ruled out by my policy of involving other scientists directly in my experiments; but the first alternative must be considered more seriously. To what extent have I been deceived in my observations? The instrumentation of metal-bending phenomena is technically straightforward. The difficulty lies in 'social components involved in the assessment of scientific findings, a process normally thought of as being in some way immune from social forces'.[3]

The reader must make his own assessment of my competence as an observer and experimenter. Alas, a lifetime's experience of these things has left me only too conscious of my own shortcomings. But I would take issue with those who assert that experimental scientists are especially gullible and unqualified to investigate psychic phenomena. Nearly all of those who first investigated Uri Geller have been subject to smear attack by people unwilling to consider the possibility of the existence of anything which is not entirely materialistic or behaviouristic. Such attacks are more familiar in party politics than in scientific investigation, and it may be that their comparative rarity in science is connected with the fact that politics is much as it was two thousand years ago, whereas science has been able to make advances.

These chapters are not the place to refute such attacks as have been made on me, but I have answered[4] in detail elsewhere one particularly inaccurate account of my activities.

Although Uri Geller has not been caught red-handed in faking a paranormal physical phenomenon, yet adverse circumstantial evidence about his public performances has been given wide publicity. This exercise has created an atmosphere in which not only Geller but also the researchers into metal-bending have come to be regarded as suspect by the scientific community. Colleagues have been polite, but blasts of icy wind have often reached me.

It has sometimes been difficult for me to maintain an objective attitude in such an atmosphere. The reactive response of becoming partisan has had to be avoided. But it is also difficult to avoid feeling aggrieved that much uninformed as well as informed criticism has appeared. If my caution has in any way been strengthened by affairs in the public arena, then it is all to the good. But it will be clear to experimental parapsychologists reading this manuscript that my attitude is not 'hard line'. My approach yields apparent results quickly, but for this reason the greater caution is necessary. The consequences of the teleportation phenomenon for physics are so serious and fundamental that it is necessary to be very careful before accepting the evidence for its existence. The worst thing that could happen would be the polarization of the scientific community into professional sceptics and professional believers.

Yet this polarization has to some extent appeared, and has been promoted and encouraged by popular writings. It is stated by the science writer Martin Gardner that 'the researchers, almost without exception, are emotionally committed to finding phenomena'. But we might with equal justice claim that many science journalists are emotionally committed to finding that there are no phenomena. I have become just as sceptical of such reporting as I am bound to be of reports of paranormal physical phenomena.

After five years' work I am still largely committed to the policy outlined in chapter 1: 'Believe nothing that you hear and only half of what you see.' But if this policy is universally accepted, then who is going to believe me? And if someone is sufficiently trusting to spend time doing similar work, then who is going to believe him? There is thus a 'regression of disbelief', similar to the 'regression of observation' in the quantum theory of measurement. The regression of disbelief is surmountable only by a more intensive concentration of orthodox scientific effort on these alleged phenomena. But it is also true that scientists are emotionally committed: to a belief in their own scientific method.

A criticism I have often heard is that 'we all wanted the events to happen.' This is in some degree true, *and it may be that this is why they did happen*. There is an unmeasured parameter in the experiments, namely the attitude of the observers. But I did not always know exactly what it was that I wanted to take place; and sometimes what did take place was different from what I expected.

It is of course not possible for an investigator of psychic physical phenomena to choose exactly the field in which he makes his observations; to a great extent he must accept what turns up, and subject this to rigorous test.

But it must be admitted that when it comes to a choice of paranormal physical effects to investigate, the metal crystal lattice has several advantages. It is both stable against thermal and other normal external changes, and its own physical behaviour is well understood. It does not require isolation in a container, as does a liquid or gas, and its high electrical conductivity damps out potential gradient and electrostatic charge. By contrast, biomolecular systems and living organisms are less well understood structurally and are rather more difficult to maintain in a completely stable state. Gases, liquids and especially plasma are subject to various instabilities. For example, 'Kirlian photography' of high frequency discharges around the body can show interesting effects, but such discharges are complex and difficult to understand quantitatively even in the absence of possible psychic influences.

Effects due to impurities, and in particular surface effects, are equally troublesome in all materials; they represent the principal source of awkwardness in physical science, and should be avoided as far as possible. It is well-known among scientists that 'God made matter, but the Devil made surfaces.' At least the surface area can be minimized for a metal crystal, and much is already known about the effects due to impurities in metals and semiconductors.

So although paranormal physical phenomena (sometimes known as 'occult phenomena') represent possibly the greatest challenge to physics at the present time, at least metal-bending can be said to be the easiest part of that challenge.

In collecting the observations I have called on the help of many people, and it has been generously granted. I gratefully acknowledge finances for the research which have come from Mr Instone Bloomfield, through the London Society for Psychical Research, and more recently from Mr Donald Webster, through the New Horizons Research Foundation of Toronto. My colleagues in research have included above all David Robertson; and I have had the expert assistance of Nick Nicola, Sadeq Kadifachi, Ken Jacobs, Brian Warford, Tony Walker and two Bill Marshes. Charles Lane has performed the glassblowing. Much encouragement and advice have come from David Bohm, Arthur Ellison, Arthur Koestler, Brian Inglis and George Owen. The excellence of the photographs has been due to David Rookes, and of the drawings to Roy Abrahams. Computer programming and numerical analysis are largely by Lech Jankowski. In the preparation of the text the burden of typing has fallen on my wife, Lynn.

But it is to the metal-benders themselves and their families that the greatest debt of gratitude is owing. There could have been no study of the phenomena if they had not spent long patient hours with me, waiting for things to happen. I will not single out any for special mention at this point since there are so many who have contributed; but it will be clear from the text how generous with their time and effort many of them have been.

Thank you, metal-benders.

Chapter **1**

An introduction to metal-bending: involvement of the author

In retrospect, it seems curious that it all started in the mid-seventies of the twentieth century.

- Has it been going on unnoticed for centuries, or is it something quite new, brought on by our advancing technology and social system?
- Does it really happen at all? Are the claimants merely frauds?
- How rare is it, and who is really responsible? Can it be pinned down to the responsibility of one person, or is it just a fact of nature, a sort of local disease?
- Can it be developed or taught?
- How long does it last, and how frequently do the attacks come on?
- Is it a symptom of something else?
- Do other phenomena accompany it?
- Can any use be made of it? Is it likely to have much effect on human society?

We cannot answer all these questions in concise sentences; but at least we can describe the researches which will find answers for the most agonizing question of them all:

- How is metal-bending possible within the framework of the physical science that we have come to accept?

The essential phenomenon is this: a very few people appear to be able to deform and fracture pieces of metal, and occasionally other materials, just by stroking them between their thumb and fingers, or even without actually touching them.

At first the household cutlery becomes deformed, no one knows how; perhaps a spoon or fork is seen to bend on its own. Usually the phenomena are first noticed after a television appearance by Uri Geller, the best known, first and 'strongest' of all metal-benders. When the household first becomes aware of the bendings, it is often not known who is responsible. Nearly always it is one of the children, who finds that if he or she strokes a spoon between fingers and thumb it sometimes softens and bends.

It is apparent that metal-bending should be classed as a 'psychic' phenomenon, to be grouped together with such things as water-divining, telepathy, faith-healing, mediumship. I cannot claim to be a life-long authority on these things (I have always found physical science more interesting and more immediately important), but I have come to regard them as worthy of serious study. What has really led to my taking an active part in 'psychic research' is simply that it is very difficult, and therefore very important, to reconcile psychic phenomena with physical science. Of course this is why many scientists, probably the large majority, refuse to believe in the reality of psychic phenomena at all. The area must be classed with others, such as the workings of the brain and the origin of the universe, in being only speculatively interpreted.

Within our present society there are strong social overtones to psychic phenomena; it is possible to make money, and even to achieve some power, through their use. Therefore there have been some who have eked out their sparse psychic effects with fraud, and some who were entirely fraudulent. Naturally this has led to much scepticism among thinking people, and it has been scepticism not only of mediums but of investigators. It is useless for a person who has experienced psychic phenomena merely to claim that this scepticism is of the 'closed mind' variety.

There are all sorts of sociological reasons for these strongly-held attitudes, even within science itself. In such a field, any seriously interested person must start by finding things out for himself, without paying too much heed to the opinions held by others. My own initial attitude was: 'Believe nothing that you hear and only half of what you see', and it is only more recently that I have come to realize that I was perhaps arrogant in ignoring some good investigations that previous psychic researchers have made. I have seldom taken this attitude in other fields of science. Yet proportionately there has been almost as much bad science done as there had been bad psychic research. Some years ago there was an outcry when a National Bureau of Standards physicist working in atomic processes claimed that 90 per cent of the published papers in this field were wrong (at least in the sense that the real data were subsequently found to lie outside the published error bars). We must concede that it is easier to make mistakes in psychic research than it is in physics. Nevertheless, although opportunities may be lost, the community of scientists (and this includes the psychic researchers) will always get there in the end, by virtue of sheer persistence.

My first target was to answer to my own satisfaction the question of whether there was anything in paranormal metal-bending worth investigating at all – i.e., was it a real phenomenon? And in this I was very lucky in obtaining reasonably good evidence at the very first attempt; I doubt if the single instance described would be sufficient on its own, if nothing subsequent had happened; but at least at the time it was sufficient to prompt me to start a serious research programme. My account of what happened reads naively in the light of all the scorn that has since been heaped on such observations by some sceptical science-writers; indeed, no publisher would even consider publishing this account back in 1974. But I stand by every word of it, and have been unable to find any errors of fact in the account which follows.

First observations with Geller, 5 February 1974

It was already five o'clock. There was a television camera in the hotel lobby, fixed so that anyone walking in would be photographed. I had never seen this in an English hotel, but perhaps one day it will be nothing to notice especially. I was told that the hotel was popular with Israeli airline pilots, who needed security. But it made the evening seem a little unreal to me.

David Bohm and I were on our way to meet Uri Geller, the young Israeli who was visiting England and bending spoons on the television. I had seen his interview on the David Dimbleby 'Talk-In' show, and, sure enough, a spoon had apparently become quite soft in his fingers.

I am an experimental physicist, and David Bohm is a senior theoretical physicist; he developed the concept of the hidden variable in quantum theory. We had both come by taxi from the laboratories at Birkbeck College, which is part of the University of London. In my pocket I had four polythene envelopes each containing a brass latchkey, cleaned up and carefully examined for scratches. When I was an undergraduate, my laboratory training in chemistry included months of gravitational analysis, making weighings of chemicals to verify that 'matter can neither be created nor destroyed'. So I developed the usual skill at handling chemical balances, and thought I would use this skill on the latchkeys. If they weighed the same after they had been handled by Geller, something would be learned.

This was my first venture into anything that could be described as 'psychic research', and I think this applies to David Bohm as well. The whole field is contrary to the huge weight of experiment and experience which make up the physicist's life. The history of psychic research is spattered with doubtful reports and contradictions. What is one to believe?

I made up my mind, as most physicists would do, to take nothing on trust and believe nothing that I had not actually seen clearly myself. What a state of affairs! How fast would physics advance if we had to restrict ourselves to this cautious attitude? The young scientist is taught (in the words of Newton) that he has the advantage of 'standing on the shoulders of a giant'. What if the giant had lied to him? On the other hand, I had often told my research students to take nothing on trust.

We found the hotel suite and were introduced to Uri Geller by Brendan O'Regan. Brendan is a research consultant who had met Geller at the Stanford Research Institute in America. It was he who at the instigation of Californian physicists Fred Wolf and Jack Sarfatt had persuaded Geller to talk with Bohm and myself. But he was more or less unknown to me, and I thought at first that he might be a colleague of Geller's; this suspicion was helped by what happened next. David Bohm and I took seats, and Brendan and Uri went off together for a minute or so. I wondered what they could be cooking up, and tried to think how I could keep my eye on Brendan as well as Uri. But when they returned, Brendan kept well in the background, whilst Uri sat between David and myself around a plastic-topped wooden coffee table; I had already looked underneath the table and found nothing there. After all, spoons do not bend when they are stroked, and people were already saying that Geller was a very clever conjuror.

There was another scientist present – Dr Ted Bastin; he had with him a piece of electronic equipment which was not working; Uri Geller put his hands on it and tried to heal it but without success. I had the impression that Uri was rather nervous and unsure of himself in the presence of a new crop of scientists (he had already spent some weeks working with physicists at the Stanford Research Institute in California). So we started by talking about what Geller had been doing at Stanford, and after that he tried to receive telepathic messages from us. We drew pictures on paper, which he could not see, and he tried to guess what they were; but I had already decided that I would not investigate claims of telepathy at all seriously, since I had no experience, and the conditions were poor. I was waiting for the opportunity to produce my latchkeys. I judged that Geller had to be feeling confident before he would agree to try. I also wanted to make sure that the conditions were just right, so that David Bohm and I could get a really close-up view. I hoped that nothing would go wrong, and although I was in a mood of suspense, I tried not to let this be communicated to the others.

At length Geller said he would try, and asked for a hotel spoon. But I produced two latchkeys in polythene bags before he had a chance. I took them from the bags and laid them on the table.

Many spoons are so weak that anyone with moderately strong hands might bend them. But latchkeys, particularly the large ones issued by the Automobile Association, are much tougher, and I know few people who can bend them between the fingers; it is, however, not very difficult to bend them with one hand pressed against a hard surface. Also I knew all about my latchkeys, and my knowledge of the weights would enable me to test for chemical corrosion and abrasion.

Geller was quite happy with the keys, and at once took one in each hand, holding it lightly between the forefinger and thumb; I did not take my eyes off them once, not even for a moment. I can affirm that I did not see Geller's other fingers touch the keys (except at pick-up) and that he did not move them more than about an inch from the table surface; they were in my field of vision the whole time. Nothing happened for about forty seconds, and then Geller put the keys flat on the tables about two inches apart and stroked them gently, one with each forefinger. All the time Geller was talking, but I never took my eyes off the two keys and I am certain they never left the table for a surreptitious bend to be performed. After one more minute's stroking, the end of each key started to bend slightly upwards, one (the one stroked by his right forefinger) distinctly more than the other. The angles were $11°$ and $8°$, as measured afterwards.

Geller picked up one key and held it a few inches above the table to see if it would bend further, or if the metal would soften extensively. But no more bending took place that I could see, and when Geller handed me the key I quickly put it back in the polythene bag and into my pocket. It was not even warm. During the entire time this key had spent out of the bag its movements had been very simple; table, Geller's forefinger and thumb, table, pick-up by Geller, handed to me, back to the bag. I am quite sure that I did not take my eyes off this key or the other, and I am quite sure that Geller's handling of the keys was light and gentle. Although the operation had taken little more than two minutes, the strain of the close observation was beginning already to tell on me. I do not think that I could have continued at this intensity for very much longer.

The other key had only a smaller bend; Geller tried by stroking to get it to bend further. We took it into the bathroom and held it under a running tap, but to no avail. It remained only slightly bent, and it is my opinion that all of this slight bend ($8°$) had occurred on the table during the stroking. I dried the water off and put the key back in the polythene bag; we said goodbye to Uri Geller, who was happy about what had happened. He promised to come to our laboratory when he returned to England, and David Bohm and I went off into the hotel lobby, past the television camera and out into the street. Altogether we had been in the hotel for an hour and a quarter.

We caught a taxi straight back to the chemistry laboratory where I had use of a balance, and I weighed both keys; next morning I weighed them again. Within the reproducibility which I was getting, there was no change of weight:

	AA key	*EFG key*
Morning	12.3264 g	12.5023 g
Afternoon	12.3267 g	12.5024 g
After bending	12.3265 g	12.5013 g
Next morning	12.3271 g	12.5023 g

One reason why I carried out this weighing routine was that I had heard that paranormally bent or fractured specimens had sometimes lost weight. This might be attributed to corrosion by chemicals or to scratching or chipping; but if normal causes were ruled out, something most peculiar must have happened. Metal can be changed chemically, or vaporized, or filed away, but it cannot just disappear, unless it is converted into energy, as in a nuclear reactor. But I now had evidence that this bent key did not lose appreciable weight. I was later to repeat the weighing — paranormal bending — weighing observations more than twenty times, and with one unreliable exception, no specimen was found to have lost or gained in weight.

More recently a weight loss of 0.03 g has been reported by Dr Sachiro Okada at Tokyo University in a spoon bent by Jun Sekiguchi: this report remains unique.

This was my personal introduction to the metal-bending phenomenon, and whilst it is obviously not worth very much on its own, the conditions of the observation were sufficiently good for me to claim that a conjuror could not duplicate exactly what I reported. But no attempt was made to video-record the events, so that all we have as a permanent record is my own testimony and that of the other physicists present.[5] Such testimonies are perhaps not worth very much in isolation, but when similar reports accumulate, as they have done, they amount to more than video-records.

During the late 1950s the young Israeli Uri Geller had the following experience. He writes:[6]

One time my mother had made some mushroom soup. There was good white bread with the soup, and I dipped the bread into it and ate. Then I started eating the soup with my spoon. I'm left-handed, so I held the spoon in my left hand and took several sips of the soup. My mother was standing by the kitchen stove. I was lifting a full spoonful up to my mouth, when suddenly the bowl of the spoon bent down and spilled hot soup into my lap. Then the bowl of the spoon itself fell off. I was left there holding the handle. I called to my mother. 'Look what happened!' She came over and looked at me, then at the spoon. And then she started laughing. 'Well, it must be a loose spoon or something,' she said. Now I knew that was silly. You don't just have 'loose spoons.'

I laughed, too. But then I started to put two and two together. Something was happening around me that was very strange, and I had no way of explaining it or knowing what to do about it. I only knew that, whatever it was, this kind of thing didn't seem to happen to anyone else. And it was not comfortable.

Try to imagine such a thing happening to you as a child of eight or nine. You have a spoon full of soup, and it suddenly breaks and spills the soup into your lap. What do you do? The first reaction is to jump back in surprise, then to get angry at the spoon. And if it happens again the reaction is: Wait a minute. What's going on here? What is happening? And then if it continues, as it did with me, up to thirty or forty times a year, it becomes disconcerting and worrisome, to say the least.

The worst part of it was that there was no place to turn for help.

Neither of my parents could believe what was going on, and I couldn't exactly blame them. I didn't want to talk to my teachers about it, and my classmates would either laugh or say it was all just a trick. I was too ashamed even to ask anybody about it, because I knew they would laugh at me.

In view of what has happened during the 1970s, we are forced to wonder whether occasionally in the past there have been other children who have had similar experiences, which did not become widely known, and which eventually ceased altogether, as has been the case with nearly all those children studied more recently. We shall discuss pre-Geller metal-bending in the next chapter.

Uri Geller, having a strongly outgoing personality and a talent for performance, started to give public demonstrations of metal-bending and other things in Israel. 'Having an audience even seemed to help,' he wrote. But then:

When the manager urged me to add the magician's trick to the regular demonstration, I didn't know what to do. He was very persuasive, and I was young and inexperienced. He insisted that everything was going to fail unless I added the trick material. I figured, well it won't last much longer anyway. We'll soon cover all of Israel, and that will be it. Maybe I'll be able to save enough money to open up a coffee shop or something like that. I really didn't have any conception about the gift that had been given to me . . .

I finally gave in to the manager's pressure. I felt it was wrong the minute I agreed. I didn't realize, though, how big a mistake I was making, one of the most crucial mistakes of my life. After all, the more I became known all over the country, the more controversy would grow as to whether what I did was real or phoney. I added the trick to the legitimate demonstrations and I hated myself every time I did it.

Uri Geller's demonstrations in Israel did not convince the world that a new phenomenon was occurring; but the news reached Dr Andrija Puharich, a medical and electronic researcher in the United States, and Puharich made two visits to Israel with simple physical equipment and recorded various observations. At the instigation of astronaut Edgar Mitchell, Puharich brought Geller to the United States, via West Germany, in 1972. A number of physicists then became involved in investigating the effects: Dr Karger of the Max Planck Institute in

Munich, Dr Targ and Dr Puthoff of the Stanford Research Institute in California, and others.

Most of Uri Geller's activity was in the form of 'performance' rather than laboratory investigations; the performance did not convince everybody, but it was found that the community, including scientists, polarized into every shade of opinion between complete believers and complete sceptics. One could with some success predict how a person would react if one personally knew him and his background. What was more important, the scientific community had now had their attention drawn to the metal-bending phenomenon, and here and there some physicists and engineers started to make more careful observations and even experiments.

In 1974 the 'induction effect' began to occupy attention. During Geller's television performances other people both in the studio and in their homes would find that a latchkey held gently in the hand would bend of its own accord. In most West European countries, as well as Japan, South Africa and others, the television companies received letters and telephone calls reporting cutlery bending of its own accord in viewers' homes. Hundreds of such cases have been followed up in West Germany, and in Britain by the Society for Psychical Research; investigations were made by mathematical physicist John Taylor,[7] who wrote of his experience with children, the 'mini-Gellers' who could produce metal-bending effects on their own. In nearly all cases the effects began during or after the television performance. Moreover it is quite possible that a deliberately faked performance or account has actually induced real paranormal metal-bending.[8]

In January 1974 I became involved myself, and slowly developed my research with Uri Geller, and more extensively with British children. This will be described in subsequent chapters. In 1975 the first scientific conference to discuss the effect was held, called by Andrija Puharich at Tarrytown, USA. At this time certain professional conjurors and science-writers started what has since become an organized campaign to convince the public that the entire phenomenon was fraudulent.

In 1976-7, what might be termed 'second generation metal-benders' made their appearance in Europe. These people, some of whom are adult rather than children, came forward not as an immediate result of Geller's own performances but rather as a result of their own personal experiences that such a thing existed, and their gradual realization that it was affecting them to an extent that could not be ignored. The onset of the bendings was a long time, as much as three years, after the first Geller performances. The Frenchman Jean-Pierre Girard and the Bernese

Silvio Mayer are examples of this second generation. The attitudes of the children and of the second generation of benders are rather different from each other and from that of Geller himself. There is no longer much possibility, as there was with Geller, of becoming an international 'star' or entertainer. They do not spend their entire life demonstrating the effect; they continue with their careers and as far as possible co-operate with researchers and the media in their spare time.

At this time it cannot be said that thinking people, and especially the scientific community, are convinced of the reality of these phenomena. One important reason is that the phenomena do not connect up with physical science, and that as yet there have been no good hypotheses for such a connection. Hypotheses must wait until definitive quantitative information regarding metal-bending becomes available. To this information I attempt to contribute in the forthcoming chapters; and I shall follow this with some speculation about the possible physical basis of metal-bending.

Another reason for popular scepticism is that the metal-bending is rare and spontaneous, and cannot be reproduced to order. Many times I have been approached by television producers with the request that one of the metal-bending children demonstrate his or her 'powers' in front of the television camera. I have nearly always advised the family not to allow such a 'performance', because the chance of success is usually small. Nevertheless some successful television recordings of metal-bendings by children and also of strain gauge experiments (chapter 4) have been made, and have appeared in various countries. But there have also been unsuccessful attempts, and these have caused great frustration and unhappiness. Nearly always the metal-bending effects must be taken to be 'spontaneous' and not readily reproducible to order.

How did I reach the conclusion that the metal-bending phenomena are genuinely paranormal, or inexplicable? By accumulation of observations of events in which it was my good luck to participate. A few of these I shall describe below; some are simply retained in my notebooks.

When metal is bent paranormally the yield strength becomes temporarily abnormally low; in other words, the metal softens. It is difficult to observe this directly, because the effect does not have to be large for bending to occur, and usually it is not such a large effect that it is obvious to the observers. On rare occasions, however, the metal becomes as soft as putty. The first time that I saw such a phenomenon, it made a deep impression on me. I wrote at the time:

Before he [Uri Geller] had been in my office for two minutes, I spoke of my experiences with the children, and handed him one of the stainless steel spoons which had been bent by the girl.* Geller held the handle and did not touch the bend.† Within a few seconds, and under my close scrutiny, the bend in the spoon became plastic. It quickly softened so much that the spoon could be held with one end in either hand and gently moved to and fro. I had never seen Geller produce a really plastic bend before, and I asked him to hand the spoon to me in one piece. I took one end from his left hand into my right and one end from his right hand into my left. The acute angle, about 60°, was essentially unchanged in the handing over.‡ I could sense the plasticity myself, by gently moving my hands. It was as though the bent part of the spoon was as soft as chewing-gum, and yet its appearance was normal. I continued a gentle bending movement for about ten seconds, and then decided that it might be more interesting to try and preserve the spoon in one piece than to pull it apart. As carefully as I could, I laid it on the desk. It was not appreciably warm. I did not dare touch the bent part for fear of breaking it, and it lay on the desk apparently in one piece for a few minutes; but on attempting to move it I was unable to prevent it from falling apart, a 'neck' having developed.

This was the first time I had clearly seen a really 'plastic bend', since these are much rarer than the slow bends I had observed previously. I do not think there can be any question of fraud when a really plastic bend is produced under close scrutiny, unless there is serious chemical corrosion, such as that produced by mercuric salts. Even then, the metal behaves quite differently, becoming wet, discoloured and brittle, but hardly plastic. Chemical corrosion is accompanied by a change in weight; therefore I was pleased that I had recorded the weight of this spoon as follows:

Original weight	24.3526 g
Weight after bend by child	24.3533 g
Combined weight of pieces after fracture	24.3529 g

These variations are within the limits of weight changes, both up

---

* Valerie P. Actually it was her brother, Graham P., who had bent it.

† It has been supposed that Geller performed the well-known conjuring trick to prepare a near-fracture by working the spoon to and fro, covering it between the finger and thumb, and gradually revealing that the spoon is bending.

‡ A photograph of myself holding this spoon appears in Geller's book, *My Story*.

and down, which have been observed in other bent specimens. The errors are due to dirt and to moisture condensation and evaporation.

To be quite sure of such softening, one must be able to inspect it at close quarters both with the eye and by handling.

A piece of metal that has been critically weakened by bending to and fro can be held rigid at the weak point between finger and thumb. A gradual series of bends can be made apparent by suitable manipulation, but all the time the weak point is held firm, and the movements are made against the restraining force of the flesh of the ball of finger and thumb. The conjurer Mr Randi has demonstrated this trick to me, and it is most effective. It caused me to pause and think: was the Uri Geller spoon-softening, or others that I have observed, of the same character? No, the character was not the same, in two important details: first, there had been no opportunity for Geller to weaken the spoon by working it to and fro; and second, the part of the spoon which softened and bent was clearly exposed to view, and not held firm. In fact, I was able to hold the end of the spoon myself, and sensitively probe the softening by movements of the hands against the resistance of the metal. It was an uncanny experience.

I have more recently obtained a video-tape record of a vertically mounted stainless steel teaspoon in a floppy condition. Metal-bender Stephen North succeeded in softening a point on the spoon without even touching it. He then gently pushed and pulled the bowl about, so as to demonstrate the floppiness. Eventually the bowl fell off.

I have obtained similar video-records of the bending of long thin aluminium strips, which are mounted vertically by standing them on pieces of Plasticine. Stephen holds his hand close to the metal but does not touch it. Suddenly a softening at one point causes a sharp bend, the upper end of the metal strip collapsing to one side under gravity. This type of rapid metal-bending event, which can be seen on only a few frames of the video-record, is not infrequent. It almost seems as though metal-bending takes place either too slowly or too fast for the viewers to have an easy task observing it. No doubt this has contributed much to the slowness of its acceptance by sceptical people.

When a strange physical phenomenon is reliably observed and even instrumented, the possible causes must be assessed. First, there may be a natural physical cause, such as the relaxation of previously developed internal stress. In many cases of metal-bending, such causes have been eliminated by previously annealing the metal. Second, there may be the conscious or unconscious 'action', by means as yet unknown, of one or more humans (or animals). Third, such action may be brought about by one or more discarnate entities — 'spirits' of living or dead humans (or animals) or, alternatively, deities. Finally, the action may be brought about by one or more inanimate physical objects, such as haunted houses. In principle, any one of the above, or any combination of more than one, could have been the cause of the phenomenon.

It is difficult to see what proof might be offered of the responsibility of these entities. Even if communications were received, repeated demonstrations would have to be given, with the communicated message before each one.

The most that can be expected at present is that a link with a human can be established. Uri Geller is said to cause metal-bending because it happens frequently in his presence, and sometimes when he thinks that he is intending it. But the phenomenon is said to be 'spontaneous' because sometimes it occurs when he thinks that he is not intending it.

A sudden event observed in an early session of Uri Geller in my laboratory was the bending without touch of a disc-shaped single crystal of molybdenum of about 1 cm diameter. This had been provided by Dr Anthony Lee of the Cavendish Laboratory, and I personally kept it secure in a plastic box in my pocket before its exposure to Geller's 'action'. Physicists David Bohm, Ted Bastin, Jack Sarfatt and also Brendan O'Regan were present as witnesses. Geller asked for small metal objects to be placed for him on a large metal plate, so we placed on the table a machine-shop working plate. I took the crystal from its box and put it absolutely flat on the plate. Sarfatt extended his hand a few inches above the crystal and the other objects on the plate. Geller moved his hand above Sarfatt's, until a tingling sensation was reported by the latter. Geller tried to 'concentrate his action', and it was suddenly seen by the observers that the crystal had changed its shape, and was now slightly bent, through an angle of about 20°. I could not swear that the bending was not accompanied by a tiny metallic sound. But I was absolutely certain that neither Geller nor anyone else had touched the crystal since I placed it on the metal plate; nor did he drop anything on the metal plate.

I replaced the crystal in its box, which I returned to my pocket; a physical examination of the crystal would be necessary. I eventually found that a physical property (the magnetic susceptibility) of the crystal was anomalous, but I have not previously published this fact. It will be discussed in chapter 11.

Unfortunately a precise account of this event never appeared at the time, partly because an unauthorized and imprecise account was released to the press by one of those present. Sceptics had a field-day on the basis of this account, and even now it is doubtful if many readers who remember it will be much influenced by my own version. But I myself was impressed by what I had seen, and was reasonably certain that it could not have been a piece of conjuring. This is partly because conjurors do not know about how to change the physical properties of very pure molybdenum; nor could it have been known just what investigation I was going to make.

But it must be admitted that there were no conjurors present at our session, and that numbers of that profession have written very sceptically about metal-bending. Notwithstanding this, there is a less vocal minority of conjurors who are convinced of the reality of the phenomenon. Particularly is this the case in French-speaking Europe, where metal-bender Jean-Pierre Girard has given many 'demonstrations'.

One of the deepest impressions I received came from the observation of a bend by Jean-Pierre Girard. I had been asked by chemical physicist Dr Wolkowski of the University of Paris to participate in a discussion on the French radio, and the next day he telephoned to say that as a result of the broadcast a young man had come forward and demonstrated that he could bend metal. Girard was employed in selling pharmaceuticals, but was interested in conjuring and had performed as an amateur. He found himself able to concentrate deeply on pieces of metal, so that eventually they would bend. Very soon there was a television demonstration, of which I received a filmed version. Girard was seen to handle metal rods which bent; it was clear that manual force was not involved. Those of us who watched the film immediately saw that it could have represented a previously bent rod being slowly rotated so that the bend appeared. Such a procedure would have to have involved the film technicians, and when I mentioned this fact in a public lecture, the television company threatened legal action. Although the film was perhaps suspect, I determined to see Girard for myself. The opportunity came as late as July 1977, when I monitored a similar filming in Paris for Alan Neuman and the National Broadcasting Company of America (NBC). We made sure that the protocol was tight; large identified aluminium alloy bars were provided by the Pechiney Aluminium Company, and a suitable one was chosen on camera; after a filmed bending, it was returned on camera. The subsequent tests showed that the manual force that would have been required to make this bend was equivalent to 17 Newton metres (Nm) moment. The average limit of human strength under these conditions is 25 Nm, but a case has been reported of a man achieving a 38 Nm bend by force. The witnesses were unanimous that manual force was not used, and the published film shows this clearly (NBC holds the complete footage of the bending, and a report from me). Girard's pulse-rate was monitored during the event, and at the critical period it was as high as 160 beats per minute. The entire proceedings took place with Girard sitting at a flimsy glass table, which could very easily have been broken if strong force had been used on the metal bar.

It is never easy to achieve a metal-bending event under the conditions required in the television studio. The delays and adjustments which are necessary to the production contrive to develop an atmosphere of excitement, impatience, confrontation and even stage-fright. If video-evidence is desired, it is much better to allow a child metal-bender to accustom himself to the equipment for several days in his home, and practise metal-bending in view of the camera, with one of the family operating the equipment. I have then been able to visit and monitor (for example, from Stephen North and Julie Knowles) the recording of stroking bends, and of bends without touch; also of strain gauge records of the type described in chapter 4.

One very unusual record was obtained by my colleague David Robertson of the action of the metal-bender Julie Knowles on a very long thin strip of aluminium (50 cm X 8 mm X 0.8 mm). Such strips can be waved about flexibly and are bent very easily, so I have used them for practice and encouragement of the metal-bending children whom I have studied. Julie held the strip upright by one end and remained still; it soon became apparent that the top end was forcing itself towards her, and then springing back again. She was able to press the strip quite hard against this invisible force, and also to move the strip about and turn it to the horizontal; it was obvious from the video-record that the 'invisible force' was not in fact produced by a thread or 'moti', as it is called by Indian conjurors. Eventually Julie forced the strip sufficiently hard against the 'invisible force' to bend it right over in a smooth arc of nearly $180°$.

Here is a final example which illustrates well the spontaneity, even capriciousness, of metal-bending happenings; also the difficulties that we encounter in bringing ourselves to come to terms with them.

During 1978 a Japanese boy, Masuaki Kiyota, was invited by a television company to visit London and attempt to 'demonstrate' some optical phenomena of the type to be described in chapter 22. I decided to examine his metal-bending, and brought with me two freshly-purchased stainless steel teaspoons and two of my own household dessert spoons; all of these I quickly identified by nicking their bowls in various places, using wire-cutters. I also traced their outlines on paper and located their magnetic poles (chapter 11). I kept them securely in my pockets during Masuaki's visit.

On the first day I pulled out a dessert spoon from my pocket, quickly checked the identification by touch and offered it to him during a break in the filming at Birkbeck College; he straightway placed it in his left-hand trouser pocket and withdrew his hand; I could see a bulge, presumably (but not certainly) made by the spoon. No one else who might have received the spoon from him came near us. He then asked to be shown to the toilet, so I took him there myself, unaccompanied. Before we had reached the toilet, while we were walking together along the basement corridor of the College, Masuaki pulled a spoon from his pocket and gave it to me; there was a single 180° twist in its neck, which appears in Plate 1.1a (2). By touching the nick in the bowl, I found that it was my spoon, and I kept it in my hands until I returned it to my pocket. Of course I did not see the twist take place, but my observation was that the necessary tools (such as hand vices or wrenches) could not have been used on his person without my noticing; therefore I deduced that Masuaki's twisting of the spoon, whether carried out with two hands, with one, or with none, must have involved local softening of the metal.

Similar twisting of the spoons shown in Plate 1.1a (1 and 3) took place during Masuaki's visit, but I was not personally responsible for observing them. The last teaspoon I continued to keep in my pocket, and after checking the identification I offered it to Masuaki two days later in a taxi while I was sitting beside him. He played with the spoon one-handed, all the time in my field of vision; within two minutes it became twisted (Plate 1.1a (4)). It happened too fast for me to get a really clear visual image of the happening. I again checked my nicking and returned it to my pocket.

The identification of a spoon by touching the nicked bowl is easy and quick, perhaps embarrassingly so. Later during the day I pulled a teaspoon from my pocket without checking it and showed it as evidence of the taxi event to another investigator. I had earlier explained my identification technique, and he was able to see that it was in fact another teaspoon altogether (Plate 1.1a (1))! I pulled out the 'taxi' teaspoon and this time there was no trouble with the identification. My face was undoubtedly red, but this is no reason why the observation should be invalidated.

I describe these events in order to show the difficulties of observing spontaneous phenomena. Had Masuaki been sat down in front of the

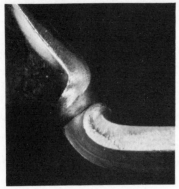
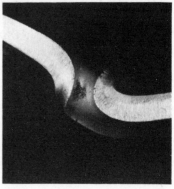

television cameras and invited to bend metal, there would not have been a very high chance of success. But Nippon Television in Tokyo have during 1979 achieved some good video-recordings of twists.

My description of metal-bending events will not in subsequent chapters be arranged in correct historical order, but rather by classification of the different types of physical phenomena and the experiments necessary to obtain some understanding of them; these 'no-touch' experiments have mostly taken place in the homes of metal-bending children, to which I have carried portable equipment, attempting to approximate to 'laboratory conditions' without removing the child from his natural environment.

The chapters will read as though the sessions have been one continuous success story, but in fact this has not been the case. There have been many long hours of observations without any 'paranormal effects' to show for them. My policy has been to set up the most suitable social and psychological conditions for metal-bending to occur. I have no detailed recipe for success, nor do I consider that public demonstrations are likely to be successful, except in rare cases.

Plate 1.1a (Opposite above) Stainless steel spoons twisted by Masuaki Kiyota
Plate 1.1b (Opposite left) Enlargement of twist in spoon 1
Plate 1.1c (Opposite right) Enlargement of twist in spoon 4

Chapter **2**

Metal-benders and world reactions

Although this book is principally about my own observations, I cannot avoid giving some account of the activities of metal-benders I have not investigated in detail and of the behaviour of the many people who have reacted to the emergence of an apparently paranormal pheno-menon. I shall try to set the stage by taking a global view of the events.

At the outset the question must be posed; why did mankind know nothing about metal-bending before the appearance of Uri Geller? Had the phenomenon actually occurred before, did it fail to be recognized as such, did it just pass into legend? We can certainly find descriptions of events which might be classified as paranormal metal-bending; but what authority are we to give them? Psychic phenomena have usually occurred in waves, partly due to an 'induction effect' (chapter 17), and partly due to the alerting of observers and recorders; we might cite such examples as outbreaks of witchcraft, and Victorian table-lifting. Did previous waves of metal-bending occur?

Before the industrial revolution metal objects were of course much rarer than they are today, and it must be remembered that the widest use of metal, apart from coins, ornaments and tools, was for weapons. Swords have historically been treated with reverence, sometimes given individual names, and even regarded as possessing magical properties. Not only are there legends of swords such as Excalibur being immovable except by a magically endowed individual, but there are also legends of magical renewal of the metal itself.

One of the Galahad adventures in the *Morte d'Arthur* reads as follows:[9]

Then Eliazar, King Pelles' son, brought before them the broken sword wherewith Joseph [of Arimathea] was stricken through the

thigh. Then Bors set his hand thereto, if that he might have soldered
it again; but it would not be. Then he took it to Percivale, but he
had no more power thereto than he. Now have ye it again, said
Percivale to Galahad, for an it be ever achieved by any bodily man
ye must do it. And then he took the pieces and set them together,
and they seemed that they had never been broken, and as well as it
had been first forged. And when they espied that the adventure of
the sword was achieved, then they gave the sword to Bors, for it
might not be better set; for he was a good knight and a worthy man.

This does not read like an account of blacksmithing, but is more like
the 1970s feats of the Romansh-speaking Swiss metal-bender Silvio
Mayer, who has been able to bond together the pieces of teaspoons that
he has already fractured without the apparent use of force. German
physicists and parapsychologists have investigated these claims, and do
not regard them as frauds; and indeed the spotless nature of Sir Galahad
was never gainsaid. Perhaps there is a connection, far-fetched though it
seem.

No real proof exists that metal-bending phenomena occurred in
witchcraft, but there are good reasons for believing that this might have
been the case. Crooked pins were usually vomited by victims of witchcraft,[10] and at least one authority[11] considered this to be a legal
diagnostic of bewitchment. In some instances the victims found crooked
pins poking into their skin. These things were counterfeited, probably
more often than they occurred naturally, and this makes it difficult to
know for certain how the pins became bent and how they got where it
was claimed they did. The reason we have for proposing that the
phenomena may have occurred paranormally is their similarity to
certain modern events, described in later chapters. I have witnessed
teleportation of objects into the mouth with the same psychic subjects
whom I have witnessed bending clusters of pins in plastic boxes; all that
is missing is the composite event, resulting in bent pins in the mouth or
at the body surface. There are modern cases of pins being found in large
numbers within the arms and legs of human victims of voodoo.[12]

All through the nineteenth and twentieth centuries, metal cutlery,
knitting-needles, etc., were in common use in the home, and there have
been many reports of poltergeist hauntings and other psychic phenomena with physical content; but very few included events which might
be classified as metal-bending. One such case was unearthed by Scott
Rogo;[13] an article by Mrs I.K. Reno in 1905 reports: 'Frequently
during the meal hour, milk, tea, coffee and soup were flying into the

faces of those at the table, several times inflicting painful scalds and burns. Spoons were broken, or suddenly twisted out of shape in their hands.'

The English medium Bertha Harris remembers as a child the bending of her brothers' model railway lines; but nothing came of it except nursery strife!

There was the incident of Jung's knife. The psychologist Carl Gustav Jung organized spiritualistic seances in his youth, and in one of these a breadknife in a drawer inexplicably snapped into four parts, with a sound like a pistol shot. The four pieces of the knife are still in the possession of the Jung family.[14] We shall see in chapter 12 that fractures are very much part of the metal-bending phenomenon.

There was the wave of paranormal or 'preternatural' bell-ringing described by Major Edward Moor, FRS, in the Victorian monograph *Bealings Bells*. I came across this little-known piece of psychic research only because Major Moor was a great-great-great-uncle of mine. In a house at Bealings, Suffolk, which I remember as a child, the bells were of the tinkling variety pulled by wires taken around corners by dogleg levers. Each bell was mounted on a curved piece of spring metal.

Major Moor experienced inexplicable ringings of his bells. He set about excluding the possibilities of mischievous pulling by humans, birds, etc., but he never succeeded in explaining them, and when he published his account of the events several other families came forward with similar accounts. The generally assumed interpretation was that something preternatural had been pulling the wires.

But an equally sound interpretation would be that the metal springs received paranormal extension or contraction pulses of the type to be described in chapter 4 and frequently observed in my experiments. In fact, I shall describe a similar no-touch experiment in miniature (carried out months before I came across *Bealings Bells*): a galvanometer mirror mounted on a small piece of spring metal experienced paranormal elastic jerky movements, each giving rise to the deflection of a laser beam. Some time after I became acquainted with *Bealings Bells*, the extraordinary similarity between the two constructions occurred to me. Perhaps Major Moor was experiencing an attack of paranormal metal-bending.

Since the reports of Major Moor's experiences first appeared, other instances have come to light; and even after the First and Second World Wars cases continued, such as in the former hospital building at South Mimms, Herts.

Notwithstanding these examples, the accounts of pre-Geller metal-bending are sparse, and credit must undoubtedly be given to Uri Geller, whatever the defects in his career, for bringing the phenomenon to the notice of members of the scientific establishment. We can now at least count the numbers of serious groups researching the subject in double figures: in the USA, the late Dr Wilbur Franklin at Kent State University, Dr Targ and Dr Puthoff at Stanford Research Institute, Eldon Byrd at the Office of Naval Research Laboratories, Washington, Dr Ronald Hawke at Livermore and Elizabeth Rauscher at Berkeley; in France, Dr Ducrocq, Dr Wolkowski and, more recently, scientists at the Pechiney Aluminium Company; in West Germany, the Freiburg University group; and also Dr Wälti in Switzerland. Professor Dierkens in Belgium, Dr Mattuck and Scott Hill in Copenhagen, Professor Ferdinando Bersani and Dr Aldo Martelli in Italy, Dr Charles Osborne in Melbourne; the New Horizons Group in Toronto, and also Dr Bob Cantor; in Japan a number of different laboratories, from among which I would single out that of Professor Shigemi Sasaki in Tokyo; and finally there are reports of serious researches in China.

The contributions of many of these groups will become apparent as we proceed with our account. But their activities have not gone unnoticed. Sceptical science-writers, eventually organized in the USA and elsewhere into a committee, succeeded in obtaining widespread publicity for the defects in the picture. To be sure, much has been publicly claimed in the media which would not stand up to close scrutiny; and since most psychic histories appear to be an inextricable mixture of reality and fraud, we would not expect to find an exception in metal-bending.

When a fraud is 'exposed' (whether or no the exposition itself would stand up to close scrutiny) this is by no means a proof that genuine events have not taken place as well at a different time. Indeed the inextricable mixture appears to be the norm, so that the psychic researcher must choose his methods with extreme care.

Before embarking on the account of my own observations, I shall report briefly on the early history of Geller's metal-bending – a sociological exercise for which I myself am perhaps rather inadequately qualified. But the exercise must be carried out, so as to remove various misconceptions that have taken hold of the public mind.

Geller was 'discovered' in Israel in 1971 by Dr Andrija Puharich, an erratically brilliant field-worker in such fringe science areas as psychic surgery and hallucinogens. Puharich could not become extricated from the idea that Geller's 'powers' originated from extra-terrestrial beings, but he reported many observations of teleportations (chapters 18 and 19) happening around Geller, and he introduced him to former astronaut Edgar Mitchell, through whose auspices further research was financed. Geller began five weeks of experimentation with the physicists Dr Targ and Dr Puthoff at Stanford Research Institute. The published part of these researches concerned not metal-bending but the telepathic transmission of information, in which field Targ and Puthoff have since carried out extensive work.[15]

Geller toured the USA giving lectures and demonstrations, but comparatively few scientists were convinced, largely because trouble was not taken to set up the conditions exactly right. He also performed on American television shows, but never made sufficient impression for large numbers of telephone calls to be received from families who reported cutlery bending in the home. As we saw in chapter 1, this is what happened in West European countries as well as Japan, South Africa and elsewhere.

In Britain Geller made several successful public television records of apparently paranormal bendings of cutlery, and many children came forward and claimed, sometimes even demonstrated, similar happenings. Mathematical physicist John Taylor, who was present in the studio, started a programme of field-work and invited numbers of the children to his laboratory.

He published accounts in a book entitled *Superminds*, and publicly affirmed that he believed paranormal metal-bending was a real effect. Later he was to announce something of a change of heart, brought about by his failure to detect the presence of electromagnetic radiation during metal-bending. The reasoning was that bending must have been brought about by such radiation, and since none was observed, the bending may well have been produced normally, presumably by manual action previously undetected. This reasoning is difficult for physicists to understand.

Later, I spoke to many of these children; I had formed the opinion that it was a mistake to conduct initial observations in the laboratory; the children would find the environment strange and would be anxious to achieve success by any means available to them. In fact, sociologist Dr Harry Collins[3] at the University of Bath was able to show this by inviting children to his own laboratory and viewing them stroking spoons through a two-way mirror. Five were seen to alleviate their failure by cheating; the sixth, Julie Knowles, will appear in later chapters.

Occasionally child metal-benders have been able to recall instances of bending occurring before the Geller revelation; but they failed to recognize it as unusual. Masuaki Kiyota makes this claim.

A fanatically sceptical conjuror, known as 'The Amazing Randi', started a campaign to probe the weaknesses of much of the reporting.

His publications contained interesting material, but I found it extremely easy to find faults in his reporting; he attempted trickery during a visit to my office, and the level of the interview was so low that I have decided that a detailed discussion of it here would serve only to embarrass him. Other conjurors have contributed a rather more balanced view; two of the British, David Berglas and Ali Bongo, whilst sceptical, have responded to my requests for advice and help. A number of others observed Geller and other metal-benders and stated publicly that they could detect no fraud. These included Zorka and Abb Dickson in the USA, Leo Leslie in Denmark, Henk Vermeyden in the Netherlands, Ranky in France and Rolf Mayr in Switzerland.

Geller's public performances represent a grey area into which the serious student should not venture. It is reported that his business associate, Yasha Katz, publicly alleged trickery, which Geller has denied. I have myself been present at only five performances, two in London and one each in Southampton, Longleat (near Bath) and Tokyo. Although I found no evidence of trickery, I was not personally responsible for the arrangements, so that the protocol was not always as I could have wished. It is worth mention that the softening of the large piece of heavy silver cutlery produced at Longleat was almost beyond dispute genuine. For the visits by Geller to my laboratory I was responsible for the protocol, such as it was (not what I would have wished, for several reasons!); again, I found no evidence of trickery, although a number of incidental strange events happened unwitnessed, and therefore could not be taken as evidence. I believe that this also applies to the visits by Geller to the Kent State and Berkeley Laboratories in the United States.

It will be valuable at this point to enumerate the names of various metal-benders in different countries who have allowed investigation of their talents by scientists and others. Most of these were children at the time when the 'powers' first became manifest, nearly always after watching Geller's television appearances. The exceptions include Jean-Pierre Girard, whose abilities will be discussed in chapter 13; Silvio Mayer, who also paints pictures of a visionary nature; Christine Wild, a housewife from the English Midlands; James Blevens from Verona, Wisconsin, and Mrs T.W. of Detroit.

Child metal-benders were sometimes known as 'mini-Gellers' and in Italy 'Gellerini'. Two of the Italians are Paride Giatti, who has been investigated by physicist Professor Bersani, and Orlando Bragante. The latter, investigated by Dr Aldo Martelli, is reliably reported to have bent cutlery enclosed in a sealed box. Other Italian metal-benders include

Lucia Allegretti, Sandro Gasperini and Giovanni d'Emilio. In Israel, sixteen-year-old Ori Seboria has been investigated by Dr H.C. Berendt and others; when Ori visited Australia, scientists at the Caulfield Institute of Technology in Victoria also made observations, and other Australian children showed some powers. Sometimes, as in the case of Lisa in Denmark and Bernard in Belgium, real names are not published in order to preserve privacy. In Switzerland, observations have been made with Edith Aufdermauer. In Japan, the most dedicated metal-bender is Masuaki Kiyota; but there are also Hiroto Yamashita, Yasushi Murasawa, Makoto Hirota, Toro Osaki, Jun Sekiguchi, Seiyuri Tanaka, Satoshi, Masao and Koji.

Finally we come to the British metal-benders; John Taylor has compiled a list of at least thirty-eight. My own investigations have covered rather fewer. There are those who not only have strong 'powers', but who have had the patience to collaborate extensively with me; they include Nicholas Williams, Andrew G., Stephen North, Julie Knowles, Willie G. and Mark Henry. There are also those who have successfully participated in at least one experiment with positive results. They include Belinda H., Graham P., Richard B., David and Steven Nemeth, Susan Clarke, Clifford White, Alison Lloyd, Neil Howarth, Gill Costin, Kim Griffiths and Ian L.

There are some others with whom I have not had the chance to work, such as David Jefferies, Douglas Smith, Russell Jennings, Stephen Coates, Mark Shelley, Janet H., V. S. and Heidi Wilton.

Two English adults fall into unique categories as metal-benders. One is Matthew Manning, who as a child experienced strong poltergeist phenomena and has written much about his psychic experiences. When he visited Canada, several investigators at the New Horizons Research Foundation in Toronto observed his metal-bending; but he has since lost interest in the phenomenon, and seems never to have been at home with it.

The second is Dr Rob Basto, a space physics researcher who became seriously involved with transcendental meditation. He undertook to practise for hours at a time over a period of several weeks; after this he was able to produce effects on sensitive detection equipment, to my own and his satisfaction.

Chapter **3**

Techniques of validation when touch is allowed

Most of the experiments I shall describe are on the measurement, by means of sensitive equipment, of physical effects produced on metal specimens which the metal-bender is not allowed to touch during the entire session. However, before I settled down to such experiments, I made observations of bendings and fractures produced merely by stroking, in order to satisfy myself that manual force was not being widely used to bring about the bending, either intentionally or unintentionally. These observations are not as easy as they sound, particularly when curved household objects such as spoons are used. Clearly, small changes in the curvature are difficult to detect without precision measuring equipment. The use of a curved comparison template such as a similar spoon is not a particularly sensitive or satisfactory method. I therefore used flat strips rather than cutlery, and am surprised that some other observers are still watching children stroking spoons! This chapter is in part directed at those who wish to play a part in psychic research, but approach the subject with very little experience or technical knowledge.

The normal bending of a metal strip is brought about by loading, most simply the three-point load $\underset{\uparrow\quad\uparrow}{\overset{\downarrow}{\rule{2cm}{0.4pt}}}$, which produces a uniform cube-law curvature, and the four-point load $\underset{\uparrow\quad\uparrow}{\overset{\downarrow\ \downarrow}{\rule{2cm}{0.4pt}}}$, in which the centre section is free from stretching force, and a square-law curvature is produced. When the loading (stress) is light, the deformation (strain) is elastic, and is proportional to the load. When the loading is increased beyond the yield point, the deformation becomes plastic, that is to say, permanent rather than temporary. Deformation progresses until work-hardening prevents further distortion. If the loading is sufficiently large, the work-hardening will be insufficient to prevent fracture.

The first task which an observer faces is to become thoroughly familiar with the magnitude of the forces required to bring about normal deformation; he must also become familiar with the appearance of human hands and arms when such forces are being exerted.

Since it is a moment (force multiplied by distance) which produces deformation, both the yield strength and the length of a metal specimen need to be considered. We also need to know the limits of human strength, using either two hands or a single hand. Systematic tests of large numbers of people were made by the French researchers. For a two-handed bend on a specimen 25 cm in length, the average limit of male strength is 25 Newton metres moment (25 Nm), and the average female limit about 15 Nm. The limits of children vary between 5 and 20 Nm. The record achieved by the strongest man tested by means of a dynamometer was 38 Nm on their 25 cm specimen.

When observing bending by stroking, we need not insist that a bend beyond human strength be produced (unless there is a large gap in the observation), but only that the human strength required should be easily recognizable when it is being exerted; physical strength between one-half and two-thirds of the limit is easy to recognize. Unfortunately opinions occasionally differ about what is recognizable as manual force, even when studying video-tapes; but a consensus opinion is of value. I have carefully studied a video-tape of a bending by the French metal-bender Jean-Pierre Girard, under strict protocol, of a specimen that he was able to deform by an amount that would require 14 Nm; although his stroking action looks beyond suspicion to me, and to many who have seen the tape, a French physicist of distinction has claimed that the finger forces could have been rendered especially strong by athletic training.

For a single-handed bend the situation is more complicated. When a specimen is held and stroked between fingers and thumb, parts of the specimen are concealed from view by parts of the hand. This screening is minimized when the observers view from different angles and different heights (e.g., with a mirror-surface table). A three-point load can most easily be applied to a specimen, using one hand, by (a) the ball of the thumb, (b) the first or second joint of the forefinger, and (c) the base of the palm. The bend will then be centred on the point of application of the forefinger. If the specimen is only about 5 cm long (e.g., a latch-key), then it is not possible to apply a three-point load in this way; instead the thumb and two fingers would be used; in this operation much more of the specimen is exposed to view. I have used latchkey specimens for this reason. On occasions I have noticed that paranormal bending takes place beyond the end of the thumb and fingers, which would be impossible under normal bending from a physical three-point load. When the bend is gradual, it is difficult to be certain that there is no physical three-point load throughout the time of bend. But on one occasion a single crystal of zinc was stroked between the fingers and thumb by Graham P., under good conditions of observation; I observed an instantaneous cleavage beyond the end of the fingers and thumb. The end of the crystal dropped to the table, leaving the remainder of the crystal exposed, projecting beyond the fingers and thumb. A sudden event of this sort enables the observer to be certain that the position of cleavage is not between the two outer loading points and, therefore, that physical force of the fingers and thumb could not have caused the cleavage.

It has been pointed out that although latchkeys are excellent for exposure for bending in one hand, they are relatively easy to bend if one end is gripped in a slot in a piece of furniture, or in the open end of a metal tube; the observer must watch carefully for such things. Latchkeys can be bent with two bare hands only by a strong man, and I have never encountered anyone able to bend one using one bare isolated hand. But it is possible to do it by pressing one end of the key onto a hard surface, using a single hand only; one latchkey has also been linked through the hole of another to increase the leverage.

For a one-handed bend using fingers only, the limit of human strength is about 10 Nm, depending on specimen length. Another operation is possible to a metal-bender: the production of two bends simultaneously in a long (40-50 cm) specimen held in both hands. One bend is produced under each hand, so that an S-configuration is formed. Any tendency to produce only a single bend between the two hands should not be accepted. Two bends each requiring $\geqslant$ 10 Nm can then be accepted as validation.

The tight twisting of the handle of a stainless steel dessert spoon (see chapter 1) through 180° requires typically a torque of 7-8 Nm. This is beyond human strength even if the handle of the spoon is held rigidly, for example in the keyhole of a door; the typical male human limit is 4 Nm. Thus the tight twist is good validation under observation, even though few metal-benders are able to achieve it, as will be further discussed in chapter 11. The stainless steel teaspoon requires 5 Nm, whereas the limit of torque that can be exerted on the bowl by an adult male is typically 2 Nm.

A few examples of well-observed bends will now be given. A latch-key bend by Uri Geller has been described in chapter 1, and I have observed others by Uri Geller and by Nicholas Williams and Andrew G., including fractures. I have observed a 23 Nm metal bar bent by stroking by Jean-Pierre Girard, under good protocol; a moving picture exists of this event, also described in chapter 1. Dr Crussard and Dr Bouvaist, whose researches with Jean-Pierre Girard are described in chapter 13, have observed his bendings of several metal bars of up to 75 Nm yield moment. Uri Geller, tested under similar conditions, has achieved an 80 Nm bend. I have offered an AU4GT4 aluminium alloy bar to Julie Knowles and she has obtained a 45 Nm bend; although there was a gap in the observation, there were no visible signs of force being used on the carefully polished bar, and it needs more than twice her physical strength.

We have seen that for observation (with or without video-camera) of bending by stroking, the specimen should be chosen to be sufficiently strong to require considerable muscular effort to deform it; with careful watching this effort can be recognized by the observers; at the same time the use of absurdly strong specimens is unlikely to result in there being any measurable deformation. The most sensitive methods of measuring permanent deformations are by means of a micrometer gauge of suitable design, or by the unevenness of roll of a cylindrical bar on a flat surface. In the latter case a deformation of about 0.1–0.2 mm can be detected; in the former, one may achieve 0.01 mm sensitivity. The specimens should initially be accurately machined *and the residual deformation measured*. The use of matching cutlery as templates is much less accurate.

The preparation and yield-testing of metal specimens require standard metallurgical and engineering techniques. Destructive yield-testing can to some extent be avoided by making use of the fact that for many alloys the hardness (a non-destructive test) is a good indicator of the yield strength.

When metal-bending by stroking is to be observed, there are two central problems of validation.[16] One is that the specimen be prepared and identified beforehand, and examined and identified properly afterwards. The other, as we have seen, is that the observation of absence of serious normal force should leave no room for doubt. Under no circumstances should the observer allow himself to be manoeuvred into a situation in which (for example, because of unidentified specimens) sleight of hand could be used for substitution. This is possibly the most difficult operation for an observer to detect, even if he is practised.

The object of visual observation and video-tape recording is to determine whether or not physical force has been entirely responsible for the bending, and to determine whether the specimen or any other object has been substituted at any moment. Visual observation is a deceptively simple exercise; it requires careful preparation and practice to perform well. The best number of observers is three or four; any more will introduce cross-currents which distract the attention; in addition, the field of view of each observer is diminished. Fewer observers would certainly ensure that the field of view of each was very large, but probably larger than each could successfully watch. There should if possible be more than one observer, since the chances of catching a sleight of hand are increased by the presence of several. Attention should be paid to good lighting to minimize shadows, to the background surface and to the avoidance of all distractions, whether originating from the subject, from the observers or externally. The maximum time for which a really high standard of visual concentration can be maintained is about two to three minutes. If the event takes longer than this, then undoubtedly moments of lapsed concentration will occur, increasing in frequency as time proceeds, thereby increasing the probability that the concentration of all observers will lapse simultaneously.

An important consideration is the width of field of view which it is required to observe; this should not be larger than about 0.05 steradian,* otherwise motions of eyes become unsuitably large. With chart-recorded experiments this presents problems, since there are several widely separated points which must be simultaneously watched. But the observation of bending of a metal specimen held in a stationary hand, or situated within inches of the hand, is much simpler, since all that is necessary is to concentrate very hard on a narrow field of view. A distance of about two or three feet between the observer's eyes and the specimen enables the maximum of detail to be recognized without widening the required field of view unduly. An important task of the observers is to ensure that the intended and identified specimen remains in view from the moment it leaves the possession of the investigator until the moment it is returned to him.

The purpose of recording by video-tape is twofold: to obtain records by means of which a physical event can be studied repeatedly, and to obtain records to increase the credibility of the investigator. Although the achievement of each purpose is important, the temperamental nature of the metal-bending ability is such that some investigators

* The steradian is a unit of solid angle; about fourteen of them subtend the entire surface of a sphere from its centre.

(myself included) do without the luxury of video-tape recording for most of the time. It is important to assign the correct priority, as between experimentation and moving picture production, and to maintain a suitable proportion of each. It is my experience that if the experimenter is also the cameraman, then he cannot also perform adequately as observer. The technical operation − field of view, lighting, panning, etc. − occupies most of his time. Observer and cameraman should therefore be two different people.

When a video-record is taken, the field of view of the action should also contain a stop-clock, in order that the record should be seen to be in real time; no cuts have been made. Another technique, employed by Harry Collins, is to include a burning candle, whose flame readily shows up any cutting.

Specimen identification and examination is of great importance. The primary purpose of examining a specimen is to identify it before and after bending, and to measure the magnitude of distortion. The most powerful simple identification is by accurate weighing; an accuracy of $\pm$ 10^{-4} g can be achieved on a chemical balance. What appear to be identical specimens exhibit different weights, even if only by a few milligrams. Considerable careful machining would be required to prepare specimens giving identical readings on the chemical balance. Weighing will also detect weakening by filing, chemical action, condensation of moisture and perspiration.

However, there is another purpose in making detailed physical examination of a specimen. Changed physical properties might be con- sidered as possible indicators of the paranormal character of a bend. They would be valid indications only if the structure of the metal were noticably different, as between paranormal and physical bending. We shall enumerate examples of suitable physical properties that have been used for such tests. In most cases, the difference between paranormal and normal bends is undetectable, but there are several physical properties − magnetic and structural − which can be measurably abnormal in a paranormally bent specimen. In chapters 13 and 16 this will be discussed in detail.

The orientation of grains in a polycrystalline specimen can be monitored by X-ray reflection; at my instigation in 1974 Dr Paul Barnes and his students[17] made measurements on a brass latchkey al- legedly paranormally bent by Geller, and found the data indistinguish- able from those for the unbent parts of the latchkey. Mr Wälti[17] at the University of Bern has confirmed this finding, on other specimens.

In the following year micro-hardness measurements were made at my instigation by Dr Desvaux[18] on polycrystalline and single crystal specimens paranormally bent by our child subjects. The data (e.g. Figure 3.1) did not show extensive differences from those which would be expected for physical bending. Thus neither of these techniques is in general suitable for validation by examination of bent specimens.

A possible technique of validation by specimen examination is the study of paranormal fractures by electron microscopy. In our college Dr Paul Barnes and his students made electron micrographs of para-normal cutlery fractures, but although some features were found which would not be expected in normal fractures, the complications were such that recognition of a paranormal fracture from the electron micro-graphs was by no means certain. It was also reported by the late Dr Wilbur Franklin[19] that electron micrographs of paranormally fractured stain-less steel spoons were similar to those of normal room temperature ductile fractures. It must be recognized that the study of fractures by electron micrograph is a specialization in itself. In chapter 11 the subject will be further discussed.

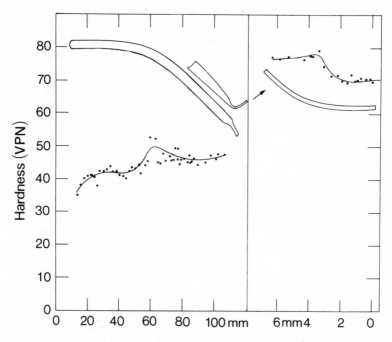

Figure 3.1 Hardness measurements on copper single crystal, of cross-section 5 mm square, bent under good observation by Graham P. The end of the ingot, bent under good observation by Belinda H., is shown on an enlarged scale

Also in the category of validation by proof of paranormal structural change are the experiments of Eldon Byrd, and later those of Bob Cantor[20] and Melanie Tokofoyu, on mechanical memory metals. The mechanical or shape-memory effect (SME), also known as marmem or martensitic memory, is especially strong in the near-equiatomic nickel–titanium alloys or nitinols. A marmem alloy is set up by machining or mechanical distortion to have a certain shape at a certain temperature. When it is plastically deformed, for example by manual force, at a temperature below the original temperature, it will revert to its original shape on heating to a temperature above the shape-memory transition temperature.

Eldon Byrd set up pieces of nitinol wire for Uri Geller to deform, which he did allegedly paranormally. On appropriate heating the original shapes were not achieved; new shapes were formed. This has been taken as proof that the action was paranormal in that it produced some structural change in the metal. It would be difficult to propose an alternative explanation with confidence. Later, nitinol specimens were exposed to a number of the British metal-bending children. Of these, half succeeded in destroying the mechanical memory and half did not.

When deformation of ordinary metals is unusually extensive, a simple validation technique using specimen examination becomes possible. We know from studies of stress-strain data that permanent plastic strains of greater than a certain value cannot be reached by the normal application of stress; this is because of the existence of a maximum in the stress-strain curve; when this is reached, the strain can increase rapidly until fracture results. The percentage strains which cannot be reached have been given as: aluminium 13%, soft copper 23% and mild steel 17%.

If such large strains are reached at the convex surface of a bent specimen, without cracking, then we know that some treatment such as heating to a high temperature, or paranormal softening, must have been necessary to produce the convex surface cracking. If crackless sharp bends of thick specimens through sufficiently small radii of curvature are obtained, then their existence points to the action of something other than normal force.

Neglecting hump-back distortion, the strain $\epsilon_0 = t/2r$ at the convex surface of a circular bend of radius r at the neutral axis of a strip of thickness t. For a strip of width $2r$ twisted with pitch p, $1 + \epsilon_0 = (p^2 + 4\pi^2 r^2)^{\frac{1}{2}}/p$. Thus we may readily calculate whether the maximum strain has been exceeded; we have found it to have been substantially exceeded in bends produced by Andrew G. and Julie Knowles, and in twists produced by Stephen North and Andrew G. The twisted spoons produced by Masuaki Kiyota and shown in Plate 1.1a (1,4) fall into this category. It should be mentioned that Professor Uphoff has also observed the boy producing such twists on identified stainless steel teaspoons; first the metal was softened by stroking with the forefinger, and then a quick twist of the wrist produced the necessary (but much reduced) torque. Professor Uphoff has offered a monetary reward for a performance of this operation by normal means under his specified conditions. The circumstances under which Masuaki produced the twisted spoons for me are described in chapter 1.

Thus we are introduced to the conception that the paranormal phenomenon is not precisely metal-bending, but *temporary metal-softening*; during this softening, a smaller, sometimes a very much smaller, degree of manual force is necessary for permanent deformation. So we return to the concept of validation by requiring the bend (to be produced by stroking) to be beyond human strength.

A recent example is the distortion of bowls of tablespoons. Plate 3.1 illustrates examples produced by Julie Knowles; some of them were observed and some not. I needed to know whether both orthogonal radii of curvature of the spoons — lengthwise and crosswise — were changed by Julie's action, and I therefore measured them before and after the operation; I found considerable changes in both. In consultation with metalwork craftsmen I have investigated how such effects could be produced by normal manual force, and have reached the conclusion that there must have been paranormal softening.

Of course it is not unknown for a child to exert more manual force than he should do. I have devised a rather wicked test for such behaviour. I offer a piece of a special metal which, although in appearance soft and elastic, is in fact brittle and cannot be bent quickly without a precisely monitored dynamic force. If the metal-bender attempts to use force, then there is an extremely strong probability he will break the specimen.[16] Although this tactic has been kept secret for a long time, nearly all the metal-bending children have failed to break the brittle specimens I have offered them.

The normal loading of a metal strip causes an elastic deformation proportional to the load, but beyond a certain 'yield point', any further deformation which takes place is plastic or permanent in character. The strip work-hardens as it deforms, so that its resistance to deformation increases with time until it is sufficiently large to resist the loading entirely; no further deformation then occurs. But if the resistance is insufficient to resist the loading, fracture then takes place. There are brittle metals and alloys in which the work-hardening is so slight that uncontrolled plastic deformation terminates in fracture. Such metals will not bend plastically, except by 'creep', a process which is appreciable

Plate 3.1 Bowls of spoons deformed by Julie Knowles by stroking action

only at temperatures greater than one-half of the absolute melting temperature. Thus low-melting point brittle alloys may be deformed by creep at room temperature, but cannot otherwise be deformed plastically just by the imposition of a load. An attempt to cause plastic deformation of a brittle material must involve a load which increases steadily with increasing time. Since it is virtually impossible to terminate a manual load suddenly during the very brief period when the metal is being plastically deformed, it will be impossible to bend manually a suitably chosen specimen of brittle material, except in a long period of time during which creep occurs.

Creep is the deformation produced very slowly by the continuous application of a load. The rate at which deformation occurs is not constant; according to Andrade's law, the deformation is proportional to the cube root of the time for which the load is applied. Although the law is an incomplete description, it applies reasonably well to the eutectic alloy of bismuth, tin and cadmium (54% Bi, 26% Sn, 20% Cd) (m.p. $103°C$). At room temperature the loading of a 6 mm $\times$ 8 mm specimen, supported by two knife-edges 10 cm apart, with a 3.2 kg load for 4.25 hr, produces a bend through $16°$. A sudden application of 3.5 kg under the same conditions fractures the specimen.

A suitably dimensioned specimen of this alloy cannot be bent by normal force through a large angle in a time of the order of minutes. When it is normally fractured there is often the appearance of a bend at the break. Even in boiling water the alloy is still brittle and fracture will occur. In order to produce normally a large angle bend without fracture, a machine producing a time-varying strain would have to be constructed.

A specimen of this alloy can be used for testing a metal-bender without concentrated observation, since the continuous application of surreptitious force will almost inevitably cause fracture. However, these tests have not deterred the children. Specimens 15 cm in length and 6 $\times$ 8 mm in cross-section have been bent without fracture by Andrew G. and Nicholas Williams as follows: $135°$ in 10 min, $100°$ in 5 min, $67°$ in 3 min, $62°$ in 2 min, $40°$ in 10 min and $34°$ in 6 min. At one session Nicholas W. placed four specimens in his coat pocket, and within five minutes all four had been bent through angles $111°$, $135°$, $160°$ and $170°$. As with bends that have been produced by creep loading for much longer periods, there was very little work-hardening, as can be seen from the data in Figure 3.1. The action must have been paranormal.

The bending of valuable items of porcelain in the private collection of a Swedish woman, recently investigated by Professor Hans Bender and Dr Hans Betz, fall into the category of paranormal bending of brittle material.

Another validation experiment which involves a task beyond human powers is the rupture of epoxy-resin bonds made to thin strips of metal. In the early experiments I had bonded pieces of different metals together in order to see which bent the most when exposed to subjects; but usually the resin bond fractured. I therefore obtained from Mr K.F. Thompson of Ciba-Geigy (makers of Araldite) a large number of tested epoxy-resin bonds of pairs of thin aluminium strips, each 1 inch wide. I then exposed these to the stroking action of child metal-benders. Although some strips merely bent, a significant proportion of the bonds fractured. The shear strengths (against fracture by pulling) are several thousand Newtons, well beyond human strength. However, the peel strengths are much lower and are within human strength. Therefore only those fractures are genuinely beyond human strength in which the

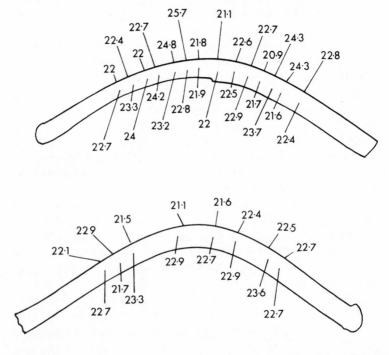

Figure 3.2 Two pieces of eutectic alloy of bismuth, tin and cadmium (6 × 9 mm × 15 cm), paranormally bent by Nicholas Williams. Hardness measurements (VPN) on side faces and convex faces.

two pieces do not show the distortion that inevitably accompanies a peel fracture of thin strips of metal bonded together. Table 3.1 lists the fractures achieved as of March 1977; the nineteen undistorted fractures must be regarded as paranormal.

Another device for avoiding the application of manual force for bending metal strips has been used successfully by Dr Osborne, a physicist who has researched metal-bending children in Australia. A precisely flat metal strip is recessed into a thick bar of clear brittle plastic, being held tightly in the recess at the ends and sides, but not actually stuck with adhesive. The possible elastic bending of the plastic without fracture is arranged so as to be insufficient to cause a permanent bend of the metal strip. Thus any permanent bend must come about as a result of suppression of the elastic properties of the metal; that is, a temporary softening.

Dr Osborne, like Professor Taylor in England, has made use of a spring balance, of the type used for weighing mail, to avoid the use of manual force by a metal-bender. A metal strip is securely attached to the pan of the balance, and the movement of the pointer is watched by the observer while the metal-bender gently strokes the strip. Testing of such a device shows that the application of strong manual bending moment to the strip without causing deflection of the balance pointer is extremely difficult.

'Homework' techniques

By far the most difficult type of validation is that of metal-bending unobserved at the time of action. It would be convenient if one could with certainty accept as genuinely paranormal some of the specimens which have been claimed to be paranormally bent by the children in their homes. But this is very difficult to do. One way would be if by good fortune the properties of paranormally bent metal turned out to be obviously different from those of physically bent metal; but we have already seen that this is unusual. Hardness measurements, for example, are often well within the range of normally bent specimens. I have therefore accepted 'homework tasks' as evidence of paranormality only when the metal specimens were enclosed within laboratory glassware.

Two of the British metal-bending children produced their most effective work in the privacy of their own bedrooms; one, Andrew G., invented the 'paperclip scrunch'. Under his action, paperclip wires curled up into all sorts of shapes; they would twist together and tighten

Table 3.1 Expoxy-resin bond fractures (length of each strip 11.4 cm; width of each strip 2.5 cm; area of epoxy-resin bond 1.5 cm × 2.5 cm)

Description of resin	Thickness of metal (mm)	Strength against tension (N)	Peel strength (N)	No. of undistorted fractures	No. of fractures with bend	No. of bends without fractures
Standard (twin pack) Araldite AV/HV 100	0.914	6000–7000	–	12	4	1
Redux K6 (phenolic based)	0.914	9360	200	2	3	6
Araldite AV 1523 GB (single component)	1.651	9190	369	5	1	1
High strength Araldite AV 1566 GB (single component)	1.651	10,000	144	–	1	5
ATI powder	0.914	–	–	–	11	–

up, making decorative forms. Little men and animals began to make their appearance; at first they were formed from only four or five paperclips, but eventually Andrew worked with as many as fifty or a hundred. Some of the most impressive are illustrated in Plate 3.2. The action used to take place quite fast, but failed to occur under visual observation, although audio and magnetic observation (chapter 7) have occasionally been successful.

Obviously it is possible to fabricate paperclip scrunches with the fingers, but in order to determine whether the action was paranormal, I decided to find out whether Andrew could produce them inside glass globes. It turned out that he could do this only when the globe contained a small orifice. Very little success was achieved with completely sealed globes; but when a hole even as small as 2 mm in diameter was allowed, and straightened paperclips were inserted through it, then wonderful scrunches were obtained. Straight metal strips were also inserted; they bent in such a way that they could not be extracted. Two of the twenty-two spheres are illustrated in Plate 3.3.

It is possible, as Society for Psychical Research member Denys Parsons showed, to unravel a scrunch with the use of tweezers, etc., and to extract it through the orifice in the globe. This exercise was carried out on the scrunch in sphere P, and it showed that the scrunch was apparently prefabricated in small sections. Of course this does not mean

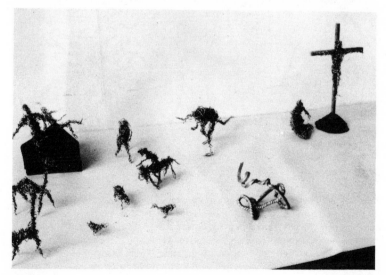

Plate 3.2 Part of an exhibition of paperclip scrunches mounted by Andrew G

that the scrunch tightening was not paranormal. To cast doubt on Andrew's scrunches we would need to reproduce similar ones by normal means, using tools. The first such replication was done by David Berglas, but in the opinion of many who saw the result it was not very convincing. Eventually Society for Psychical Research members Richard Alabone and Denys Parsons produced two impressive normal scrunches; but on inspection we found that the wires were not so tightly bound as in Andrew's scrunches. Also the time taken for fabrication was rather long, and the tightening was carried out on the entire assembly of paperclips. Andrew, on the other hand, could do the operation in stages, taking only a few minutes per stage; two of his scrunch histories were recorded photographically and the photographic history of one of these appears in Plate 3.4. In my opinion the tightening of the paper-clips within the globe is possible in these short periods of time only when some paranormal distortion takes place; equally rapid achievement of really strong tightening by normal means using tools has not been achieved.

The globes have been widely exhibited and inspected and have impressed many people with the reality of unobserved paranormal metal-bending. However, it has been argued by others that the validation

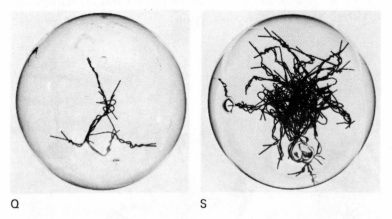

Q   S

Plate 3.3 Scrunches within glass spheres produced by Andrew G.

Sphere Q, made of unusually thin glass, diameter 127 mm, orifice diameter 3 mm. Scrunch of eight paperclips made in four stages of 2½ minutes, 5 minutes, 10 minutes, and inspected after each stage by the family.

Sphere S, diameter 132 mm, orifice diameter 8 mm. Made in nine stages of a few minutes each, and photographed by the author after each stage.

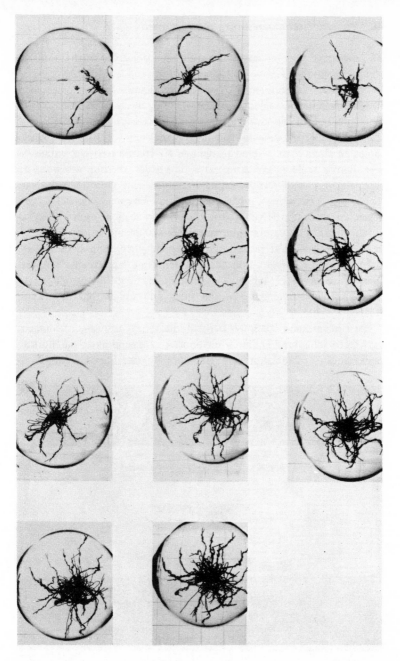

Plate 3.4 Serial history of fabrication of scrunch T within sphere of diameter 132 mm, orifice diameter 8.5 mm. Successive stages of eight paperclips in 9 min, five in 7, six in 7; eight in 8, five in 13, five in 11; three + eight in 7 + 6, six in 9, six in 15; five in 10, and six in 6 min.

of unobserved phenomena by this technique is not watertight, and I did not pursue the work beyond this stage.

Stronger testimony now exists in the shape of metal pieces bent inside hermetically sealed glass tubes. These bends are small and undramatic, but there is no doubt that they have been obtained.

I first recorded such a bend in a 3 cm length of 3 mm × 0.5 mm annealed alpha-brass offered to Belinda H. The flatness was within 0.1 mm before sealing, and after extraction a deformation of about 0.6 mm, together with some twisting, was recorded. More recently Mark Henry has bent for me a piece of alpha-brass 7.6 cm × 1 cm × 0.77 mm sealed inside a plastic tube with epoxy-resin seals at each end by Dr Brian Millar. The deformation was 1.55 ± 0.04 mm; since there had been no annealing, I heated the deformed strip to 350°C, but the deformation, although reduced, still remained permanent. I experimented to see whether such deformations could be produced by prolonged violent shaking of the tube, and found that they could not.

Dr Crussard and Dr Bouvaist of the Pechiney Aluminium Company in France (chapter 13) have also reported the bending of metal inside hermetically sealed laboratory glassware by metal-bender Jean-Pierre

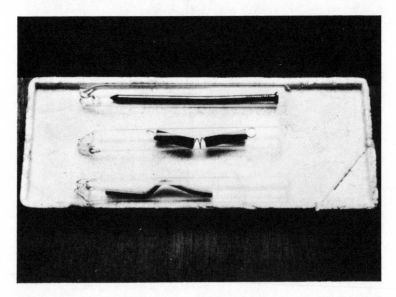

Plate 3.5 Metal items (nail, spring and brass strip) bent by Jean-Pierre Girard within glass tubes sealed by Dr Wolkowski

Girard. Only 0.5 per cent strain was recorded — comparable with the small bends obtained by Belinda H. and Mark Henry.

Dr Wolkowski, who conducted the first experiments with Jean-Pierre Girard in Paris, has also reported unobserved bending within sealed tubes. Three of his sealed tube experiments resulted in more dramatic bends, which are illustrated in Plate 3.5. What is different about these glass tubes is that the sealing is not hermetic; they would probably not hold a good vacuum, since the glass at one end was softened and pinched together by Dr Wolkowski rather than drawn out in a single thread under rotation. However, since such bends could not be produced by the operation of tools through these very small vacuum leaks, the validation is good.

Dr Wolkowski writes:[21]

We then embarked on a more sophisticated experiment, which consisted of sealing different metal objects in Pyrex glass tubes; these were completely sealed with a torch. They were weighed with a precision of 10^{-4} g and measured with a precision of 10^{-4} m, and were left with Girard. Inside we had placed different metal objects such as metal paperclips and steel springs of the coil kind; when they were returned to us they were quite remarkably bent, from $10°$ to $30°$. The steel spring, for example, which was straight at the beginning, was now so distended that at one point it could no longer move freely in the Pyrex tube. All the tubes were still the same weights and the same dimensions, and the glass blower could not detect any tampering.

Chapter **4**

The detection of metal-bending action

It occurred to me at a very early stage, during the Society for Psychical Research 1975 experiments carried out with Graham and Valerie P. at City University, London, that very small elastic deformations might be of common occurrence in metal-bending sessions; they would be undetectable by eye, and would result in no permanent deformation; but they could possibly be detected by instruments. Therefore I thought it would be useful to provide the metal specimens with a sensitive device capable of detecting small *strains* (elongations or deformations), such as are produced by, or at any rate associated with, *stress* (force or moment). I found the *resistive strain gauge*[22] to be by far the most suitable instrument for this purpose. One modern type of gauge consists of a thin film, typically of the alloy constantan, in the form of a folded filament, deposited on a small thin plastic sheet (see Figure 4.1). The gauge is either stuck onto a metal surface or onto the inner surface of a cavity machined in the metal; the plastic is sufficiently thin ($\leqslant 0.05$ mm) for it not to reinforce the metal but to bend or extend with it. The electrical resistance of the constantan filament varies proportionally to its length (normal length plus strain), so that a suitable battery-operated electrical bridge circuit and amplifier (Figure 4.1, as first built by my technician Nick Nicola) produces a time-varying voltage proportional to time-varying strain. This 'analogue signal' can be recorded on magnetic tape, or better still on a chart-recorder; thereby we obtain a measure of how long the strain lasts and how large it is. Suitable design enables very small strains to be measured, so that weak 'powers' of a paranormal metal-bender can be detected even though the specimen is far below the condition of permanent deformation. Calibration of the instrument is summarized in Table 4.1.

I built the device with electrical screening of the wires, sufficient to

Table 4.1

Strain sensitivity	$\Delta l/l = \epsilon =$	3.33×10^{-6}/mV
Moment sensitivity on Al strip 12 mm wide, 0.75 mm thick	$\sigma l =$	2×10^{-4} Nm/mV
Temperature sensitivity of the thermistor	$\Delta T =$	2×10^{-3} °C/mV

Standard deviation of sensitivity for six channels, for identical stress, ± 0.03.

ensure that artefacts would not occur from electrostatic or electro-magnetic causes. In the initial version a gauge was stuck onto a brass strip by Mr Chapman at the City University, and the boy whom we were studying (Graham P.) was allowed to stroke the strip with the ball of his forefinger. To our surprise some sharp little pulses appeared on the chart-record. When I myself stroked the sensor in a similar manner

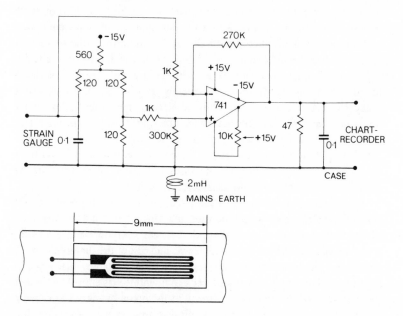

Figure 4.1 Bridge and amplifier circuit for use with resistive strain gauge and chart-recorder; strain gauge (Micro-Measurements type EA09 125 BT 120) is shown enlarged.

no pulses appeared. But at this stage Chapman and I were not convinced that we had recorded the phenomenon for the first time. We were both sceptical and thought that electrostatic artefacts must have been responsible. The signals were small, and I thought it possible that they could have arisen from the finger's jumping from point to point, in the manner of chalk producing an involuntary dotted line on a blackboard. In retrospect it now seems possible that these were genuine paranormal signals, but I decided at the time to make two drastic changes:

1   The strain gauge was to be enclosed within a cavity in the metal, and electrically screened as far as possible.
2   The child must not be allowed to touch the metal with his fingers.

With the new policy I started exposing strain gauges in latchkeys to the children I visited, Belinda H., Julie Knowles, Andrew G., Willie G., Richard B., Nicholas Williams, Alison Lloyd, Mark Henry, David and Steven Nemeth, Clifford White, Gill Costin and Neil Howarth. All of them managed to produce signals without touch, and I have since successfully exposed the sensors to other subjects in other countries.

Children enjoyed playing with the latchkeys in which the first strain gauges were mounted (Plate 4.1). When the key is deformed elastically between the fingers and thumb, a deflection can be seen on the chart-record, with the paper moving typically at a speed of 1 inch every 5 seconds. A latchkey is difficult to deform permanently by finger pressure alone, so the chart-recorder trace returns to approximately its original level. The device is such a pleasant toy that we might recommend its production commercially. Of course we must avoid the use of ferromagnetic metals, since spontaneous relaxation of domains might cause signals due to the Barkhausen effect.

The moment of truth for a metal-bender is when he realizes that similar signals appear when neither the fingers nor indeed any part of the body touches the latchkey. Sometimes I would place the latchkey on a plastic dish or in a glass bowl, and allow the metal-bender to stroke the glass beneath it. The best part of an hour was often necessary to produce the first paranormal signal, and it was almost as though the experimenter were coaxing it out of the metal-bender. The viewing of the chart-recorder is a form of biofeedback, and is best when the sensitivity is raised until the electrical noise shows as 'grass' on the trace; a tiny artefact is as much encouragement as the appearance of a tiny paranormal signal, and it does not matter if at first the two are confused. Larger signals are then to be expected. If they appeared when the key was resting in a glass bowl, I would then remove the bowl and allow the key to hang by its own electrical connections. The child would then just sit facing the key, possibly pointing his forefinger, or even stroking his fingers and thumb together.

Of course the apparatus must be allowed to run 'quiet' for as long as possible (sometimes hours) before exposure to the metal-bender. No signal must appear when the metal-bender is not present. Battery operation is preferable, and precautions must be taken against inductively

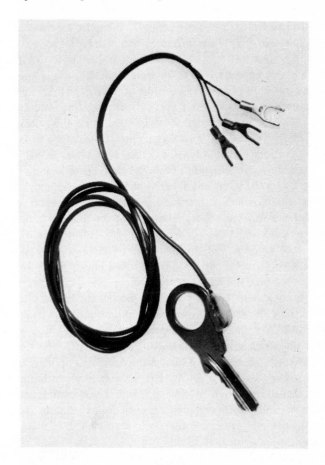

Plate 4.1 Latchkey with milled slot containing resistive strain gauge. Epoxy-resin potting and screened lead, as used in early experiments with Nicholas Williams

coupled mains artefacts and atmospheric artefacts (e.g. those arising from strong walkie-talkie radio sets). Dummy resistances, circuits and chart-records are used for this purpose, and any signal appearing also in the dummy channel must be rejected.

The drift experienced on the strain gauge amplifier, although by no means large after the settling period, is not such that slow variations of strain could reliably be studied with the direct current system. The use of an oscillatory input, with or without phase-locked loop, would readily allow of this investigation, but we have postponed it for the time being.

The latchkey is suspended from its wires so as to minimize mechanical coupling; the child can point his fingers at the metal, at about six inches distance. We must watch carefully to see that there is no touching, but we should not appear to do so. If signals are still forthcoming, then the distance can be slowly increased. Most of the successful metal-benders have succeeded at distances of up to about three feet; Andrew G. and Stephen North have succeeded at up to eight feet and Nicholas Williams has regularly worked at fifteen feet, and once obtained a signal at thirty feet. Occasionally the latchkey or piece of metal actually bends permanently during its suspension from the strain gauge wires.

Figure 4.2a–e shows the entire chart-record of the first really impressive strain gauge session, which resulted in a permanent deformation of the latchkey. Nicholas Williams was seated by my side on the sofa in the lounge (see Figure 5.1) whilst the key was hanging by its wire from the mantelpiece on the opposite wall. We had a long wait before signals appeared, and I gave Nicholas cutlery which I asked him to bend. He twirled the pieces around, and in the course of time several displayed a 'curly bend'. My object in allowing him to handle cutlery was to encourage his possible 'power' to blossom and spill over onto the strain gauge specimen. Also his hands were occupied, so that any question of tampering with the strain gauge specimen was ruled out. During the session I changed the sensitivity of the chart-recorder amplifier at appropriate times. I shall never forget my increasing excitement as the small, doubtful signals increased in size, although I was completely confident of the reliability of my equipment, since prolonged tests had been made in Nicholas's absence, and there were no signals. Eventually the latchkey developed a permanent bend.

A most important lesson which is taught to the metal-bender by use of the strain gauge detector is the avoidance of over-concentration; he must learn 'sudden inattention' if he wants results. The insomniac who concentrates his mind on going to sleep will have little success; it is often the same with paranormal metal-bending. The strongest events often take place, it appears, when the subject relaxes directly after concentration. He must learn to be patient and not to 'concentrate on concentration'. If the experimenter makes it obvious that he is scrutinizing or is suspicious of the subject, then the effects are likely to be weak or altogether absent; if the experimenter conceals his scrutiny, and the metal-bender avoids over-concentration, then some signals may come. Parapsychologist Julian Isaacs has embarked on a series of experiments with groups of subjects and an audio-recorder, studying the psychological tensions at moments when signals are recorded.

Of course this 'learning of inattention', on the part of all present, is particularly unfortunate from the point of view of the observer. On the one hand he must develop reliable techniques of observation and instrumentation; on the other hand he must learn to *appear* inattentive if he wishes the effects to be stronger. Obviously some compromise is necessary. Most of the time is spent keeping a careful watch; but if

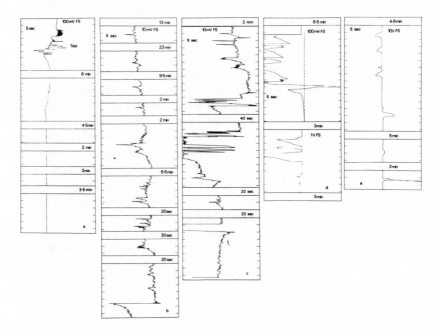

Figure 4.2a–e Chart-record of dynamic strain gauge signals produced at the first session with Nicholas Williams. Vertical time scale markings of 5 sec are interrupted during quiet periods (e.g. 6 min, 4.5 min). Full-scale sensitivities are 100 mV, 10 mV, 100 mV again, 1 V and 10 V; square-ended signals indicate full scale.

rapport between the experimenter and the child is sufficiently good, then there is less danger of touching if the head is turned. One must judge whether the child is himself really interested in the experiment; in that case he will report an inadvertent touch. But always the experimenter must return to the pattern of good video observation. If bad habits of touching should develop, we can make use of the touch detector discussed further in chapter 15; we can also use partial screening of the target, and even a moving target.

When the child and the family first realize that bending can take place without the necessity of the metal being touched, this is a great step forward in their understanding. Sometimes the child is a little frightened by this realization, and sometimes he never faces up to it at all.

If we are to make the detection of strain within untouched metal a valuable method of investigation, then we must encourage its use by other investigators. At the time of writing, ten other groups of workers have successfully used essentially the same equipment as ours; their reportings of signals obtained with various subjects can be regarded as an important confirmation of our findings. The most extensive experiments have been carried out in France and in Japan.

I have several times made video-records of strain gauge experiments, notably with Julie Knowles and Stephen North; also I have made a point of asking physicists and others to be present at the production of strain signals in the homes of these families. On occasion I have been asked to provide a metal-bender to produce signals on a television programme. Four times Stephen North has attempted this, and twice he was successful, twice he was not; but the effects cannot usually be produced to order, particularly when there are television lights, continual delays, photographic tests, make-up, and so on. I had the impression that Stephen was acting the part of a metal-bender rather than being his normal self. Certainly, Uri Geller, Jean-Pierre Girard and Masuaki Kiyota have learned sufficient control to work under these conditions. But there are many reasons why the metal-bending children should not be encouraged to follow in their footsteps.

An important choice the experimenter must make is the size of the metal specimen and just how the strain gauge should be mounted in it. When a strip of metal is gently stretched, the extension (strain) which causes the signal is directly proportional to the tension (stress). The thinner and narrower the strip, the larger is the extension for the same tension and the more sensitive is the equipment to force. When we require the greatest sensitivity, we may stick the gauge onto a metal strip only 0.75 mm thick and cover it with a thin piece of foil for electrostatic shielding. But the experiments concerned with the details of strong effects, such as those with Nicholas Williams or Jean-Pierre Girard, require much more robust specimens.

We must of course use the recommended strain gauge adhesives; there is a danger of paranormal forces tearing away the strain gauge from the metal (chapter 9). To attach the strain gauge with adhesive tape (a reported procedure) is quite inadequate. If the strain gauge itself is fractured by paranormal action, then the experiment terminates; but I have conducted sessions in which there was fracture of the specimen without destruction of the strain gauge and it was still possible to continue work.

When the strain pulses are sufficiently strong for the specimen to be deformed permanently, the chart-recorder trace may also show a permanent deflection. There might be a correlation between the magnitude of this deflection and the observed angle of the bend; an effort has been made to reproduce the data graphically in Figure 4.3 for sensors mounted in latchkeys in the Nicholas Williams experiments.[23] But the correlation is not an accurate proportionality, partly because the bend does not always take place exactly at the position of the strain gauge and partly because, as we shall find in chapter 6, the signal may correspond only to a permanent extension and not to permanent bend. A latchkey will usually bend somewhere along the part that goes into the

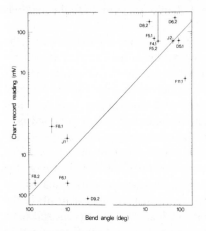

Figure 4.3 Comparison of permanent deflection chart-records with observed bend angles of latchkey during the Nicholas Williams sessions summarized in Table 5.1. The 45° straight line is merely a fitting to the data.

lock, while the strain gauge has been deliberately mounted in the handle and will continue to function even when the latchkey is fractured. In the first session with Stephen North, using a long thin strip of aluminium, a very large visible bend or curl through 540° was produced more than an inch from the strain gauge, and no permanent deflection of the chart-record was manifest.

Sometimes the electrical connections to a strain gauge are bent or fractured paranormally during a session; in some early experiments it was my practice to embed them in solid epoxy-resin; but it is sometimes important to avoid alteration of the mechanical properties of the specimen.

When the strain gauge is embedded in the metal, the subject has no direct knowledge of its form, and it is very likely that any paranormal action will be on the metal itself. We have found evidence from subsequent experiments with several sensors mounted inside one specimen that it is usually the metal and not the strain gauge which experiences the 'action'.

During the first ten hours' experience with strain gauges exposed to metal-benders I learned much about their use from mistakes that were made. But after nearly two hundred hours of exposure I consider that I know sufficient to avoid mistaking drifts or artefacts for paranormal signals, and vice versa. Among others, physicists Ron Miller, David Robertson and Elizabeth Rauscher have taken part in the exposures of strain gauges and have brought a fresh critical approach to the methods I use.

It is of course important to verify by other experiments that the signals do not arise from paranormal action on the electrical equipment or on the pen of the chart-recorder, or simply from electric mains or electromagnetic artefacts coupled inductively to the battery-operated equipment. Two subsidiary experimental programmes were mounted for this purpose. In the first a galvanometer mirror was mounted on a very thin spring steel strip, with strain gauge attached. One end of the spring was attached to a stable horizontal surface under a glass dome, and an optical beam from a helium–neon laser was passed through the dome and was reflected through it again from the mirror and onto a scale. The overall optical path was about 6 m. Small movements of the light spot were seen to synchronize with strain gauge signals, and some ringing was observed, due to the long-period mechanical resonance in the system. One spring exposed to Stephen North became permanently deformed. This is the experiment which seems in retrospect to have been a miniature of the *Bealings Bells* situation (chapter 1).

In the second type of experiment a dummy strain gauge is included with real strain gauges on a metal strip. Signals are observed on the real strain gauge chart-record throughout a session, but *signals are not recorded from the dummy gauge.* Sometimes a stable resistor mounted on or near the metal is used as a dummy strain gauge. Sometimes a resistive thermal sensor (Micro-Measurements type STG 50D) of 70 Ω resistance is connected with compensation in one channel of the electronics. In physical appearance the thermal sensor is similar to the resistive strain gauge (Micro-Measurements type EA09 125 BT 120), but its resistance is insensitive to strain although highly sensitive to temperature. Sudden temperature changes are unknown to us in para-normal metal-bending sessions, although temperature drifts usually occur, arising from convection currents (chapter 14). Paranormal strain signals on the other hand are sudden, in that they are sharp-fronted pulses; the measured durations are now known to be, on occasion, less than a millisecond.

The use of a chart-recorded dummy strain gauge channel is now standard practice in our experiments. Both types of experiments have vindicated the interpretation that paranormal action develops an internal strain in the metal or the strain gauge or both.

Naturally I have given much thought to the question of whether I consider the many thousands of strain pulses recorded in these sessions to be merely artefacts. It is quite possible to devise electronic methods of simulating signals, using electromagnetic coupling, but I am releasing no detailed information about how this might be done! The dummy strain gauge would show up such simulations, as it shows up artefacts arising from local electrical disturbances. Any signal also occurring in the dummy strain gauge channel (and such an event is rare) is discarded. There is also the possibility of someone jogging the chart-recorder mechanically or tampering with the electronics; obviously I am aware of this possibility, but I have never known it happen except accidentally. I think it possible that very small electromagnetic artefacts (about 0.2 mV in magnitude) might appear on the strain gauges but not in the dummy channel. But the vast majority of paranormal signals are much larger than this, and I do not see how they can represent anything other than paranormal strains.

Action on 'nude' strain gauges which are not stuck onto pieces of metal was observed at several no-touch sessions with Nicholas Williams. Typically the strain gauge was stretched between two rigid mounting points, and in some experiments a small piece of insulated wire was allowed to rest freely on it. The purpose was to search for any downward quasi-force exerted during bending of the wire. In fact such quasi-forces were observed each time the wire bent visibly. Their magnitudes sometimes exceeded those of the force exerted by the entire weight of the wire resting on the centre of the horizontal strain gauge. Thus these quasi-forces appear not to be simply changes in the weight of the metal; the interpretation of this type of experiment is at present rather difficult.

I believe it likely that the action was not on the strain gauge but on the wire, which bent. But in later experiments a strain gauge unloaded with wire was found to experience signals; possibly these were electrical in origin (chapter 15).

I have successfully exposed strain gauges mounted on many varieties of material; tungsten, brass, aluminium, copper, silicone rubber, wood, plastics, glass and fused silica.

With the strain gauge I have attempted to measure the strains experienced by a metal specimen during no-touch bending action. The action occurs in occasional bursts. There are characteristic patterns which these data exhibit. First, the signal rise times; are they sudden or gradual in their onset and their termination? Inspection of the data shows that nearly always the strain pulses have sharp onsets and usually sharp terminations. The time-resolving power of the chart-recorder (about 0.1 sec) is in fact the limit of the observed sharpness, but other methods of recording have been used. It is rare for a more gradual onset of force to be recorded. When signals are a thousand times more powerful than typically, the rise times are slower, partly because the chart-recorder amplifier is slower. But typical signals show onsets which are sharper than those which can be recorded from finger action on the metal; finger signals, except for the smallest, are softened by muscular response and flesh distortion.

I have amplified the paranormal signals and listened to them acoustically; they are bumps rather than clicks; i.e. frequencies greater than about 500 Hz appear to be insignificant. Occasionally there is acoustic ringing of the metal specimen, and occasionally the metal specimen is seen to swing a little on its wire suspension.

Second, the duration of the signals; although most are of less than a second, a few are of several seconds' duration. Occasionally the pulse (Figure 4.4a) appears to be continuous with wobbles superposed. Possibly this represents an unresolved group of shorter signals. There are some signal events in which a pulse in one direction is followed immediately or after one or two seconds by a pulse in the other direction (Fig. 4.4b). Activity continuing for more than about ten seconds is rare; although sometimes there is minor activity ('nibbling', Figure 4.4c) which can occasionally last for more than a minute. Sometimes there is extensive structuring of the signals (Figure 4.4d). Sometimes the elastic component of the strain is suppressed, so that a bend is achieved without overswing (Figure 4.4e). Sometimes an elastic pulse in one direction is followed by a plastic deformation in the other (Figure 4.4f).

Third, the magnitude of the signals. Considered as stress signals they depend upon the strength of the specimen on which the strain gauge is mounted. Results of calibration experiments of the system in terms of strain and stress are given in Table 4.1. Signals during a metal-bending session can be distributed over several orders of magnitude, from a few millivolts to a few volts on the chart-recorder, so that it is difficult to make precise predictions. Both lower and upper limits are instrumental, the former being the electrical noise, and the latter the upper limit of the chart-recorder (10 V) and sometimes the fracture of the sensor or of the metal. It is usual for the signals to increase from small to large during a session; only occasionally are the first signals the largest. Sometimes there is a continuous train of signals of similar magnitude, either

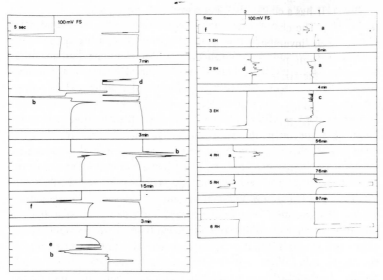

Figure 4.4 Some dynamic strain pulses showing distinctive features. All are from Nicholas Williams sessions B–F. Time scale intervals are all 5 sec. Two-channel measurements (chapter 5), with sensors numbered 1 and 2, in separate latchkeys.

a, signals with reasonably flat tops; b, signal followed immediately by one in the opposite direction; c, nibbling; d, structured signals; e, permanent deformations in which the elastic components are suppressed; f, elastic strain pulses in one direction followed by plastic strain pulses in the opposite direction.

small or large. There are many factors, psychological and physical, which determine the signal magnitude, and they will be discussed further in chapter 17.

Fourth, the structure of the signal events in time, which we have already illustrated and described in Figure 4.4. Examination of even this small amount of Nicholas Williams data will give some idea of the great variety and unpredictability of the structure. Such records should be rare in purely physical experiments, where the structure should show at least some regularity; the signal records are strongly reminiscent of biophysical or environmental data, which, of course, they are. Any attempt to explain their origin must take account of this variety of fine structure. Some of it cannot be produced by hand. There is some discernible variation between the patterns of signal as between different metal-benders. Most signals produced by metal-benders are simply sharp peaks, but a few are followed by reverse peaks, or overswings, which are not instrumental in origin. The reverse signals are in this case just as sharp as the parent signals preceding them.

An interesting type of signal makes its appearance in Figure 4.4 (3 EH f). It has a curved tail, always of the same form, an 'exponential' $\exp(-t/\tau)$. The characteristic time τ varies only with the design of the sensor; it is invariant during a session, for example. Perhaps these tails arise from physical relaxation of internal stress in which both the metal, the strain gauge and the adhesive play their part (see chapter 9).

During the reception of signals, I have studied the no-touch movement of a specimen and strain gauge suspended from its electrical connections; this has been done visually, and on several occasions by means of a video-camera. I noticed that when a relatively strong dynamic strain pulse was produced by Nicholas Williams the key would sometimes be joggled a few millimetres and would swing for perhaps a second. This motion was first recorded on video-tape with the co-operation of Dr Ron Miller. But the magnitude of the movements was small, and we cannot make any further generalizations from a study of the tapes, other than that the key was not touched by any visible agency. A stop-clock was included in the field of view, in order that the small movements of the key could be synchronized with the signals recorded on the chart-recorder.

Subsequently David Robertson and I made video-records of strain gauge experiments with Stephen North and Julie Knowles. When a long, thin (0.75 mm X 8 mm X 40 cm) metal specimen suspended at each end received paranormal strains at the centre, it sometimes continued its bending oscillations, which were recorded until they died out in a few seconds due to physical damping.

A feature of the sessions with both Stephen North and Nicholas Williams was the slow start with gradually increasing frequency of occurrence of signals. It is possible that they were learning during the session to lose their inhibitions against producing signals. Several children have commenced sessions with small signals, separated by long periods of time; but not all of them make the transition into the more powerful regime, when signals come thick and fast.

In the next chapter we proceed to the discussion of the information that can be obtained by the use of more than one detection device at a time.

Chapter 5

Simultaneous strains: the 'surface of action'

There have been many reports by families of several metal objects being found bent at the same time. Of course it is difficult to observe two widely separated objects actually bending at the same moment, since the eyes cannot subtend a wide field of view; but occasionally there are good reasons to suppose that two or more bendings may have taken place simultaneously. We are forced to pose the questions: Did these involve simultaneous strain pulses, and if so, how extensive was the region of action? Were any strains experienced elsewhere, and where was the subject at the time? Does his location affect the strains, and can he direct his 'powers' at several objects at the same moment? Is there conceivably a terrestrial effect – a preferred orientation for signals?

A physicist might suppose that some sort of wave-front issues from the subject, like ripples from a stone dropped in water. If this were so, objects equidistant from him would receive signals at the same instant. Does this occur?

We have investigated these questions using the strain gauge equipment described in the previous chapter. Synchronized chart-records and independent strain gauges, bridges, amplifiers and batteries were used.

The first studies with two, and later with three, independent strain gauges were undertaken in thirteen sessions with Nicholas Williams during the first half of 1976. At first he simply attempted to influence both chart-records while the two metal specimens were about a foot apart; his own position was not fixed during the session. We found that signals did appear on both chart-records, sometimes simultaneously, and therefore it was possible to proceed to more controlled experiments.

Since it was necessary that Nicholas should be in one location during the entire session, a suitable occupation had to be found for him. He was already an experienced builder of model aircraft and ships, using

commercial assembly kits, glue and paint. He was asked to do this at a
work surface in the open-plan ground-floor living-area of his house;
individual latchkeys, each containing its own strain gauge, were arranged
in suitable locations, suspended from their own electrical connections,
so as to minimize mechanical coupling between them. A plan of the
area is shown in Figure 5.1; the circle S represents Nicholas's location,
but that of the observer (myself) is not shown. It varied between the
lounge sofa, the kitchen and even the stairs; and sometimes I would
have to move to the apparatus to make adjustments. As far as possible,
other observers were excluded from these sessions, but on some few
occasions the presence of Nicholas's father, Dr Terry Williams, Dr Miller
and one or two family friends was recorded.

The routine was as follows: I would arrive around noon and set up

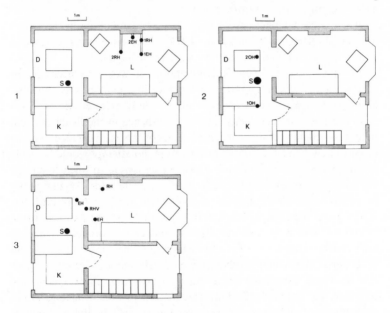

Figure 5.1 Plan of ground floor of Nicholas Williams's house, in which sessions
with two and three strain gauges were conducted.

S, the subject, Nicholas Williams; 1EH,2EH, two strain gauges in the equidistant horizontal configuration; 1RH,2RH, two strain gauges in the radial horizontal configuration; 1OH,2OH, two strain gauges in the opposite horizontal
configuration; RHV, two strain gauges in the vertical configuration, or in the
radial-horizontal vertical configuration (with RH).

L, lounge; D, dining area; K, kitchen.

My own position was on the lounge sofa, in the kitchen, or occasionally
watching from the stairs.

the equipment. It was then allowed to run quietly in the empty house for as long as possible, with Nicholas out of the house for as much as two hours. When we returned, the chart-records were found to be free from artefacts. The afternoons were used for exposures of about two hours each. On several afternoons the suspended latchkeys spontaneously bent to and fro, and ultimately fractured.

The latchkeys were suspended in various configurations with respect to Nicholas, as described in the caption to Figure 5.1. There were four configurations with two latchkeys: equidistant horizontal, signified by the caption EH; radial horizontal, signified by RH (here the two keys were on a horizontal line stretching radially from Nicholas); opposite horizontal, OH (in which they were horizontal and at directly opposite sides of Nicholas); and vertical, V, in which one latchkey was directly above the other, at the position shown.

When three latchkeys were used they were mounted in the radial-horizontal-vertical configuration, RHV. The three keys defined a vertical plane stretching radially outward from Nicholas.

For the most rigorous experimentation it would be necessary to change from one configuration to another in a random way, possibly after every signal event or even at randomly selected times. Such procedures would cause considerable disturbance in the living-area and of course could not be concealed from Nicholas. I decided that he should know what the configurations were; no attempt would be made to screen the sensors from view; but the decisions as to when to change the configurations would be made by me, usually after a small number of events. This would not be a completely random procedure, but regularity in the changes was carefully avoided. In later sessions I made efforts to induce Nicholas to learn to induce synchronous signals in each configuration; when he achieved success, the configuration would be changed; ultimately a change would take place after every three events. These procedures were followed because of my increasing certainty that the configurations were matters to which Nicholas would probably react differently at each session; at first he did not express much interest in what configuration was being offered; but in the end he was motivated to try as hard as he could to produce the maximum 'control' over the sensors in each configuration. This 'control' was understood to be the production of synchronized signals on more than one sensor.

In some events there are signals on one sensor only. In some, both traces display signals, but one is obviously in advance of the other. But in some the signals appear, within the accuracy of the equipment

Table 5.1 Classification of events in Nicholas Williams sessions A–G

Configurations: EH, equidistant horizontal; RH, radial horizontal; V, vertical; RHV, three sensors, radial horizontal and vertical, with two vertical sensors closest to subject; 30°, inclination of subject to line joining two horizontal sensors (90° would represent EH); Up, subject upstairs, sensors downstairs; OH, opposite horizontal; RHS, radial horizontal with one sensor screened; OHS, opposite horizontal with perspex screen over one sensor.
Synchronization classifications: U1, 2, signal unique on 1 or 2; S, synchronous; NS, non-synchronous; SS, signals on one sensor suppressed (small magnitude), but still synchronous.

Session	Date (1976)	Designation	Configuration	Synchronization	Range (mV)	Remarks
A	9 Mar	1	≃EH	U1	0.1	
		2	≃EH	NS	0.1	
		3	≃EH	S	0.1	
		4	≃EH	S	0.1	
B	18 Mar	1	30°	S	0.1	
		2	30°	NS	0.1	
		3	30°	NS	0.1	
		4	30°	S	0.1	
		5	30°	U2	0.1	
		6	30°	S	0.1	
		7	30°	NS	0.1	
		8	Up	S	0.1	
		8a	30°	U2	0.1	
		9	30°	S	0.1	
		10	30°	S	0.1	
		11	EH	NS	0.1	
		12	30°	NS	0.1	
		13	RH	S	0.1	
		14	30°	U2	0.1	
C	23 Mar	1	RH	S	0.1	
		2	RH	S	0.1	
		3	RH	S	0.1	
		4	RHS	NS	0.1	Screening by kitchen foil
		5	RHS	NS	0.1	Screening by kitchen foil
		6	EH	NS	0.1	
		7	EH	NS	1	
		8	EH	NS	1	
		9	EH	NS	1	
		10	EH	NS	1	
		11	EH	NS	1	
C1	23 Mar	1	EH	S	0.1	
		2	EH	S	0.1	
		3	EH	NS	0.1	
		4	RH	S	0.1	

Table 5.1 continued

Session	Date (1976)	Designa-tion	Configura-tion	Synchron-ization	Range (mV)	Remarks
		5	RH	S	0.1	
		6	RH	NS	0.1	
D	9 Apl	1	RH	S	0.1	
		2	RHS	NS	0.1	Glass screen
		3	RHS	NS	0.1	Glass screen
		4	RHS	U1	0.1	Brass screen on key 1, which bent to 70°
		5	RHS	NS	1	Steel screen on key 1, which bent to 135°
		6	RHS	NS	1	Steel screen on key 2, which bent to 60°
		7	RH	NS	1	Key 1 fractures, key 2 bent at 60°
		8	RH	NS	1	Key 2 bent to 80°
		9	EH	NS	1	Key 2 bent to 85°
		10	EH	NS	10	Key 2 partially fractured
		11	EH	U	10	Key 2 fractured
E	15 Apl	1	OH	U1	0.1	Fracture of table-spoon with sensor
		2	OHS	NS	0.1	Perspex screen on eutectic alloy specimen
		3	OHS	NS	0.1	ditto
		4	OHS	NS	0.1	ditto
		5	OH	NS	0.1	
		6	OH	S	0.1	
		7	OH	U1	0.1	
		8	OH	S	0.1	
		9	OH	S	0.1	
		10	OH	U1	0.1	Intended key 1 only
		11	OH	U2	0.1	Intended key 1 only
F	23 Apl	1	V	S	0.1	Unwitnessed alleged paranormal shooting of piece of metal from tube
		2	V	S	0.1	
		3	V	S	0.1	
		4	V	SS	0.1	25° bend on key 1 Failure of chart-pen

Table 5.1 continued

Session	Date (1976)	Designation	Configuration	Synchronization	Range (mV)	Remarks
		5	V	SS	0.1	45° bend on key 1, 25° bend on key 2
		6	V	NS	0.1	Some misalignment of configuration; 35° bend on key 1, 25° on key 2
		7	V	SS	0.1	Some misalignment of configuration
		8	V	SS	0.1	10° bend on key 1; 45° on key 2
		9	V	SS	0.1	10° bend on key 1; 45° on key 2
		10	V	S	0.1	
		11	V	NS	0.1	Intended delay, 135° bend on key 1; 45° on key 2
		12	V	S	0.1	Key 1 fractured
		13	EH	NS	0.1	
		14	EH	SS	0.1	Some misalignment of configuration
		15	EH	S	0.1	
		16	V	SS	0.1	
		17	V	NS	0.1	
		18	V	S	0.1	
		19	EH	SS	0.1	
		20	EH	S	0.1	
		20a	EH	S	0.1	
		21	V	S	0.1	
		22	EH	S	0.1	
		23	RH	S	0.1	
		24	RH	S	0.1	
G	30 Apl	1	RHV	S	0.1	
		2	RHV	S	0.1	
		3	RHV	S	0.1	
		4	RHV	S	0.1	
		5	RHV	S	0.1	
		6	RHV	S	0.1	
H	27 May	1	Single		0.1	All viewed on television monitor
		2	Single		0.1	
		3	Single		0.1	
		4	Single		0.1	
		5	Single		0.1	

(0.2 sec), to be recorded at identical times. The signals are not of the same magnitude, or even in the same sense, but their time structures are very similar; they are, basically, *synchronous signals*.

The classification of the data from all these sessions into synchronous and non-synchronous signals is clearly a valuable exercise. Usually it is as simple as has appeared from the above example, but there are a few signals in which the classification is doubtful, and these have not been included. Table 5.1 lists the classification, which can be summarized as indicated.

Configuration	Synchronous signals	Non-synchronous and unique signals
Radial horizontal	9	3
Vertical	6	3
Radial-horizontal-vertical	6	0
Opposite horizontal	3	1
Equidistant horizontal	4 (+ 6 in session F)	13

It appears that synchronism is most characteristic of the radial horizontal, the vertical and the radial-horizontal-vertical configurations. But it is not characteristic of the equidistant horizontal configuration, apart from the very successful 'learning' of session F. If the situation were reversed, one might seriously consider the possibility of a circular or spherical wave-front proceeding outwards from the subject. The very existence of large numbers of synchronous signals makes it necessary to consider what might be causing them. The experiments establish that essentially simultaneous strainings take place, and that most commonly they take place on a vertical plane passing through the location of the subject.

It could be that synchronous paranormal action was taking place elsewhere as well, but we had at that time no evidence for this; the minimum hypothesis is that it took place on a surface which is not necessarily planar but is sufficiently so for three widely separated points on it to lie on a vertical plane. Let us propose the following physical model: that there can exist, in the neighbourhood of a subject, a 'surface of action', at points on which strain occurs on objects. We do not know that all points on the surface are so affected, we have information about only three (and more usually, only two; but in the further experiments with Stephen North with as many as six strain gauges, the results described below are essentially similar); nevertheless, strain throughout the surface of action is the simplest assumption. We can then discuss the phenomenon in terms of the extent, the configuration and the movement of the surface of action. This surface might plausibly be regarded as a sort of invisible extension of the human body, perhaps even of the human arm or the haptic system.

The surface is considered to move slowly about the room, presumably under the influence of the unconscious mind of the subject. When one strain gauge displays a signal in advance of the other, it is because the surface has moved from one to the other. Although we do not know that it has moved directly, or at uniform speed, we might estimate from the data that if we did assume these things, the speed of the motion of the surface would be typically 1-100 cm/sec.

During 1978-9 David Robertson and I repeated the configurational experiments using five separate strain gauge specimens; Stephen North was the subject. The data bear out the original conclusions that the most usual configuration of a surface of action is that of a vertical plane passing through the body of the subject. They are summarized in Table 5.2. Since Stephen's action takes place at rather smaller distances than that of Nicholas, the experiments were on a scale between four and five times smaller. The use of five sensors made it possible to define the plane of experimentation in more detail.

For the analysis of the new data we defined a synchronism ratio s for an event as the ratio of the number of synchronous signals to the total number of sensors exposed. The mean value of s, denoted $\bar{s}$, was calculated for a session. We also tabulate a mean value $\bar{s}_w$ weighted according to signal magnitudes. It is clear from Table 5.2 that both $\bar{s}$ and $\bar{s}_w$ decrease in the order RV > RH > EV. The surface of action is similar to that in the first series of experiments.

Stephen behaves differently from Nicholas in sessions, in that he cannot rid himself of the idea, which seems to be a correct one in his case, that metal-bending action usually extends from his hands or arms. Normally he points one hand, or even one finger, in the direction of the sensors. When these are mounted in a radial vertical configuration, it is natural that there are synchronisms on several sensors; the 'surface of action' appears to be an invisible vertical extension of Stephen's arm.

The occurrence of equidistant (E) sensor synchronisms in Stephen's sessions was therefore of particular interest. It became apparent to me during my observation of them that possibly both hands might be involved simultaneously. As will be seen from Table 5.2, the horizontal distances between the synchronous sensors were quite small; although Stephen was asked to produce action on the entire array, he was accustomed to point his left hand at the left-hand sensor; on occasion the right hand would also point, as though he felt that this was the

Table 5.2

Session	Configuration	Number of sensors	Horizontal or radial extent (cm)	Vertical extent (cm)	No. of signals	$\bar{s}$	$\bar{s}_w$
EE	RV	5	26	26 ⎱	14	0.69	0.90
PP	RV	4	21	13 ⎰			
GG	RH	5	26	7 ⎱	19	0.41	0.49
LL	RH	5	30	8 ⎰			
FF	EV	6	36	15 ⎱	33	0.31	0.29
HH1	EV	4	18	15 ⎰			

natural way to produce a wider action. When both right and left hands were pointed, synchronisms would sometimes occur at the sensor at which they were being pointed. Thus it is possible that more than one surface can be produced by one subject.

A pair of remarkable sessions was held with Stephen using one sensor strapped to the forearm and one suspended in front of him. The forearm sensor was in the form of a circular disc with a rosette of three strain gauges at the centre; with this equipment the direction of the individual strain vectors can be determined (chapter 10). The disc was mechanically decoupled from the forearm by being mounted only on its screened leads, so that it was raised about 1 cm above the hairs on the forearm. If signals were obtained on this sensor, the experiment would show to what extent the strain vectors were aligned along the forearm. Also there was the question of whether synchronous signals would be observed on the forearm sensor and the suspended sensor.

The data from these sessions do not support the notion that the forearm sensor strain vectors show any tendency to be aligned along the forearm; the angular distribution appears to be fairly random.

However, the arrangement in time of the dynamic strain signals on the forearm and suspended sensors turns out to have tantalizing features; each set of signals on the forearm is followed after an interval by a signal on the suspended sensor. Of course this is only one of several possible interpretations, but it is nevertheless worthy of notice. What is surprising is the very long series of times between the corresponding signals. If this interpretation is correct, a very slow speed of the surface of action is indicated.

The notion that the surface of action passes through the subject (in opposite horizontal synchronous events) is somewhat imprecise. Are some part or parts of the body involved, and are they always the same parts? There is a common belief that the hands are involved. There is a case of a boy obtaining bends by placing the specimen outside his thigh, and success has also been achieved under the armpit. Two metal-benders are reported to have produced bends with their toes and two have used their foreheads. The neglected but classic experiments of Crawford[24] on table-lifting phenomena in the Goligher family led him to conclude that a 'cantilever arm', which was similar to our 'surface of action', came out of the lower half of the body, often the feet. Perhaps there are extensive differences between different subjects. More experimentation is needed; one series of experiments of my own was carried out not with strain gauges but with orthodox psychokinetic apparatus: a pointer suspended within a glass dome (chapter 20). One subject made detailed attempts to sense the parts of his hands and arms (e.g. the acupuncture points) which were most effective when placed under the suspension; but no special points were found. My experience with metal-benders suggests that what is important is the unconscious mind; the part of the body is dictated by psychological rather than by physical considerations.

A question often asked is: 'Does the right hand act more effectively than the left in a right-handed subject?' We have carried out a quantitative experiment with Julie Knowles, an ambidextrous subject with some right-handed bias. It is necessary that both hands should produce detectable action over the same period of time, in order that time-dependent variables (such as learning or decline effects) be eliminated. For example, strain gauges could be mounted on two metal specimens, one in the vicinity of each hand. An even simpler experiment was attempted with Julie, in which a long metal specimen (3 mm × 1.3 cm × 70 cm) was grasped with both hands, mutually separated by about 15 cm, under video-camera observation. It was found that an S-bend was produced, and at 5-minute intervals the magnitudes of the two parts of the S were measured by tracing onto paper. The data showed that the action of the right hand was 'stronger' than that of the left.

We can also consider the question of the maximum distance at which metal-bending effects are still possible. I have never conducted metal-bending experiments in a large hall or in the open air, so that the limits of action have always been set by the small room in which the subject and the specimens were situated. Nicholas Williams was able regularly to affect strain gauges at 5 m distance, and on one occasion very large signals were observed in synchronism, with a distance of 9 m between them; one strain gauge was on the ground floor of his house and another on the third floor, where Nicholas himself was situated.

On several occasions during an afternoon with Nicholas, we left the strain gauges and chart-recorders switched on in a locked empty house and went for a walk together. It was possible that signals would be recorded while we were out, since Nicholas was intending that they should. But nothing of significance was recorded.

At present I believe that metal-bending is limited in distance to the psychological 'immediate surroundings' or 'territory' of the subject; perhaps to the room in which he is situated. Further 'distance effects' will be discussed in chapter 8.

During the sessions with Nicholas Williams some experiments were carried out with partial screening of one of the sensors. The screens, of glass, brass and mild steel, are drawn in cross-section in Figure 5.2. The procedure was to wait until synchronous signals were obtained, and then quickly surround one of the strain gauges with a screen. It was found that the synchronism was destroyed, while the strength of the signals remained unimpaired. The data of Table 5.1 demonstrate this finding, but the statistics are poor. I have conducted further experiments with Stephen North, which confirm that signals are not impaired in strength by partial screening with transparent plastic. Total screening by a sealed glass sphere seriously inhibits metal-bending action, as we have seen in chapter 3. But the partial screening serves merely to delay the action by seconds.

We can conclude this chapter with the generalization that reliable synchronous strain gauge data tell us much about the metal-bending action; the action is repeatable in that different experiments are similar, each to each. It takes place at a 'surface of action', which may be regarded as a kind of invisible extension of the subject's arm.

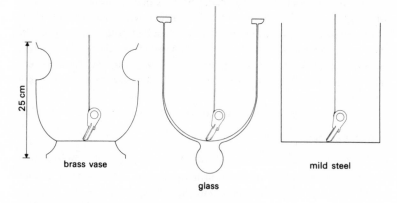

Figure 5.2 Cross-sections of screens drawn to scale.

Chapter **6**

Extensions and contractions

In the last chapter I attempted to interpret synchronous strains by invoking a physical model of a moving 'surface of action' at which strains are experienced. This might be regarded as some sort of field of dynamic strain or of stress, but it is a field with unusual properties; we imagine the strain to be zero or very small at points in space which do not lie on the surface; but at points which do lie on the surface, possibly at all these points, bending strains or stresses are experienced. The surface moves slowly in space, possibly under weak control of the subject.

However, everybody knows that to bend a strip of metal it takes the action not of one force but of at least three, arranged thus: $\frac{\downarrow}{\uparrow \quad \uparrow}$. This action is known as a 'three-point load'. It might be supplemented by other forces acting at neighbouring points, or even by a continuous array of forces; yet always there must be two opposed torques, centring on different points within the specimen (a shear). How can such torques be produced at a 'surface of action'?

In the Nicholas Williams data there are strain gauge signals which indicate a permanent deformation of a metal specimen, without any actual bending being visible. Examples (not illustrated) are signals A 4(2), B 2(2), C 1(2). I did not enter such events on the sensitivity graph (Figure 4.3) since, being drawn fully logarithmically, it cannot display zero bend angles.

The signals indicate either a permanent extension or a permanent bend (since the strain gauge is not on the neutral axis). But since no bend is visible, a permanent extension must be indicated. Possibly many of the elastic deformation signals are also extensions rather than bends. For the bending of a strip of metal there is extension on the convex side and contraction on the concave side, so that a single strain gauge would be inadequate to distinguish a bend from an extension.

There is another group of experiments which supports the idea that the action consists of extension or contraction pulses, and not necessarily bending pulses; the fracture of epoxy-resin bonds between thin strips of aluminium (Table 3.1). The most likely interpretation of these fractures is that one strip is expanded without the expansion of the other; a shear force produces fracture, and no bend is observed.

However, the issue of whether there are only single extension pulses, or more complicated action, can be decided only by studies with more than one strain gauge. The first data with two strain gauges mounted inside a single specimen were obtained using as a subject a physicist and transcendental meditator, Dr Rob Basto, who has on several occasions proved his ability to produce paranormal signals under observation. The two strain gauges were mounted within a thick metal specimen, parallel to each other and to the neutral plane; all the principal signals extended both strain gauges, and no permanent deformation was observed. But this represented the results of only a single experiment.

When thirteen-year-old Stephen North became known to me as a metal-bender, I set up the strain gauge equipment in his home; within half an hour I found that he was producing an abundance of strain pulses, under good conditions of observation. His sister Sarah, his mother and his father sat round in the most natural and informal way possible while these phenomena developed. I determined to give priority to the exposure of several strain gauges mounted on a single metal specimen.

A session was arranged with a 250 × 9 × 0.75 mm aluminium strip mounted horizontally, opposite the subject, and with the surface of the strip vertical. It was suspended from a wooden stool by the electrical connections to three strain gauges; these were mounted on one side of the metal, and were evenly spaced along it. It was about half an hour before Stephen settled down to produce a series of synchronous signals. What was significant about them was that the signals on the left-hand and centre strain gauges were contractions, while the right-hand strain gauge signals were extensions.

I was forced to the conclusion that there can be simultaneous extensions and contractions on a single piece of metal; I must therefore design experiments to measure the distributions of sign and magnitude throughout the thickness of a metal strip. This requires the use of an array of strain gauges through the metal; but at first I had to be content with one strain gauge mounted on the front and one on the back. If the observed nominal strains were equal, and of opposite sign, then there would be pure bending about a neutral plane passing down the centre of the strip. On the other hand, if the signals were equal and of the same sign, the simplest inference would be that there was no bending, but only pure extension or contraction. During sessions of about 100 minutes, I usually observed rather fewer than 50 pairs of signals, which were analysed as follows:

Suppose that the signal I_1 at strain gauge 1 on the convex surface of a bent metal strip consists of a contribution s_t from a stretching pulse and a contribution b from a bending pulse, so that $I_1 = s_t + b$. The signal I_2 at strain gauge 2 on the concave surface is $I_2 = s_t - b$. We define a 'proportion of stretching' $R = s_t/(s_t + b)$ for each pair of signals, and for a session we calculate the arithmetic mean R of values of R. This quantity defines the 'proportion of stretching' in the action of the subject in a particular session. The distribution of individual signals about these means is defined by the standard deviations $\sigma(s)/\bar{s}_t$ and $\sigma(b)/\bar{b}$, where

$$\sigma(s_t) = \{\sum_n (s_t - \bar{s}_t)^2/(n-1)\}^{\frac{1}{2}}$$

where n is the number of pairs of signals in the session.

Metal specimens of different thicknesses t were offered on different occasions to Stephen North, Mark Henry and Rob Basto; the data are summarized in Table 6.1. The subject was normally situated within one metre of the specimen, and was observed throughout the session, not being allowed to touch the specimen.

It is apparent that $\bar{R}$, the proportion of stretching, shows variation over about one order of magnitude, and that this correlates well with the thickness t of the metal specimen. The quantity $\bar{R}/t$ is seen from Table 6.1 to be reasonably constant in this range and a plot of $\bar{R}$ against t is shown in Figure 6.1. Presumably this correlation relates to the psychological approach of the subjects to the metal specimens, which were of course seen by them. A subject has sufficient confidence with a thin specimen to 'produce' pure bending forces, but when presented with a thick specimen he has not this confidence and 'produces' a large proportion of stretching.

The distribution of individual signal pairs about the means is always fairly wide, since the proportional standard deviations $\sigma(s_t)/\bar{s}_t$ and $\sigma(b)/\bar{b}$ do not differ greatly from unity (mean value 1.05). An exception to this rule is the short burst of signals recorded within 1 minute from Rob Basto; these were remarkably self-consistent. Apparently it is much more difficult to maintain this consistency over an entire experimental

Table 6.1 Analysis of bending with stretching sessions

Subject and session	Specimen dimensions l (cm)	w (mm)	Material	No. of visible deformations	No. of signal pairs	$\mathscr{I}$	$\bar{s}_t$ (mV)	$\bar{b}$ (mV)	$\bar{R}$	t (mm)	$\bar{R}/t$	$\dfrac{\sigma(s_t)}{s_t}$	$\dfrac{\sigma(b)}{b}$
RB	11	7.5	Eutectic	0	11	0	1.23	1.09	0.53	6.5	0.08	0.094	0.086
SN E	10.2	7.5	Aluminium	1	52	0.14	0.20	2.74	0.068	0.75	0.09	1.34	0.85
SN F	10.2	14	Brass	0	32	0.39	2.30	0.87	0.725	5.0	0.15	2.71	0.73
MH 1	18	12.5	Aluminium	0	14	0.10	0.41	1.84	0.182	1.25	0.15	0.61	0.62
MH 2	10.2	7.5	Aluminium	0	37	0.43	0.51	5.06	0.092	0.75	0.122	1.27	0.72
MH 3	10.2	7.5	Aluminium	0	56	0.21	0.85	5.08	0.143	0.75	0.19	0.95	0.70

RB, Rob Basto; SN, Stephen North; MH, Mark Henry.

session lasting about 100 minutes; this would be expected in any human phenomenon.

No distinction has been made in this analysis between signals of different polarity; i.e. contraction as opposed to extension, or bending in one direction as opposed to bending in the opposite direction. Nevertheless there is considerable alternation in these polarities, and I have chosen to characterize it in the following way. Each closely-spaced group of signals, or each isolated signal, is called an 'event'; the 'indecision parameter' $\mathcal{I}$, is defined as the ratio;

$$\mathcal{I} = \frac{\text{number of changes of polarity during session}}{\text{number of events during session}}$$

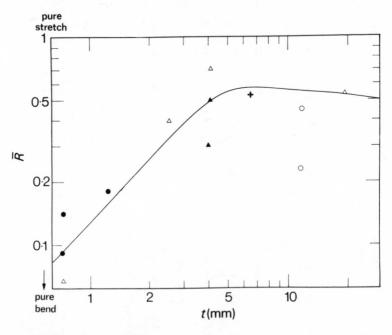

Figure 6.1 Variation of mean value R, of bending-stretching ratio during sessions, with thickness t of metal strip, on each side of which two resistive strain gauges were mounted.

Closed circles, Mark Henry; closed triangles, Julie Knowles; open triangles, Stephen North; crosses, Rob Basto; open circles, Jean-Pierre Girard.

For thin metal strips there is some justification for a linear R–t dependence (i.e. the thinner the strip the purer the bending). For the thick metal bars there is a tendency for R/t to approach 0.5 (broken line) (i.e. signal on one strain gauge only; failure to penetrate the thick bar). Only in one session with Jean-Pierre Girard was a good 'bending purity' obtained with a thick bar.

Values of $\mathscr{J}$ have been recorded in Table 6.1 and elsewhere. Since the unweighted mean of tabulated values of $\mathscr{J}$ is 0.18, there is on the average a change of sign after every five events.

Since conducting these experiments I have been able to work with the adult French metal-bender Jean-Pierre Girard, using a very thick bar of aluminium. In one session he produced pure bending signals, but in the

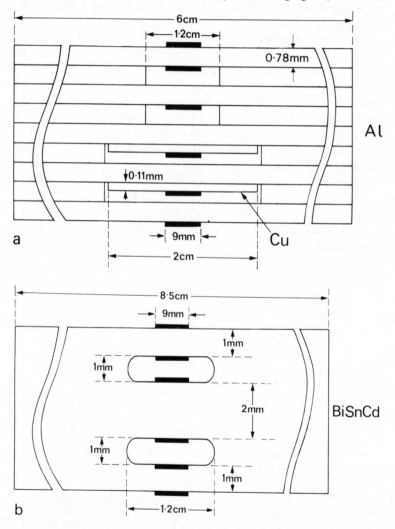

Figure 6.2a,b Dimensions of thick metal strips containing six resistive strain gauges for profile studies: (a) laminar, (b) slotted.

second session nearly all the signals were on the top strain gauge only (his hand is always above the metal). The two values of $\bar{R}$ are shown in Figure 6.1, and it is clear from this representation that a value of $\bar{R} = 0.5$ (i.e. signals on one strain gauge only) is approached for large thickness t. There may well be signals of opposite sign within the metal, but they do not penetrate as far as the other side. Further sessions with thick metal specimens acted on by other metal-benders showed similar results, and are included in Figure 6.1.

I could not abandon the possibility that the profile of stretching and contraction across the thickness of a metal strip might be more complicated than the simple bending and stretching envisaged so far. I therefore designed thick metal strips with six strain gauges distributed across the thickness, and successful exposures of them were made with Stephen North. The dimensions of these specimens are given in Figure 6.2 a and b and typical profiles from amongst the hundreds of signal events are shown in Figure 6.3. It is seen that the action is in fact more complicated than a simple bending or stretching. There is an important fraction of events in which the sign of the signal changes more than once as we proceed across the thickness of the specimen. They are neither stretching, contractions nor bending events — they are distortions. The metal is not being bent; an attempt is being made to churn it up!

A simple characterization is by the number of times the gradient

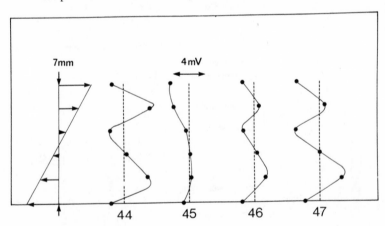

Figure 6.3 Profiles of a typical run of signals, in Stephen North's session S, from six resistive strain gauges mounted across thickness of a metal bar. Signals to the right are extensions, signals to the left are contractions. Thus in the schematic representation of a pure downwards bend shown on the left the arrows represent the expected signals. The recorded signals are three Ws and a Ʌ.

changes across the profile. In a pure bend, as can be seen from Figure 6.1, there is no change of gradient. In the remainder of the events in this Figure there are changes of gradient, and we characterize events 44, 46, 47 as W events. Also possible are V, ∨∧ and ∧∨∧ events. During the three Stephen North sessions Q, S and T, the distributions of these events were as indicated. Thus it appears that there is a distribution of complexities of profile; the simplest and most complex are perhaps less common than the mean.

Profile type	Session			
	Q Laminar EH (fractured)	S Eutectic RH	T Eutectic EH	No. of gradient changes
Bend or stretch	5	11	1	0
V	19	10	2	1
∨∧	11	11	8	2
W	4	18	11	3
∧∨∧	1	5	2	4

I have recently conducted experiments with strain gauges mounted within solid specimens: cubes and spheres. The strain tensors are complicated. In the first experiment with a sphere of 1 inch diameter, by far the most powerful signals were recorded on the strain gauge pointing radially to the subject. Almost no signals were recorded on the one pointing radially away from him. Integrated signal strengths were in the proportions 501, 78, 46 and 1 at respective orientations $0°$, $60°$, $120°$ and $180°$. It is possible that this sphere experiment represents some measure of the attenuation produced by screening within a really thick piece of metal. Incidentally, the experiment could hardly be described as an experiment on metal-bending, since bending of the spherical form is not possible without a previous major distortion. Compression of the sphere between the fingers gave no observable signals, and the observed extensions and contractions in various directions are impressive as validation. The indecision parameter $\mathscr{I}$ had the unusually high value of 0.3 for the session.

The concept of 'surface of action' has therefore to be modified, in the sense that it is now only a macroscopic model, applicable over distances of several centimetres or metres, and not necessarily valid on a microscopic scale. It still might be regarded as a sort of extension of the subject's arm, but it is more of a slab-like region than a surface.

Chapter 7

Movement of the surface of action

Once we have assumed the model of a surface of action, then an inference of its speed of movement follows from a measurement of the time between signals at two or more strain gauges at known locations. It is not necessarily a good assumption that the surface travels directly between two sensors at a uniform speed. Data are being collected in order to test this and similar assumptions. But if the assumption is valid, we have seen that it is possible to make the generalization that the speeds lie probably between 1 and 100 cm/sec.

The data show that there must be times when the motion of the surface is very slow. At a multiple strain gauge session with a sensor mounted on Stephen North's forearm, speeds as low as 1 cm/sec were frequently recorded. Therefore it should be possible for a strain pulse to be produced on a specimen which is physically impelled and moves through the surface. There have been several reports of cutlery being found to be bent after being thrown in the air; Andrew G. has reported throwing paperclips in the air and watching them land in the shape of treble clefs. A stroboscopic photograph of a spoon bending in flight has been published by Japanese researchers. Willie G. told me that he was able to bend metal in flight, but I soon found that it never happened when other people were present. It did not happen on video-camera either, so I arranged that Willie should be able to take his own stroboscopic flash photographs of swinging wires. Although he never succeeded in producing a photograph in which the metal specimen was straight in one flash and bent in the next, some of his photographs showed a bent specimen swinging from a thread, and bending more and more in consecutive flashes (ten per second). In one photograph the successive angles were $37.5°$, $39.5°$ and $41.5°$, in another $80°$, $74°$, $70.5°$ and $70°$. What interfered with Willie's efforts to achieve a better photograph was his apparent production (very possibly by paranormal means) of unwanted effects on photographic film. When he felt he had timed his 'power' to coincide perfectly with the camera shutter operation, he would find he had produced a Polaroid print covered with inexplicable images (see chapter 24). I believe it is likely that Willie did in fact cause metal specimens to bend in flight, but the experimental proof is not as watertight as could be wished.

Willie and his family of course knew nothing of my proposed 'surface of action', but they did form an opinion that the bending in flight could be affected by placing a heavy piece of metal on the floor. The specimen seemed to bend as it flew past it, although this was impossible to see with any certainty.

It is tempting to interpret these reports in terms of a surface of action stationary over the heavy piece of metal; as the specimen flies through the stationary surface, it receives a strain pulse and may well be deformed. Most of the specimens used in these attempts were lengths of 2 mm diameter tinned copper wire, very easily deformed.

Recent time-recorded dynamic strain recording experiments with Stephen North have demonstrated his action on a strain gauge embedded in a metal strip rocking to and fro on a moving wooden arm attached to a musical metronome. But the surface of action could not be kept motionless while the metal moved through it. The dynamic strain signals were recorded at all phases of the metronome motion.

Not only is the speed of motion of the surface of action important; one must also consider its possible change of shape whilst in motion. Many paranormal metal bends, particularly of easily deformed specimens such as wires, have been through very large angles, often several thousand degrees (spiral); occasionally the formation of the spiral is reported to take place in one continuous motion; it can be a little frightening to the child on the first occasion. In such an event we might imagine that the surface of action to some extent follows the form of the specimen; it is as though it clings to it, exerting continuous quasi-force. Such a clinging surface would be capable of forming remarkably complicated metal shapes, and these are precisely what have been found.

Plate 7.1 shows a 'folded strip' shape which several metal-benders have formed. Nicholas Williams was already familiar with violent spontaneous bending events when he and I first encountered a folded strip. One day I offered him pieces of very easily deformed aluminium alloy 30 cm × 8 mm × 0.75 mm, which he was able to leave on its own in anticipation of spontaneous action. We took them up to his third-floor bedroom in the empty house, and placed them on a table, in the

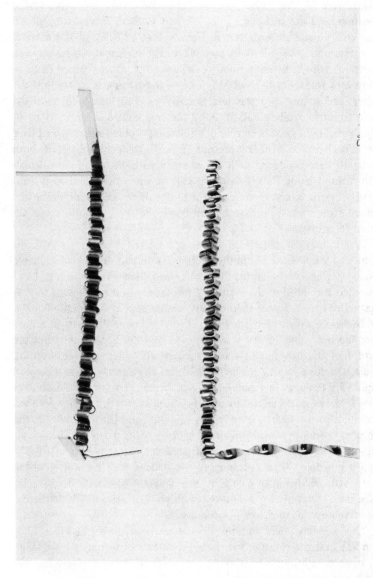

Plate 7.1 Folded crossed metal strips produced without touch by Nicholas Williams

form of a cross. We both started to leave the room, without closing the door. Within seconds I heard a scratching noise, as though the metal strips were moving rapidly on the table. We found the strips folded together, and the free end of one of them twisted. The twisting gives a clue to a possible interpretation: namely that a surface of action starts to rotate about an axis in its own plane. The surface is caught between the two strips, and as it rotates it clings to them and causes them to form into folds. On this occasion one of the strips was longer than the other, and so one end was left free. By good fortune the axis of the rotating surface aligned itself along the free end, causing it to twist. This twisting has not been found in the many 'folded strips' which have since been made. Andrew G. and Willie G., albeit unobserved, both claim to have produced such folded strips without seeing the original, and without being told what might happen when two aluminium strips were crossed. A common feature is that a single coil is formed in the folded structure. More than two strips can be used, and more complicated folds obtained.

A number of folded strips were produced by Nicholas Williams without his being present in the bedroom. I did not destroy the delicate balance of observational psychology by installing a video-camera, but I recorded the speed of the events instrumentally in the following way. A magnetized tinned steel strip of very similar appearance was, unknown to Nicholas, substituted for one of the aluminium alloy strips; a flux-gate magnetometer probe was mounted near by on the table, but the nature of the experiment was not explained. When the folding took place, the time-varying magnetic field was chart-recorded, and showed rapid variations, as in Figure 7.1. Since the metal strips move around as they fold, one might expect there to be a simple proportionality between the number of chart-record peaks and the number of folds in the finished specimen; one, two or even three peaks per fold. The correspondence between the numbers of peaks and the numbers of folds is shown in Table 7.1; it encourages us to believe that the motion of the metal strips is being observed by this simple magnetic device. Similar experiments have been carried out with pairs of wires in a V configuration fixed by the apex to a wooden board.

The magnetic field variations, such as those shown in Figure 7.1, indicate that the rotation speeds of the surface of action can be as high as three revolutions per second. But we must beware of placing too much reliance on visually unobserved experiments.

A child who could rotate surfaces could, without touch, twist a single metal strip about its own axis; metal strips were exposed singly

Table 7.1 Magnetic records of folding

	Designation	No. of folds or twists	No. of peaks in chart-record
Fold	M1 1	7	14
	M1 2	7	21
	M1 3	12	48
	M1 4	23	23
Twisted wire assembly	M2A 1	1	1
	2	1	1
	3	1	1
	4	4	4
	5	4	8
Twisted wire assembly	M2C 1	2½	5
	2	4	8
	3	2½	5
	4	4	8

rather than in crossed pairs. An important question to be answered is how does the twisting depend upon the dimensions of the exposed specimen? It was answered by allowing Willie G., Andrew G. and Stephen North to twist aluminium strips of different widths, identical in other respects. The pitches were then measured, and analysed in terms of the torque G necessary to produce twisting through an angle

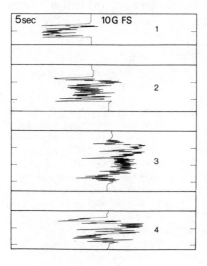

Figure 7.1 Time-variation of magnetic field in the neighbourhood of folding of crossed strips of magnetized tinned steel and aluminium. Session M1, Nicholas Williams.

θ of a strip of cross-section dimensions a and b, and linear modulus of elasticity n. This torque is given by the equation:

$$G = n\pi\theta \, (a^2 + b^2) \, ab/12l$$

The dimensions of the metal strips were as follows: $10 \leqslant l \leqslant 40$ cm, $b = 0.75$ mm, $1.5 \leqslant a \leqslant 13$ mm.

It follows that if pitch is proportional to $a^2 + b^2$, then the torque per unit strip width a is constant. The data displayed in Figure 7.2 show that this proportionality holds over more than an order of magnitude. Since the torque is force multiplied by strip width a, it follows that the quasi-force exerted by the surface of action is independent of the strip width. If the width were sufficiently small, these quasi-forces would be capable of doing serious damage to the metal; perhaps bringing about structural change. However, extrapolation through six orders of magnitude down to atomic dimensions would be too much of a liberty to take!

If the axis about which the surface of action rotates were not in the plane of the surface itself, strips of metal would not be twisted in the same way. If it were parallel to the surface but separated from it, as if the surface in rotation formed a tube, the strip would be bent into an Archimedean spiral. If it were inclined to the surface and passed through it, the strip would be formed into a helix. All these types of action have been found, but without leading the metal-bender towards a desired result. (The subject is discussed further in chapter 9.) Usually the supposed continuous rotation about a fixed axis does not continue for more than part of a single cycle. Non-uniform rotations and translational movements are the general rule. These result in the decorative

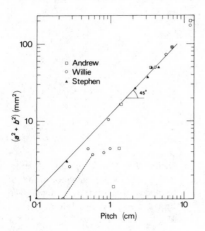

Figure 7.2 Variations of pitch of twisted aluminium strips with sum of squares of width a and thickness b. A linear variation (45° slope on fully logarithmic scale) indicates that the twisting force (not the torque) is independent of dimension. The broken line connects two points describing the two extremes of a specimen of uniformly varying width, which displays uniformly varying pitch.

shapes that some children, in particular Andrew G., claim to produce. They vary widely in size, from as large as 50 cm to as small as 1 mm. Andrew at one time must have achieved a considerable measure of control over his action so as to be able to produce the profusion of abstract and representational designs which have been seen by many people at a London exhibition and elsewhere (Plate 3.2). Julie Knowles has also exhibited art-work.

Difficulties about the conservation of angular momentum must be faced in interpreting these events. For a twisted strip to be produced by the quasi-force of a rotating surface, the strip must be held at one end, for example in the subject's hand. But some subjects insist that this is not always the case, and that all sorts of twirled patterns can be formed on their own. Although this presents difficulties of credibility, I have come at length to believe that it could sometimes be so. The solid surface on which the event takes place, a table, carpet or bed, can contribute forces; and one must also consider the possibility that two surfaces of action, or at least two parts of the same surface, could exert opposing quasi-forces. It will be recalled that suspended metal specimens receiving strain gauge signals hardly swing on their suspension wires, even though quite large strains are involved. The strains arise from within the metal rather than from an external interaction.

It occurred to us that if a strip of metal can be twisted paranormally, when it is mounted on the axis of a miniature electric generator some rotation of the axle and its rotor might be observed. This would result in the generation of recordable electric signals. Willie G. did succeed in producing sporadic recorded pulses on such a device, without twisting his wrist, but distortion of the metal strip severely limited the success of the experiment.

Chapter **8**

Distance effects

Classical physical force fields behave in a predictable manner which can be expressed mathematically by equations of vector algebra. The simplest static fields become weaker as we depart from their source, for example proportionally to the inverse square of the distance travelled. Time-varying fields are associated with wave-motion, and situations such as standing waves can arise, in which the variation of force with distance is not a uniform decrease with increasing distance from the source, but, rather, a periodic variation in a certain direction. Other more complicated distance effects are to be found in physics.

What distance effects are to be found in metal-bending phenomena? We might suppose that they differ from other physical fields in that there is some participation by the unconscious mind of the subject. They could be influenced by psychological factors.

My experience has been that the unconscious mind of the subject plays the key role in placing the quasi-force fields which bend metal. Evidently there is comparatively little bending of metal more than a few feet away from the subject. On the other hand, it is possible for the subject to 'focus' the field onto a particular point. Sometimes the subject feels that the force does not come 'from' him but 'from' outside him; is some outside entity responsible? Although the Nicholas Williams data were examined for dependence of signal magnitude on distance from subject, they showed a very wide spread. In the radial horizontal configuration, which is the most suitable for analysis, the range of variation of strength with distance seems to be more or less random.

I determined to conduct further experiments with Stephen North designed to throw light on the dependence of spontaneous dynamic strain signal magnitudes on distance from the subject. I found that with Stephen it is much slower to experiment with each strain gauge mounted on its individual metal strip than with an array of strain gauges mounted on a single strip. Synchronous data are much less frequent with individual strips. If the metal strip is chosen to be sufficiently thin, as has been shown by experiments in chapter 6, the dynamic strains can be regarded as mainly bending rather than stretching. Although they are dynamic they do not propagate extensively as shock waves along the strip. This can readily be demonstrated for normal pulses, produced artificially at the position of one of an array of strain gauges; the other strain gauges do not show significant pulses. Such an array can also be used for finding how the paranormal pulses are distributed along the metal strip. Are they all centred on the point at which the strip subsequently bends (if it does)? Or are they uniformly distributed along its length? Are the stronger ones at the end closest to the subject, or at the other end? Are they random?

In one of my first sessions with Stephen North a long metal strip carrying three strain gauges was mounted in the radial horizontal configuration, and data were recorded. After an unsettled period, the signals settled down into synchronous extension pulses, there being more than fifty such events, many of them multiple. It appeared in the first experiment that the strengths of the signals diminished with increasing distance from Stephen.

During the signals Stephen was sitting with his left hand about four inches from the end of the metal strip; he was relaxed, but refraining from movement as far as possible. I ensured that the three strain gauges were all approximately equally sensitive; this was checked by placing the entire metal strip under tension and recording the three signals. Corrections were applied if this was not the case, but in practice they were seldom more than ± 5 per cent. (Similar corrections were applied in the back-to-back strain gauge experiments described in chapter 6.)

In subsequent sessions with Stephen I repeated this distance effect experiment. But the results were rather different from those obtained in the first experiment. In general the centre strain gauge responded most strongly, while the strain gauge nearest to Stephen received rather weaker signals. I performed further experiments with three strain gauges, and later with five and six mounted on a single specimen; for each event the relative magnitudes of the signals at each strain gauge were different. It became clear to me that any 'distance effect' which might exist could best be described in terms of a 'region of action' and a 'centre of action'. At this centre the signals are strongest, and they diminish on each side of it. Thus in the first session the centre was between the subject and the nearest strain gauge, and in later sessions it was closer to the centre strain gauge. Such a concept would be consistent with qualitative observations on metal-bending; spoons do not usually bend uniformly along their length; they bend at one particular place where the centre of action is concentrated. I have on occasion observed metal strips bend into exact parabolic arcs, once as long as 40 cm, indicating a bending moment uniform along the entire length; but this type of behaviour is comparatively rare (see chapter 9).

How does the peak signal strength I vary with distances from the centre of action? A detailed analysis requires more than three strain gauges, but at first I was satisfied with fitting the data to a standard probability relationship. I used a simple Gaussian equation:

$$I = I_0 \exp\{-\alpha(x - x_0)^2\}$$

This equation represents a bell-shaped curve of width inversely related to the parameter α, and centred on a point $x = x_0$, which is the actual 'centre of action'. The variable x represents the distance from the end of the metal strip which is closest to the subject.

Each triplet of signals (or later quintet or sextet of signals) is computer-fitted to this equation with different values of I_0, x_0 and α. If the variation of signal strength over the entire metal strip were to follow this behaviour (which is the simplest assumption), the implication is that the strain signals occur in a region of variable size, centred on a point of variable position; and they are of variable strength. These variations lie within certain limits described by normal statistics; probable errors e have been calculated; and a histogram of x_0 values during a session is shown in Figure 8.1.

I repeated the three strain gauge experiment some eight times, with Stephen North and also with Mark Henry and Julie Knowles. The metal strips were of different lengths, and were arranged in three different orientations: radially from the subject, in a horizontal plane, RH; with the end equidistant from the subject in a horizontal plane, EH; and vertically, V. In each orientation the behaviour was similar; there is repeatability.

The results of fittings of different sessions with Stephen North are analysed in Table 8.1. The simple conception of a centre of action, with Gaussian variation of signal strengths, is vindicated. The extent of the region of action is, as we have seen, determined by the inverse of the parameter α. And we do not yet know how α depends upon length of specimen, since this has not as yet been varied much.

Of course I do not suggest that an exact Gaussian profile is maintained over the length of the metal strip. A single Gaussian equation with positive α can always be fitted to any three signals (provided they are convex; concave configuration yields negative α) and there is no question of over-determination. The data from five and six in-line strain gauges show the extent of the scatter; they fit much less precisely on a single Gaussian curve, as can be seen from the two examples represented in Figure 8.2. These are chosen from among the best and worst fits to signal quintets in session SN DD; the quality of the fit is related to an error parameter $e = \{(I - I_0)^2/n\}^{\frac{1}{2}}/I_0$, and this is tabulated together with the Gaussian parameters in Table 8.2. A good idea of the grouping of signal magnitudes within a single session (Stephen North DD) can be obtained from this Table.

The concept of a region of action has been investigated in detail only within a single metal specimen, since, as we have seen, Stephen North and other metal-benders obtain fewer synchronized signals on several individual metal specimens. This reduction in numbers was shown very clearly in an experiment with Stephen in which I mounted three strain gauges on a single piece of metal containing two thin sections. I recorded signals, and then cut through the thin sections without seriously changing the relative positions of the remaining metal strips; there were now three pieces of metal, each with its own strain gauge; the frequency of occurrence of signals was reduced by a factor of two, and the frequency of occurrence of synchronous signals by a factor of twenty; nevertheless the strength of the signals was not

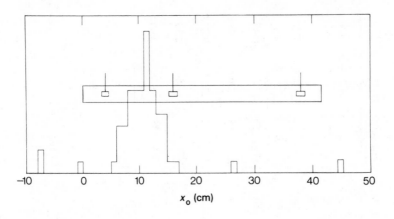

Figure 8.1 Histogram of distribution of values of the action x_0 along aluminium strip in Stephen North's session G.

Table 8.1 Analysis of distance effect data

Session	$\mathscr{S}$	No. of signal triplets accepted	No. of signal triplets rejected	$\bar{I}_0$	$\dfrac{e_{I_0}}{I_0}$	$\bar{x}_0$	$\dfrac{e_{x_0}}{\bar{x}_0}$	$\bar{\alpha}$	$\dfrac{e_\alpha}{\bar{\alpha}}$	Length (cm)	Width (mm)	Thickness (mm)	Configuration	No. of visible deformations
C	0.10	131	16	17.06	0.442	24.8	0.306	0.0041	0.244	40	7.5	0.75	EH	6
L	0.29	59	15	9.07	0.655	8.31	0.194	0.054	0.443	15	7.5	0.75	RH	6
B	0.75	91	22	15.71	0.352	6.03	1.71	0.0018	0.453	40	7.5	0.75	RH	3
G	0.11	76	3	13.68	0.397	10.15	0.348	0.0055	0.220	40	7.5	0.75	RH	1
K	0.12	18	48	3.28	0.692	14.95	0.097	0.0203	0.211	30	7.5	0.75	V	1

seriously reduced, and one of the metal strips became permanently deformed; it appears that Stephen's surface of action is greatly stabilized by the surface of the metal; at the termination of the metal strip, the surface becomes less accurately aligned.

In distance effect experiments the same feature is present as was noticed in all the earlier data: the constant changing sign of the signals. All strain gauges were mounted on the same face of the metal strip, but we observed a medley of extension signals interspersed with contraction signals. The moments of change from extension to contraction appeared to be irregular, and we have not been able to associate them with any particular psychological moment during the session. Suppose that the changing represents indecision: first the 'attempt' is made to bend the metal one way, then, when no permanent deformation is seen, an 'attempt' is made to bend it the other way. We characterize the session by its 'indecision factor', $\mathscr{I}$, defined in chapter 6 as the number of changes expressed as a fraction of the total number of signals or 'events'. Values of $\mathscr{I}$ for the distance effect experiments appear in Table 8.1. Apart from the high value of 0.75 in session SN B, a value around 10–20 per cent is common.

Since the metal-bender is not required to hold his hands absolutely still during a session, it is difficult to assess with accuracy the distance of the centre of action from the body. But I can make the following generalization. It is the perception of the target by the metal-bender

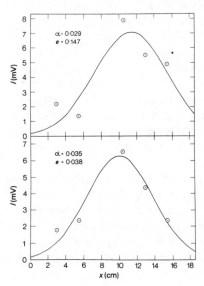

Figure 8.2 Gaussian curve-fitting to two signal quintets from five strain gauges mounted along a single aluminium strip, whose position and length correspond with the *x* axis. The quality of fit is seen to be related to the error parameter *e*. Session DD, Stephen North.

Table 8.2

Signal no.	I_0 (× 0.2mV)	α	x_0 (cm)	e
1	35.9	0.029	11.4	0.15
2	10.7	0.012	11.9	0.14
3	31.5	0.035	10.1	0.074
4	72.9	0.066	7.9	0.056
5	23.5	0.102	11.9	0.050
6	46.0	0.045	7.7	0.16
7	8.4	0.026	9.3	0.11
8	4.4	0.025	8.0	0.16
9	44.0	0.055	10.5	0.16
10	43.3	0.044	7.2	0.088
11	7.0	0.017	6.5	0.13
12	6.5	0.024	10.6	0.075
13	37.7	0.027	8.1	0.082

which is the important factor; once one has perceived it and succeeded in producing signals, the centre of action apparently moves independently of the motion of the hands or body. It assists most metal-benders to hold their hands near the target in order to obtain the first signals; some but not all prefer to keep their hand close to the metal during the entire session. The attitude of the metal-bender depends on many factors, such as previous practice, psychological mood, the witnessing, the environment and the condition of the target. Distances sufficiently great to inhibit the perception appear to hinder the production of signals. The walls of the room are usually an important factor; strain gauges outside the room in which the subject is positioned very seldom receive signals. Experiments in the open air might reveal surprisingly different 'perceptual distance effects'.

An incident which illustrates 'perceptual distance effects' very well occurred with Julie Knowles in early 1978. David Robertson and I succeeded in obtaining some video-tape records of her action on a strain gauge mounted within a table fork; her hands were nearly three feet away from it, but the signals persisted steadily for more than half an hour, and the fork and the moving chart-recorder pen appeared together in the picture.

Then we decided to add another metal specimen, with three strain gauges and another chart-recorder. Julie held her hand very close to the metal strip (mounted equidistant horizontal) and tried to induce signals on it. But the action persisted on the fork, still three feet away from Julie, and only very little appeared on the new specimen, despite the proximity of Julie's hand. We have thirty minutes of chart-record from which it is clear that the physical distance is unimportant when compared with what I have called a 'perceptual distance effect'.

Chapter 9

The localization of metal-bending action

We now address ourselves to the problem; how local is the paranormal action on metal? Obviously this is related to the problems of strain profile distribution (chapter 6) and also to the problem of distance effects (chapter 8).

The localization along a metal strip is partly defined by the width of the Gaussian curves of the last chapter, but this is of course an incomplete definition; the resolution of the experiment is limited by the distance between adjacent strain gauges, normally several centimetres. It might be that the action varies in strength, from millimetre to millimetre, or is even more localized. As will be discussed below, I have recently had the opportunity to conduct experiments with the miniaturized strain gauges now available; but at first I could rely only on less direct evidence.

In chapter 5 I suggested the model of a 'surface of action', a surface or perhaps a laminar region in which all paranormal metal-bending action takes place. If one imagined such a surface to be flat or gently curved, one might suppose that the forces were not at all local, but extended over a reasonably large area. Indeed, at an early stage in the investigations, I was introduced not only to the smoothly curving artwork of Andrew G., but to accurately formed parabolas as much as 30 cm long; these first appeared among the bends produced by David Nemeth; Julie Knowles and Andrew G. were also able to produce large arcs of parabolas, hyperbolas and even exact circles. But Nicholas Williams found it difficult to produce gentle and regular curvature. Many of Willie G.'s smooth parabolas were 'abnormal plane bends' in aluminium strip of cross-section 0.75 × 6.5 mm; they are in the plane of the long dimension, not (as would be expected) in the plane of the short dimension. To produce such smooth bends in this plane is quite a difficult operation when achieved by normal means, for example by means of a conical roller on a flat plate.

A normal parabolic bend is produced not by force applied at a single point between two supporting points (three-point load) but by a force uniform along the bent portion; this action would be produced over the central part of the specimen by a four-point load. It was the uniformity of the parabola bends which interested me in the first instance. I believed that my early observations favoured smooth and initially planar surfaces of action without strong localization. Possibly the long parabolic bends might have been produced by a uniform distribution of individual strain pulses. But just how local is it possible for the action to get? I undertook a number of experiments to throw light on this question. I offered Andrew G. metal strips scaled to different sizes, in order to see whether he could produce without touch similar objects of different dimensions; what would be the upper, and more particularly the lower limit to Andrew's paranormal craftsmanship? I found that the smallest scale objects, involving curvatures of about 1 mm diameter, were not of the same high standard as the others. Thus 1 mm diameter curved surfaces of action were not easily controlled by Andrew. This is consistent with his failure to make tight twists with the thinnest metal strips (chapter 7).

In another experiment I attached a number of resistive strain gauges close together on a circular piece of metal, in order to see whether paranormal signals were registered on neighbouring gauges. I have in one such session with Mark Henry obtained more than fifty signals without a single synchronism between any two strain gauges. The strain gauges were arranged on a circular disc radially with their inner edges on a circle of radius 8 mm. The experiment was designed for the investigation of directional effects, and other similar sessions are discussed in chapter 10. But since no synchronous signals were obtained, the only conclusion possible was that in this particular session (observed by Professor Barzilai of the University of Rome) Mark's action was all localized on individual strain gauges. The metal disc did not bend visibly.

There is some evidence that in certain signals the paranormal action is localized on the strain gauge rather than on the metal. On several occasions towards the end of sessions a strain gauge has suddenly become open-circuit, although there had of course been no touching. I always examined the open-circuit strain gauge under magnification, and found unexplained damage which I eventually attributed to strong localized paranormal action. A magnified photograph of a damaged strain gauge sensor appears in Plate 9.1b, contrasted with an undamaged strain gauge in Plate 9.1a.

It is also possible that resistive strain gauge signals showing 'tails' (e.g. in Figure 4.4b) are indicative of localized action on the strain gauge. The gauges are affixed to a prepared metal surface with one of a number of recommended adhesives. The polymer film on which the resistive film is deposited does not necessarily expand and contract at the same time or rate as the metal to which it is affixed. If the paranormal action is on the metal alone, or simultaneously on the strain gauge and on the metal, the expansion and contraction will be simultaneous. There is no tail on such a signal. But if the action is localized on the resistive strain gauge, then a mechanical relaxation, of long time-constant, in the adhesive film could influence the motion of the gauge.

(a)

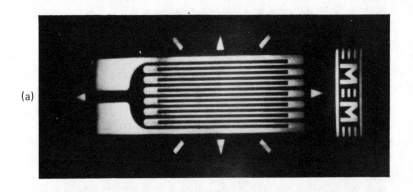

(b)

Plate 9.1 Comparison between (a) an unused and (b) a paranormally damaged strain gauge sensor. Overall length of the plastic mounting, 9 mm. The damage to the strain gauge is not to the solder tags, which are soldered in blobs, but to two of the filaments, which appear to be cut diagonally; some others show signs of incipient damage.

The time-constants for these 'tails' are of the order of 1 to 5 seconds; a thermal time constant interpretation is ruled out because compensation of the strain gauges ensures that it would require a temperature change of at least $10°$. When employing temperature sensors (chapter 14) we have never found such temperature changes on a paranormally bent metal specimen. Nevertheless the physical origin of tails on signals is not unambiguously decided, and further experimentation is necessary. Tails cannot be avoided by embedding the sensor in epoxy-resin within the metal.

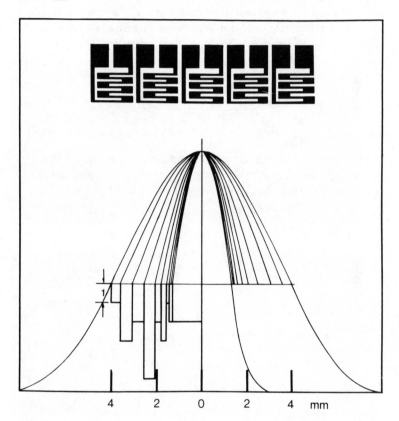

Figure 9.1 Localization of dynamic strain signals on miniaturized strain gauges, whose dimensions can be seen from the scale drawing at the top. A family of Gaussians is drawn and their localization parameters L are calculated. The localization parameters from the strain gauge session are sorted into groups according to magnitudes corresponding to the Gaussian L values. An (inverted) histogram of the strain gauge L values is shown.

Mattuck and Scott Hill,[25] like ourselves, have drawn attention to the possibility that localized paranormal action might loosen the strain gauge from the surface of the metal. In an experiment with Girard, they observed an anomalous stretching signal on a gauge attached to the concave side of a deformed bar. The 'strain gauge slip' was confirmed by a subsequent normal deformation experiment on the identical specimen, which demonstrated the failure of the strain gauge to follow the normal deformation.

I have now been able to study localization with Stephen North using five closely spaced miniature strain gauges whose working length is each about one millimetre. Wide distributions of magnitudes of signals, and even changes of sense between one strain gauge and the next, were found.

These have been found by fitting to a trigonometric series

$$I = A + Bx + C_1 \sin x + C_2 \sin 2x + C_3 \sin 3x + \ldots$$

The ratio $L = \left| \dfrac{C_3}{C_2} \right|$ can be considered as a possible quantitative measure of localization of each signal quintet, and the value of L is compared to values calculated for Gaussian curves; Figure 9.1 shows that the action can be said to be localized to distances of the order of 4 mm.

Chapter 10

Directional effects

We have seen in previous chapters that the spontaneous nature of dynamic strain signals implies that there is a distribution in their magnitude, their placement and their scale. We would expect that the directions of the strain vectors would also be distributed. But no experimental evidence has so far been presented that the strain gauges in previous experiments recorded vectors directed precisely along their maximum sensitivity axis. Since they were mounted with their axes along narrow metal strips (e.g. 40 cm × 8 mm × 0.75 mm) there is perhaps a psychological reason why the vector should have been directed along the axis of the strip. I have never come across long thin metal strips paranormally curled into straight tubes; bends across the major axis are usual. I regarded it as probable that both bending and stretching signals acted in a direction fairly close to the major axis of a thin and narrow strip.

When I started experimenting with metal strips rather broader and shorter than before (e.g. 15 mm × 20 cm × 0.75 mm), I deliberately mounted a strain gauge across the breadth of the strip, at right angles to its long axis. If all strain vectors were directly along that axis, no signals would be detected in the cross-breadth strain gauge. But small signals from Stephen North and from Mark Henry were observed on it.

I therefore decided to determine just what the distribution of directions of strain signal vectors might be in a metal-bending session. In order that an elongated shape such as a long thin strip might not affect this distribution psychologically, I chose square and circular specimens of thin metal sheet which the metal-bender would not feel inclined to bend in any particular direction, except horizontally or vertically.

The direction of a strain vector might be measured by comparing the magnitudes of the two signals obtained on two strain gauges mutually perpendicular. Ideally they would be mounted one on top of the other, on the surface of the thin specimen. But the strain at a point in a metal specimen is not adequately described by a single vector. Nevertheless the strain tensor at the surface of a thin specimen is reasonably well defined by a stretching vector in one direction, combined with a contraction vector in a direction at right angles to it. For the determination of three quantities, two magnitudes and an angle, three strain gauges are necessary; two are arranged mutually perpendicular, and the third along the line bisecting the right angle.

Suppose that the first strain gauge is directed along the x axis (Figure 10.1) and that it receives a stretching signal I_1; the second strain gauge is arranged along the y axis and receives a stretching signal I_2; the third sensor is arranged at an angle bisecting that between 1 and 2, and receives a stretching signal I_3. We assume that the strain tensor can be approximated by an extension vector I_e at an angle θ to the x axis, combined with a contraction vector I_c at an angle $\theta + \pi/2$. Then it can be shown that:

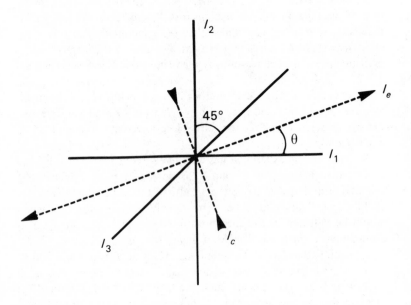

Figure 10.1 Directions of strain gauges 1, 2 and 3 mounted in the 'rosette' configuration at 0°, 90° and 45°, one directly over the other. Extension (positive) and contraction (negative) signals at these allow the deduction of the direction θ of the applied extension signal I_e and orthogonal contraction signal I_c.

$$I_e = (\alpha + \beta)/2$$

and

$$I_c = (\alpha - \beta)/2$$

where $\alpha = I_1 + I_2$
and $\beta = (I_1 - I_2)\cos^2\theta$
Also $\theta = \frac{1}{2}\arctan[(2I_3 - I_1 - I_2)/(I_1 - I_2)]$

Thus from three signals I_1, I_2, I_3, which may be of either sign, we can determine I_e and I_c, both of which may also be of either sign. There is no method by which any strain across the thickness of the metal can be determined with this arrangement but if the sign of I_e and I_c are the same, then we can infer the presence of such a strain of opposite sign.

Several experiments have been carried out with Stephen North to determine the distribution of signal directions. The data were of higher quality than in early strain gauge experiments, due partly to the increasing interest and patience of Stephen, partly to improvements in the amplifier stability and noise level, and partly to the presence of David Robertson, a physics student who assisted in this work and helped to establish a fully relaxed atmosphere.

We can conveniently express the results of an analysis of each experimental session in the form of a 'star diagram', such as that shown

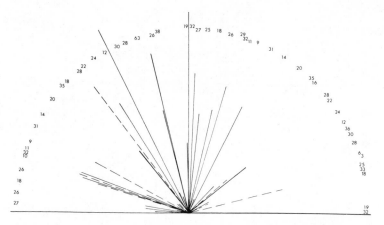

Figure 10.2 Typical 'star diagram' in which each extension signal is represented as a solid line whose length is a measure of its magnitude. It is usually accompanied by the orthogonal contraction signal, represented as a broken line; numbers indicate the correspondence. The square aluminium sheet, with the strain gauges at its centre, is suspended with one corner uppermost.

Table 10.1 Statistics of directional vectors

Session	Shape of specimen	Remarks	No. of extensions accompanied by contraction	No. of extensions accompanied by extension	No. of contractions accompanied by contraction
SN N	Square side 5 cm		33	4	0
SN O	" "		18	5	8
SN U	" "	Two permanent deformations	37	4	3
GC 2	" "		2	5	0
SN Z	Circular 3.7 cm diam.	Low coupling arm mounting	11	4	0
SN CC	" "	Low coupling arm mounting; 1 sensor fractured	11	6	0

in Figure 10.2. Each full line of the star represents by its magnitude and direction the stretching vector corresponding to a signal. Contraction vectors are represented by broken lines, and the pairs of orthogonal vectors are numbered so as to show which corresponds to which. In general the stars are of a random appearance. Specimens were mounted vertically.

Some numerical results of analysis of the direction experiments with Gill Costin and Stephen are given in Table 10.1 and with Stephen in Figures 10.3 and 10.4. It will be seen that there are events in which both orthogonal signals are stretches, or both contractions, rather than one of each. This situation represents either an all-round expansion, or an all-round contraction, rather than a single stretching vector with its corresponding contraction at right angles (i.e. pulling or pushing by four hands rather than by two). As we have seen, information about behaviour in the third dimension, i.e. across the thickness of disc, is available only by inference. Diaphragm sensors, made in the form of an Archimedean spiral, are now available for sensing strains perpendicular to the metal surface; they have an obvious application to solving this problem, and in recent experiments dynamic signals have been obtained with their use. Thus a thin disc of metal can experience a dynamic compression or thickening.

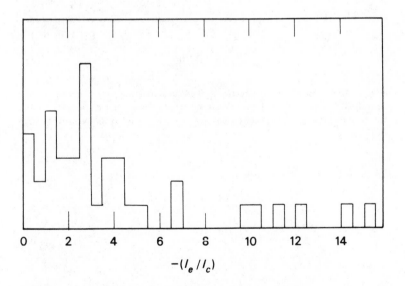

Figure 10.3 Histogram of $-(I_e/I_c)$ values for Stephen North's session U.

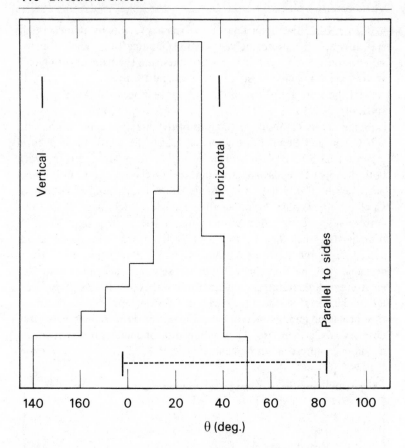

Figure 10.4 Histogram of directions of extension signals for Stephen North's session U. The square metal specimen is mounted with one corner uppermost, and the action is concentrated slightly above horizontal; it is not parallel to the sides of the square.

Chapter **11**

Hardening, softening and magnetization

Softening and hardening

At a very early stage in metal-bending investigations I posed the following questions. Is the phenomenon to be described as metal-bending, temporary metal-softening, or both? Is the bending due to the operation of 'paranormal forces', or is the metal changed in such a way that its yield point is temporarily decreased, so that relatively minor forces – gravitational, internal stress relaxation or human – would then be sufficient to deform it?

The second alternative, a temporary decrease in yield point, seems to be most likely. If the yield point remained normal, then moments of the order of several Newton-metres in magnitude would be necessary to bring about many of the bends. Assuming that such large forces could be paranormally produced, we must ask why they are always so well balanced that the metal specimen never flies across the room when it deforms and why the hand that holds it experiences no force? And why, when one suspends the specimen from its electrical connections, does it swing only slightly, if at all, as it bends?

The answers must lie in the internal origin of the forces. The metal specimen behaves as a sort of automaton, which is instigated to deform itself.

If the yield point is temporarily decreased, then any residual internal stress will be able to relax. In an early experiment I offered Belinda H. twin pieces of brass pinned together; one was annealed to remove residual stress, the other not; it was the latter which bent slightly, without the application of force; apparently, in this instance, a role could be played by residual internal stress.

Let us consider the properties of the metal after a paranormal bend, particularly its hardness, which is related to the yield strength. When a metal specimen is deformed normally, the atoms in the crystal lattice move over each other and rearrange themselves in such a way that the resulting metal is harder than before in the region of the deformation. This is known as work-hardening. Eventually this increase in hardness, being accompanied by an increase in yield strength, causes the deformation to cease, even though the applied force has not ceased.

When the normal deformation has ceased, we may measure the hardness and demonstrate that it has increased. This was also the case in the early measurements on paranormal bends which Dr Desvaux made for me (chapter 3). On the whole these data are similar to what would have been obtained from measurements on normally bent specimens. A copper single crystal was bent under good observation and the data are displayed in Figure 3.1. Although the bend was almost certainly paranormal, there was some hardening at the bend.

The only material whose hardness was found by Dr Desvaux not to have increased was the triple eutectic alloy of 54% Bi, 26% Sn, 20% Cd. This is a brittle material, but since it has a low melting-point, deformation by creep is possible. Although the times taken for some paranormal bends on this material have been incredibly short (see chapter 3), any structural changes are probably similar to those occurring in normal deformation by creep; and in these changes there is virtually no work-hardening. We found no evidence of permanent softening, but at least in this case there was no permanent hardening. In chapter 13 some further evidence for quasi-viscous creep is described.

There is some occasional qualitative evidence of quite marked temporary softening during the paranormal bending. The plasticization of a teaspoon by Uri Geller has been described in chapter 1, and, while nothing quantitative emerges, it is very difficult for me as observer to avoid the conclusion that temporary softening occurred. But there is nothing to show that any permanent softening occurred; in this case the specimen was used for fracture analysis rather than hardness measurements.

There is further evidence for marked temporary softening. Video-records have been made of the plasticization of the neck of a teaspoon and of other metal strips by Stephen North. Alison Lloyd has claimed to have picked pieces from metal cutlery with her fingernails. I have examined a coin bearing the shape of a thumb; but there was no permanent softening. There is indeed very little evidence that permanent softening is found on paranormally bent specimens which must have been temporarily soft. As examples of such specimens we select Willie G.'s abnormal plane bends in aluminium strip of cross-section 0.75 X 6.5 mm.

When such bends are photographed at high magnification, as in Plate 11.1, fine radial creases are seen at the inside edge. These creases do not appear at the outside edge; they are probably associated with compressive stresses. The abnormal plane bends could not have been produced without some local lowering of the yield point, or softening; but there is no buckling. If there were temporary softening in the region of the bend, then only a small stress would be necessary to form an unbuckled abnormal plane bend in this thin aluminium strip. In attempts to produce similar bends by normal means we have not been able to avoid local markings, and have not produced the inside edge creases of Plate 11.1. There is a strong supposition that the abnormal

Plate 11.1 Magnified photograph of abnormal plane bend in aluminium

plane bends must have involved temporary softening; and therefore micro-hardness measurements were made on the outside and inside thin edges, and on the neutral plane. However, the usual elevation of hardness on both the outside and inside edges was recorded; so permanent softening still seems to be an event of great rarity, having been recorded in only a very few of the Crussard–Bouvaist–Girard experiments described in chapter 13. In these events the paranormal action of Jean-Pierre Girard did not produce permanent deformation; but there is no doubt that local permanent softening occurred — the measurements are quite unambiguous. But this effect was found to be rarer than local permanent hardening.

Evidence for the abnormal suppression of the elastic component during paranormal deformation may be found in the data from resistive strain gauges. When a normal extension force (or bending moment) beyond the yield point acts upon a metal specimen, the temporary extension is greater than the subsequent permanent extension, because the contribution from the elastic component cannot be neglected. One can prove the point for oneself by pulling suddenly to produce a permanent stretch on a weak spring, and noting the extent to which the temporary stretch exceeds the permanent stretch.

Suppose that the temporary, elastic component of the extension (or bend) were to be paranormally suppressed; then the variation of extension with time would be more gradual, and at no moment of time would its value exceed the permanent value. Such behaviour is not uncommon in the signals chart-recorded in strain gauge experiments, especially in the Nicholas Williams sessions. A signal shown as *e* in Figure 4.4 demonstrates the behaviour, although it is atypical in having sharp pulses superposed upon it. More typical examples (not illustrated) are B 8(2), C 2(2), D 3(2), D 4(2), D 11(1), E 5(1), E 6(2), E 8(2), E 9(2) and E 11(2) (Table 5.1). These signals are evidence for the absence of hardening during paranormal deformation. Furthermore, in the Nicholas Williams sessions and elsewhere, many elastic signals in one sense, whether extension or compression, are followed immediately by elastic component suppression signals in the opposite sense. Examples include B 2(1), B 2(2), B 6(2), B 7(2), C 1(2), C 2(1), C 6(2), D 5(1), D 7(1), F 2(1), F 4(1), F 5(2) and G 4(3) (Table 5.1). In these cases there is no elastic signal in the correct sense to cause the observed permanent deformation. It follows that here, also, the elastic component of the deformation is suppressed. It is as though we could compress metal by pulling it and allowing it to spring back.

Dr Crussard (chapter 13) has affirmed that in the video-records of Jean-Pierre Girard's bending of thick aluminium bars, the elastic component suppression effect can actually be seen. The bar passes directly from its original shape to its final shape. Of course in a gradual bending a large number of very small elastic effects might take place, individually too small to see on the video-record. But there exist records which show relatively sudden bendings, without corresponding elastic components, and on these the effect is detectable. We conclude that there are both permanent hardening and temporary softening effects in paranormal metal-bending. Indeed, the structural changes which produce these can probably be taken to be the primary effects from which the visible changes follow.

Temporary softening, as is shown by evidence from the Stephen North video-tapes, can maximize and decay within a small fraction of a second. This is relevant to the problem of the tight single twists of cutlery shown in Plate 1.1. Some metal-benders, realizing that the softening can appear and vanish very quickly, wonder how the spoon twists in this short period of time. It would, of course, twist if it was already under torsional stress, being held so between right and left hand; but this a metal-bender is reluctant to do, since it would look as though unnecessary manual force were being applied.

The 'trick' is that the torsional stress is inertial in origin, being applied by twirling the spoon, rotating it between the palms of the hands rubbed together, or throwing it in the air with slight spin, or 'English'. These applications of stress look 'innocent', because the feature of the sudden softening is not yet understood by observers. One may learn a lot from throwing in the air and otherwise manipulating a bisected spoon, with the handle and bowl joined by a short length of thin tape. Intuitively the metal-bender learns that twists are puzzling and that they can be brought about by such manipulation; but he probably does not understand them in detail.

Magnetization

Some structural changes occurring in metals involve the alignment of the magnetic dipoles with the formation of ferromagnetic domains. The appearance of ferromagnetic phases has been reported in paranormal metal-bendings.

The French researchers, Dr Crussard and Dr Bouvaist, whose work is described in chapter 13, have observed the appearance, under the action of Jean-Pierre Girard, of 1.9 per cent of a magnetic phase in a specimen of non-magnetic chromium steel; no deformation took place. Each magnetic region could be clearly discerned, the susceptibility being measured by a detector which traversed the metal. Magnetic susceptibility measurements are of course routine in many metallurgical laboratories, and the monitoring of this specimen of steel before and after its exposure to Girard presented no difficulties. Indeed this type of experiment — that of witnessed exposure to metal of a strong subject and monitoring some physical property before and afterwards — is the most satisfactory from the point of view of the scientist. The technique minimizes the possibility of fraud on the part of the subject; the result is unaffected by the movement of permanent magnets concealed about the person; the responsibility for the experiment is placed securely upon the shoulders of the scientist.

I myself observed anomalous magnetic susceptibility of a specimen of molybdenum exposed to Uri Geller, as described in chapter 1. A crystal of molybdenum of outstanding purity ($\geqslant 0.999995$) and therefore small magnetic susceptibility (9×10^{-5} cgs units) was exposed on a steel plate, under good conditions of observation, to Uri Geller's action. He did not touch the crystal at any time; his hands were well above it, and Dr Sarfatt's hand was between Geller's hand and the crystal, when a small bend developed suddenly. I was not expecting any change of properties of the crystal, but when I showed it to photographer David Rookes he picked it up with tweezers which were slightly magnetized, as they sometimes are in physics laboratories. We noticed that the crystal adhered to the tweezers, and this prompted me to suspend the crystal from a fibre and make measurements of its movement in a magnetic field. I never solved the problem of why the exposed crystal came to possess a large magnetic susceptibility, only a thousand times smaller than that of iron, but I was able to arrange the determination of upper limits on the ferromagnetic impurities in the crystal as follows:[26]

Fe $\leqslant 6 \times 10^{-5}$
Co $2.7 \times 10^{-7} \pm 2 \times 10^{-8}$
Ni $\leqslant 1.5 \times 10^{-3}$

The permanent magnetization of ferromagnetic cutlery by paranormal bending can be investigated with the minimum of equipment. Much stainless steel cutlery in the home is weakly magnetized, due to normal causes such as the earth's magnetic field, local electric currents, children's magnets, etc.; perhaps some of it is magnetic when it leaves the factory. The usual configuration is with one pole on the handle, and one pole at a prong of a fork or on the bowl of a spoon. With a miniature compass one may with practice readily find the approximate positions of these poles, making certain by careful search that there are no subsidiary poles.

But when a curled bend or tight twist is produced paranormally (as for example in the Nicholas Williams cutlery bent during his first latchkey strain gauge run), subsidiary poles are usually found close to the bend, as follows:

Handle tip	*Either side of curled bend*	*Prongs*
N	S N	S

Subsidiary poles can be produced normally by the following techniques:

1 fracture;
2 heating the centre of the neck to above the Curie point;
3 prolonged hammering of the centre of the neck;
4 demagnetization followed by re-magnetization in a different way.

But as yet I have been unable to produce subsidiary poles merely by physical bending of the centre of the neck. It appears that some structural change has been brought about in the Nicholas Williams cutlery (and also in some of Stephen North's and Mark Henry's) by a mechanism we do not understand. I would not claim complete confidence about such findings, and they may well turn out to be of doubtful validity; but the simplicity of the equipment necessary to make the observations surely makes them valuable to researchers. It is also an amusing family game. Normal household cutlery can also be magnetized NSN, SNS or in more complicated ways. The effects of paranormal bending on these pieces might be complicated, so that they should be avoided when conducting household experiments on metal-bending.

Chapter **12**

Fractures and cleavages

When a strip of metal is pulled sufficiently hard or bent by normal force to and fro a sufficient number of times, fracture will occur. If the metal is brittle, a single sufficiently strong normal moment or shear force will cause fracture. The fractured surface is then of characteristic appearance, with cup-shaped depressions and conical protuberances (cup-and-cone fracture). Most metals which have been exposed to metal-benders are ductile, and would normally require working to and fro before plastic fracture occurred. The appearance of the fractured surface is then rather different; there can be fatigue bars, necking, cavitation and slip lines. Necking also appears on fractures that have been produced by pulling alone, but this requires forces much greater than the moments or shear forces described above.

Many supposedly paranormal metal-bendings have terminated in fracture. The paranormal fractures I have observed took place without any working to and fro, either before the action or during it. Chapter 1 contains the description of an event which I observed closely: the softening and ultimate falling apart of a stainless steel teaspoon, brought about by Uri Geller. I was quite certain that the spoon was never worked to and fro manually by Geller. The metal became so soft that when I received it from his hands it was difficult for me to hold it sufficiently carefully for it to keep its shape. I felt that the metal was indeed soft, and although I placed it delicately on the desk to keep it in one piece, it eventually fell apart under its own weight.

It appears that a sufficiently strong paranormal action can bring about a reduction in the yield strength of the metal. Metal-bender Alison Lloyd described this sort of event, which she personally experienced several times, as 'being able to pick holes in the metal with her fingernails'. One might interpret such a description in the following terms: tensile deformation without work-hardening is unstable; if some paranormal suppression of the work-hardening were to be postulated, then the metal would respond to a relatively small physical force with a ductile fracture.

But the appearance of paranormal ductile fractures under the scanning electron microscope is not very different from that of normal ductile fractures. Some early investigations were supervised by Dr Paul Barnes in our college.[27] A large number of electron micrographs were taken of a brass latchkey paranormally fractured by Uri Geller. Two detailed reports were written, one by each of the investigators. Although some unusual features emerged, it was not possible to isolate with certainty any properties of the paranormal fracture which would serve either as validation or as clues to the nature of the phenomenon. Similar findings have been reported by investigators in several countries, but evidence of highly localized melting has recently been reported by Professor Sasaki in Tokyo. Comparison of electron micrographs of paranormally fractured pure platinum wires with similar manually fractured specimens has shown up very clear differences; localized melting appears as rounded humps very clearly on the original micrographs.

A simpler type of break is the cleavage that occurs when a single crystal of metal is sheared. The fracture surface then follows one of the crystal planes, and can appear to be planar over quite large areas. Paranormal fractures of silicon and similar crystals have been reported in experiments with Uri Geller and Jean-Pierre Girard, and I have myself observed cleavages of single crystals of zinc by Graham P. and Andrew G., and of silicon crystals by Stephen North. The zinc crystals were 1-in.-long rods, about the thickness of a pencil, and Metals Research Ltd had prepared them with their 0001 surface perpendicular to the axis of the rod.

Each of the following types of paranormal crystal cleavage has been brought about by the observed stroking action of metal-benders:

1 The crystal cleaved straight across, leaving mirror-like 0001 cleavage surfaces on each piece. One piece remained between the thumb and forefinger, and the other simply dropped off the end, at some distance from the hand.

2 An 0001 cleavage crack developed part of the way across the length of the crystal, within a few millimetres of the end, but, again, beyond the end of the thumb and forefinger.

3 A flake of 0.1 mm thickness hinged upwards at an angle of about 45° from the end of the crystal and remained in position, although it was very delicate.

4 A slight kink developed in the crystal, but without cracking.

5 Grains of about 1 mm in size parted from the crystal, leaving the edges badly scarred. An 0001 plane crack also appeared.

It is true that even at room temperature these zinc crystals will deform and cleave fairly easily. Three-point loading of a 7 cm length with 4 kg causes some yield, followed by a cleavage. A blow with a sharp blade mounted on a weight of 500 gm dropped from a height of 15 cm also causes cleavage. Nevertheless the handling of the crystals by the children was observed by me and seen to be much more gentle than this; I hesitate to fault my own handling, or that of Metals Research.

In paranormal cleavages the surface of action presumably remains planar over a macroscopic region, and acts only in a certain crystal plane, in this case 0001. But a crack will propagate along a plane, even though the force is localized at the edge of the crystal, so that it is not clear just how far the planar surface of action extends. In the fracture of aluminium strips bonded by epoxy-resin, as described in chapter 3, the action is also planar at the metal-epoxy interface; one of the metal strips might be imagined to experience dynamic strain and the other not. These bonds are very much stronger than in the zinc crystals.

The paranormal cleavage of inorganic single crystals has been investigated by Rauscher and Hubbard.[28] Uri Geller brought about one such event, and later Elizabeth Rauscher and I observed Stephen North bring about, without touch, the cleavage of a single crystal with strain gauges attached. Electron micrographs showed up cavitation of the inorganic crystal surface. This will be discussed further in the next chapter.

Chapter **13**

The French research

In 1975 I was asked by the French chemical physicist Dr Wolkowski to participate in a discussion on the French radio of paranormal physical phenomena. On the day following the broadcast Dr Wolkowski telephoned that as a result of the programme he had been approached by a Parisian, Jean-Pierre Girard, who appeared to have strong psychokinetic abilities. Dr Wolkowski watched objects move about the table without being touched, and video-records were made of thick metal bars being bent by stroking action.

Metal specimens were sealed inside laboratory glassware tubes, and after being offered to Girard they were returned with the seals unbroken and the specimens bent. Rolf Schonbrot's photograph of these tubes appears in Plate 3.5. Dr Crussard, the chief scientist of the non-ferrous metal company Pechiney-Ugine-Kuhlmann, took up the investigations, using the extensive metallurgical facilities of his laboratories; and many observations of impressive metal-bendings were carried out. Minor bendings of metal in sealed glass tubes also took place during the Pechiney investigations.

Naturally the Pechiney metal bars were identified by engraved markings (I mention this obvious precaution simply because it has been claimed to be untrue in an article in the *New Scientist*),[29] and many of the aluminium alloy bars were sufficiently thick (8–17 mm diameter) for their 25-cm lengths to be beyond the limit of human strength to deform (see chapter 3).

As a metal deforms it work-hardens, so that the moment (force X distance) necessary for deformation through a certain angle is a smooth function of that angle; the function can be determined experimentally for an alloy of a previously defined composition and treatment. It can also be related to certain other properties of the metal, which are measurable afterwards. Thus one can know from studying a deformed bar of a known alloy the moment that would have been necessary to deform it from a previously undeformed condition. For 25 cm × 1 cm diameter bars of aluminium alloys such as AU2T4, which has been widely used in these experiments, typical moments are in the range 20–50 Nm. The mean of the maximum moments that have been produced normally by men on 25-cm bars is 25 Nm, and by women 15 Nm. Therefore many of these deformations would have required enormous strength to produce, and since the observation and video-recording was often good, one may also state categorically that the manual force used was small (say 1 Nm). The record deformation actually achieved by Girard would have required 75 Nm if produced normally; Geller, who was previously researched by Dr Crussard, once achieved 80 Nm and Julie Knowles has also achieved a bend of this order. I was present at a session at which Girard was filmed[30] in a deformation requiring 23 Nm; the protocol was good, and, as the video-record shows, the manual force was minimal. It is Girard's custom to hold one end of a bar of circular cross-section in his right hand and pass his left hand slowly over the other end for minutes at a time; he then lays the bar down on a flat surface and rests for a short while. After repeated attempts deformation gradually appears; even a small deformation can be observed if the bar is rolled on a flat surface.

Jean-Pierre Girard is little more than thirty years old; he was a rejected child brought up in the west of France in a public institution. When he first noticed his ability to produce psychokinetic effects he did not dare to tell anyone. He works in pharmaceuticals and is also an amateur conjuror; he thought his metal-bending ability might be useful in performances, so he practised in order to be able to perform in front of others. He says he had 'to learn to be an exhibitionist'. When the metal-bending occurs, he claims to feel that it is coming.

Professor Dierkens of the University of Mons has researched on Girard's electroencephalographic output, and on other physiological parameters, during the metal-bending. The characteristic feature of the EEG record is the occurrence of alpha rhythms, of highest amplitude in the parietal electrode, on the right side. Before the observed bending the alpha occurs only in bursts, but in the 'second phase', during the actual bend, there is continuous alpha. The peak frequency is 10 Hz, but there is a subsidiary peak at 9 Hz. Alpha rhythms are characteristic of sleep or of a high degree of relaxation (cerebral rest), but simultaneously the heartbeat of Girard rises to rates as high as 160 per minute. Professor Dierkens writes:[31] 'Girard is well conscious that creating PK is similar to experiencing an orgasm.'

When Girard visited me in London I found that he produced signals on resistive strain gauges which were mounted on an aluminium bar 13 mm in diameter and 30 cm long. Three sensors were used, respectively 3 cm, 8 cm and 13 cm from one end, leaving the other end free for him to hold in his left hand. This is not a very satisfactory procedure, since holding the bar in the hand can cause some deflection of the pen-records; it requires observation and experience to sort out paranormal signals, which are nearly always sharp-fronted. We recorded a great profusion of sharp-fronted signals, obtained with no touch by the right hand, and therefore believed to be paranormal. Most were on the 13 cm strain gauge but some were on the 8 mm strain gauge, not always synchronously with those on the 13 cm strain gauge. There were no signals on the 3 cm straight gauge, which is consistent with the fact that no one has reported a bar bent at the very end by Girard; the bends are always somewhere in the middle.

I mounted a competition in signal-production rate between Girard and some of the children, particularly Julie Knowles and Stephen North. Girard's signals were not larger than those of the children; in fact they were smaller than those of Stephen, but they were in greater profusion – perhaps twenty times as frequent.

When his mood is right, Girard applies himself to the task of bending with some intensity; the induction effects (chapter 17) produced on the observers can be impressive. Numbers of senior French physicists have been invited to Dr Crussard's sessions and asked to hold metal gently in their hands while the bending proceeded. I will not uncover their embarrassment when bends occurred, nor reveal their names, without permission. Sometimes a metal bar would become bent in two distinct places when held at one end by Girard and at the other end by a scientist.

The French research[32] has concentrated on the metallurgical aspects of paranormal metal-bending. This has been a suitable approach, since the Pechiney laboratories are thoroughly familiar with the physical properties and structure of the aluminium alloys they have developed for aircraft such as Concorde and the Mirage fighters. The measurements which are commonly made on each specimen before and after exposure are as follows:

1 All the dimensions were measured, especially the deformation from straightness, and the thickness; for bars of circular cross-section the diameter was carefully studied. Accuracies of about a micron could be obtained.

2 The micro-hardness, which we have seen to be characteristic of the granular and dislocation structure of the metal, was regularly measured at a large number of points; for Vickers hardness, a diamond pyramid is forced into the metal and the diagonal dimensions of the square indentation measured under the microscope.

3 The residual strain profile in the metal was measured, using X-ray diffraction techniques which are a speciality of Dr Bouvaist. The principle of the technique is basically that of Bragg diffraction. There is a linear relationship between the proportional lattice strain $\Delta d/d$ and $\sin^2 \psi$, where ψ is a certain angle measured in the X-ray diffractometer. The distance d defines a separation of planes within the crystal. The technique is used with polycrystalline metals, and is not much affected by grain size.

4 Foil specimens were often taken from the metal, and electron micrographic examination made at various magnifications. The grain boundaries are seen at low magnifications, and at high magnifications it is possible to study the forms of the dislocations and count the loop dislocations when these are seen.

5 The scanning electron microscope was used in the back-diffusion mode to obtain the dislocation density or plastic strain from the width of the channelling patterns or 'Kikuchi lines'.[33] These lines arise from the inelastic scattering of the electrons. Their absorption is different in different regions of the crystal, and their width can be related to the dislocation density below the surface.

6 Electron probe microanalysis was used for obtaining the local composition of alloys. The X-ray spectrum arising from the electron bombardment was analysed not with a spectrometer but with an energy-sensitive solid state probe.

All these measurements show changes when a bar of metal is bent, either normally or paranormally. The differences between the two sets of measurements are such as would require examination by a metallurgist in order to give a full interpretation.

One thing that is clear from these studies is that in paranormal bending the 'elastic component' is largely suppressed (see chapter 11). The dependence of applied stress σ upon strain ϵ in a metal is typically of the form of Figure 13.1a. When increasing normal stress is applied the strain increases in such a way that a point travels along the curved graph in the direction of the arrow. When the metal is stressed beyond the yield point and the stress is suddenly relaxed at a point A at the apex of the graph, the metal behaves in such a way that the point moves downwards and to the left, reaching the axis of zero stress at B.

Thus there is a permanent strain or extension of the metal, but it is not as large as was the temporary strain at point A. If we were to plot a graph of the time variation of strain it would in a normal bend have the form of Figure 13.1b (full line). The elastic component contributes temporarily a large proportion of the strain. Ultimately the elastic component ceases to contribute, and it is only the internal stress which holds the metal under its condition of permanent strain.

However, in paranormal metal-bending it seems that the path taken from 0 to B is more direct; in Figure 13.1b a possible path is represented by the broken line. In Figure 13.1b one cannot easily know the path taken, but we have seen in chapter 4 that some of the strain gauge signals are of the same form as the broken line of Figure 13.1b.

The stress that is operative in the no-touch paranormal metal-bending process is apparently an internal stress. The residual internal stresses were found by Dr Bouvaist to be somewhat different after a paranormal bend from those after a normal bend.

The residual internal strain profile is related to the profile of the applied stress. Consider the normal permanent deformation illustrated in Figure 13.2: the applied stress increases as one proceeds outwards from the neutral axis. Between the surface and the broken line planes the stress is so large that the yield point is passed and the strain becomes plastic; by contrast, in the inner region, the strain is entirely elastic. This results in the setting up of reverse strain, so that the strain profile takes the form of the final part of Figure 13.2. The residual strain profile of a normally deformed metal bar is governed by these features.

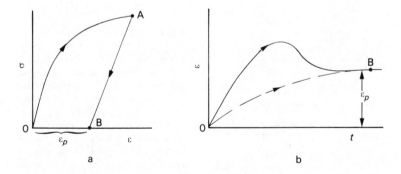

Figure 13.1 (a) Development of plastic strain ϵ_p by application of stress σ which increases from zero to a point represented by the solid circle A, and is relaxed to zero at solid circle B. (b) The time-dependence of strain developing to its final value ϵ_p in a case such as Figure 13.1a.

But the residual strains inside a paranormally deformed bar can be different. Dr Bouvaist has measured anomalous residual stress on metal bars exposed to the action of Jean-Pierre Girard.

The most significant findings of the French metallurgists have been the modifications of the physical properties of thick metal bars (150 × 30 × 4.5 mm), produced *without any bending* by the paranormal action of Jean-Pierre Girard. It is because the residual strain profile is anomalous that no bending takes place. But Girard's 'action' in these cases is probably not very different in other respects from what it is in a paranormal bend. The video-observation and the measurements made on the metal bar leave no doubt that there has been no actual measurable bending. Girard claims to feel in some way that there has been action. I have myself observed one of these events, and am of the opinion that if sufficient measurements had been carried out on other metal specimens exposed to other subjects it would turn out that this type of event was by no means so uncommon as appears at present. Up to the present only four cases of 'anomalous hardening' have been properly documented.

The feature of anomalous hardening events, as reported by Dr Bouvaist and confirmed independently by us in London, may be seen

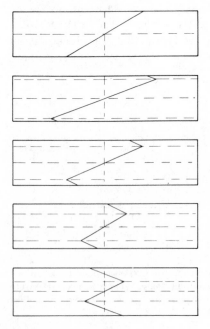

Figure 13.2 Development of reverse strain in a metal bar during a downwards bend (which for simplicity is not represented as curvature). During the elastic period (first picture) there is maximum extension (horizontal vector to the right) at the top. There is zero strain on the neutral plane, represented by a horizontal broken line. There is maximum contraction (horizontal vector to the left) at the bottom. Thus the end-points of the elastic strain vectors are represented by a diagonal line. Increasing stress produces situations represented in subsequent pictures.

in the representation in Figure 13.3. Although there is no bending, on each face of the metal bar there is localized increase in the hardness.

There is also a small localized decrease, typically of the order of 10μ, in the thickness of the metal bar ($\simeq 4.5$ mm). The residual stress increases, but not uniformly, from its original value, $\simeq -10$ MPa throughout. On one face an increase to $+80$ MPa has been measured, concurrently with a value of -80 MPa on the other. This profile of residual stress would not be typical of a bend, and in any case there was no bend throughout the entire observed event; nevertheless the hardness increased locally.

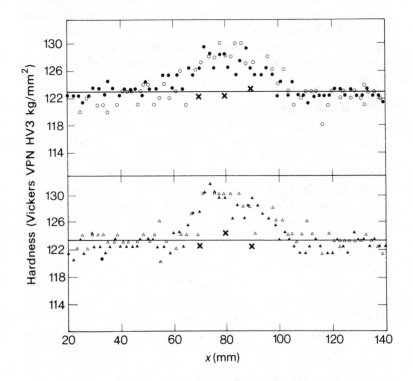

Figure 13.3 Hardness data on opposite faces of AU4GT4 aluminium bar handled by Jean-Pierre Girard on his visit to London in November 1977. The data points, before handling, are scattered about the horizontal lines and are not shown individually, except for the three crosses in the centre. The standard deviation of all these points was 1.3 VPN. Closed circles and triangles are data points taken by Dr Bouvaist in Voreppe (weight 3 kg). Open circles and triangles are data points taken by Dr Desvaux in Leatherhead (weight 2.5 kg).

Also significant are the increased densities of dislocation loops
studied with the scanning electron microscope. The density in the
original specimens was typically 7.4×10^{13} cm^{-3}: that of the surface
exposed to Girard's hand was found to be 130×10^{13} cm^{-3}; the
density of the middle was 61×10^{13} cm^{-3}. Many of the dislocations
are loop dislocations, such as are normally formed only by nuclear
radiation.

Recently the anomalous no-bend hardening action, with formation
of dislocations, has been confirmed independently in Japan by Sasaki
and his colleagues.[34]

In some ways the properties of the exposed strip of metal resemble
those of a strip exposed to crushing by a weight of 5 tons. This would
produce hardening of the correct order and also a decrease in the
thickness. However, such treatment would produce a uniform internal
strain profile and a uniform dislocation loop profile. The paranormal
action is therefore not similar to the normal application of external
force.

The strains which are associated with a paranormal metal-bending
event are in general not externally applied; we have seen that there are
dynamic strain pulses at the metal, and therefore almost certainly
dynamic stress pulses; these would probably be associated with the
formation of dislocation loops such as are found in the anomalous
hardening events. Dr Bouvaist and I decided to perform experiments
jointly to see whether there was a quantitative correlation between
paranormal dynamic strain pulses and dislocation loops induced in a
normal crystal.

We conducted the first experiment with a crystal of AU4SG (US
nomenclature 2014), which was exposed to the action of Stephen
North, with six strain gauges attached. In three 90-minute sessions a
profusion of paranormal signals was recorded, and I summed the total
of the signal strengths at each strain gauge.

It was possible that the dislocation densities at these six points
would correlate with these summed totals. But unfortunately the background of dislocations in this crystal was very high, due to precipitation
during cooling, and significant differences in dislocation density could
not be observed after exposure. There was also a high level of surface
porosity. The crystal was of a very tough alloy, so perhaps we aimed
too high in this initial experiment. A soft pure aluminium crystal with
very few residual dislocations was then exposed; no fewer than ten
permanent deformations were recorded and a high density of dislocation loops was observed; since these could have been associated with

the bends, analysis for correlation was not attempted. Silicon crystals were then exposed, but many cleavages occurred.

Despite our initial failure to quantify the correlation of dynamic strains with dislocation densities, it still seems that one primary mechanism of paranormal metal-bending is the formation of dislocation loops within the metal crystal. Metal-bending has often been found to be accompanied by dynamic strain pulses; and the dynamic strain pulses are often accompanied by dislocations.

The next step is to consider how a dislocation is formed. The normal method of formation requires some force or atomic movement brought about by action in another part of the metal. So the first dislocation cannot be brought about normally without external force, heat or nuclear radiation being applied. We have searched for macroscopic heat and for nuclear radiation, with negative results.

My own speculation is that, temporarily, a vacancy or group of vacancies might be formed paranormally; such vacancies would propagate as dislocations, by normal physical processes. In later chapters, using quite a different approach, we shall see that the appearance and also the disappearance of macroscopic objects from given locations is known to have taken place in the presence of metal-benders and other psychics; it is known as 'teleportation'. Vacancy formation might be regarded as teleportation on a microscopic scale. However, we do not know that the primary event is not the transfer of energy rather than that of particles.

A possible piece of evidence for vacancy formation comes from the investigations by Rauscher and Hubbard[28] of the surface of a crystal of potassium dichromate $K_2 Cr_2 O_7$ cleaved paranormally by Uri Geller. When electron micrographs of this fractured surface were compared with those of a normally cleaved crystal grown under the same conditions, it was found that the Geller crystal had a number of 'trench-like' features which appear to be rectangular cavities in the crystal bulk. None of these features was seen in the control crystal. It is tempting to regard these cavities (Plate 13.1) as examples of a sort of gigantic vacancy formation. However, the possibility that inclusions of air were trapped during growth should not be overlooked, and further growings and exposures are now being undertaken. Stephen North has achieved an observed cleavage of one of Professor Rauscher's crystals under the monitoring of two strain gauges.

The French researches are also relevant to the questions discussed in the last chapter. How much of the action is paranormal softening, and how much is paranormal force? Or are they both different aspects of the phenomenon? The conclusions reached about the suppression of the elastic component in paranormal bending are consistent with the idea of a temporary softening. But dislocations in general make metal harder, not softer.

But, additionally, Crussard and Bouvaist have obtained the first quantitative evidence for paranormal permanent softening. No bending took place, but the specimen (similar to the previously described one) showed permanent local softening. The aluminium alloy used was again AU4SG. The mean hardness of the particular specimen was 167 VPN; after exposure to Jean-Pierre Girard two soft regions of more than a centimetre in length appeared; in the first region the hardness tapered gradually with distance to 90 VPN, but in the second the fall to 80 VPN occurred as a sharp boundary. Electron micrographs of the first region showed a spotty appearance typical of precipitation in this alloy. Small regions of a stable structure were precipitated from a matrix of metastable structure. This type of behaviour is typical of the alloy after heating to and cooling from 625°. But no heat was applied or observed.

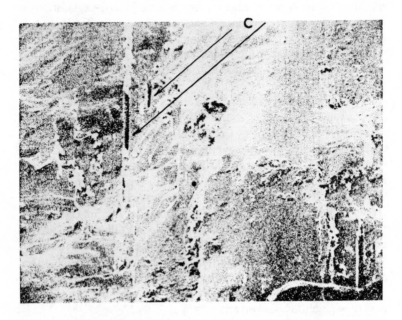

Plate 13.1 Cavities (C) shown up in electron micrographs of cleaved surface of potassium dichromate single crystal fractured by Uri Geller in Elizabeth Rauscher's laboratory

The appearance under the electron microscope of the second region was unexpected. At low magnification the grains stood out against dark intergrain films, which are characteristic of thin regions of liquid. This appearance is typical of a metal heated to near the melting-point and slowly cooled. It is typical of a metal that has experienced quasi-viscous creep.

Of course there is no question that the real temperature of the entire specimen could have reached these high values. However, on a microscopic scale, violent events are indicated by these micrographs. It is in the regions of grain boundaries, and only in these regions, that we have to postulate the rearrangement of atoms. Very few atoms need be involved; only those which form layers of liquid in the normal process known as 'quasi-viscous creep'. We still suppose that the primary event brought about by the psychic action is the local movement of atoms, or perhaps of energy. We are reminded of the 'Maxwell demon', an imagined agency for removing cool atoms so that a temperature rise could take place.

Another branch of the work undertaken by Dr Crussard and his collaborators has been the study of regions of magnetization (chapter 11) produced apparently paranormally in non-magnetic stainless steels. Austenitic-martensitic transformations have been brought about by Girard. This field of study is highly specialist, and I shall not discuss it in detail; it falls under the heading of structural changes brought about by paranormal means, and will be mentioned again in chapter 16.

One modern metallurgical technique not yet exploited by Dr Crussard or by ourselves is that of acoustic emission. The ultrasound pulses emitted during microfracture events at grain boundaries can be recorded with a modern transducer, transferred to magnetic tape, and subsequently inspected and photographed on an oscilloscope trace. In this way one can distinguish between single and multiple grain boundary fractures, and also distinguish twinning. Dr Ronald Hawke[35] has conducted no-touch experiments of this type with a Californian metal-bender (anonymous); the signals recorded were all recognizable as single grain boundary fractures.

All of these thirteen chapters have been concerned with paranormal action on metal. But there are other psychic physical phenomena than these, and in the course of my investigations I have come across various kinds produced by the metal-benders. I shall devote several chapters to discussing them, before trying to fit the whole picture into the physics background with which eventually we must all come to terms. In the next chapter I shall consider thermal phenomena.

Chapter **14**

Thermal phenomena

Sudden changes of temperature have often been reported in house-haunting phenomena. What is the possibility of there being paranormally produced temperature changes brought about by the remote action of a subject on a thermometer or similar instrument? Some years ago a report was published by the American parapsychologist Gertrude Schmeidler[36] about the thermal effects produced by the psychic Ingo Swann. It was shown that he was able to bring about resistance changes in a thermistor at distances of several metres. Some follow-up reports appeared, and one by Danish physicist Richard Mattuck[37] concerned the rising of mercury in a thermometer brought about by a Danish metal-bender. These publications, together with numerous descriptions in the literature of temperature effects in seances and hauntings, led me to consider the possibility that during metal-bending events there might be changes of temperature. Jean-Pierre Girard has been reported to have affected liquid crystal paint at a distance of several metres.[38] The changes of colour exhibited by these recently developed paints under temperature variation present an attractive goal to the psychic.

Temperature is a measure of the mean of the random speeds of motion in solids, liquids and gases, so that the elevation of temperature may not itself represent a primary physical phenomenon. For example, a shock wave produced by impact dissipates its energy in the form of a rise in temperature, and the action of a compression piston on a gas has a similar effect. The normal bending of a metal is accompanied by a local change in its temperature, and the stretching of such materials as rubber is accompanied by a fall in temperature.

Resistive strain gauges are temperature-compensated; that is, they are designed so that the resistance is invariant to small changes of temperature. Therefore our dynamic strain signals are not due simply to small changes of temperature. However, the dynamic strain pulses are probably accompanied by minute local temperature changes, to which the gauge would not respond.

There are well-known devices, including thermistors, whose electrical resistance is very sensitive to temperature, but very much less sensitive to strain. If we wish to investigate the possible existence of temperature changes during metal-bending, such devices can be attached to metal specimens and chart-records made of the time variation of their resistance. I carried out such experiments with Stephen North, using the temperature gauge type STG 50D made by Micro-Measurements Inc. The sensor, which is formed of a nickel filament enclosed in epoxy-resin and glass fibre, has a nominal resistance of 50Ω and was used with resistive compensation in our standard 120Ω arm bridge. Resistive strain gauges were also mounted on the metal specimen, and strain pulses were recorded during the sessions, including a permanent bend.

I have at no time in these sessions observed any sudden temperature change at a thermal sensor. The high thermal conductivity of the metal specimen makes it possible to detect temperature changes over an area rather wider than that of the thermal sensor, whose dimensions are 12×9 mm. The sensitivity of the equipment is such that changes of less than one-fiftieth of a degree could be detected. Thus the proximity of the subject's hands, and local air currents, were both detectable as relatively gradual temperature changes. Stephen North soon understood the magnitude of these effects and succeeded in keeping sufficiently far from the sensor to avoid serious interference. No dynamic signals of any significance were recorded on the temperature charts during these sessions, although strain pulses were recorded. I have not pursued thermal sensor studies *in extenso* because of the initial absence of signals; but it seems unlikely that anything more than highly localized temperature effects are produced by metal-benders.

However, this is not evidence that there are not minute local secondary temperature changes occurring when the resistive strain gauges receive dynamic strain pulses. Italian physicists have reported macroscopic temperature rises in specimens stroked manually by metal-bender Orlando Bragante.

It has been remarked by Dr Crussard that some structural changes instigated by Jean-Pierre Girard would have required a temperature of $600°C$ to bring them about. It might be inferred that localized regions of high temperature existed at points in the metal. Further evidence comes from magnetization data.

One reason why an elevated temperature can bring about a structural change is that chemical and physical reaction rates in general increase exponentially with temperature; thus if one structure is being formed continually but immeasurably slowly at room temperature, then an elevated temperature will favour its rapid formation. A familiar situation is that one structure is the most stable when the atoms are in faster motion, and another structure is the most stable when they are moving more slowly; the conversion from one to another is known as a phase transition. But the onset of fast motion does not imply the immediate attainment of local thermodynamic equilibrium. There are non-equilibrium ways of inducing structural change — for example, bombardment with nuclear radiation — which are effective without inducing much heat. If the psychic induction of structural change is a non-equilibrium process, then the paranormal production of temperature is only a secondary phenomenon; the atomic events leading to the structural change should be regarded as the primary phenomenon.

Chapter **15**

Electromagnetic phenomena

On various occasions during our researches into metal-bending there have occurred paranormal phenomena which might be classified as 'electromagnetic'. Electric currents or magnetic fields have been observed when so far as we know there was no normal cause for them. We shall describe these occurrences, and discuss distinctions between them and normal electromagnetic disturbances. The question must be posed: are these effects primary or are they secondary — that is to say, symptoms of a more significant physical phenomenon? If no such phenomenon is observed simultaneously, this does not necessarily mean that the electromagnetic phenomenon is primary; important additional phenomena may have taken place but escaped observation or measurement.

As an example of what I mean by primary and secondary phenomena, consider the case of a manually fractured spoon. In a normally produced fracture, the two pieces of metal take on opposing electric charges, just as do droplets of water subdivided in a spraying process. Yet it is clear that the manual action is the primary phenomenon and the electric charge a secondary phenomenon. If, on the other hand, a flash of lightning strikes the metal, causing it to melt and fracture, we would be correct in regarding the electric current as the primary phenomenon and the fracture as secondary.

We must also address ourselves to the problem of whether when we instrument what we believe to be a primary phenomenon, namely dynamic strain pulses, there may be paranormal electrical phenomena which become confused in the electrical circuitry with the strain data. We shall need to know just how common and just how large such paranormal effects can be.

As will be recalled from chapters 14 and 4, we do this in two ways. First, we substitute a dummy wire gauge or even a small stabilized resistor for one of the resistive strain gauges, re-balancing the bridge if necessary. We expose the dummy together with real gauges and await signals; but there have not been significant numbers. Any strain gauge signal recorded synchronously with a signal in the dummy channels must be discarded. Dummy channel signals usually indicate that the electrical screening is inadequate; the existence of the dummy is not normally known to the subject.

Second, we devise other instruments capable of showing whether the minute paranormal extension or bending pulses in a piece of metal do really exist; the optical lever method was described in chapter 4.

Quite early in these researches there took place some events which made me suspect strongly that I was recording paranormal electrical effects; on this occasion the subject was touching a piece of metal. It was an experiment conducted with Uri Geller in order to test whether he was able to produce paranormal effects on a Geiger counter. I described the session as follows in 'My Geller Notebooks',[39] a manuscript written directly afterwards.

We had originally planned that only myself, Bohm, O'Regan, Bastin, Nicola and Birkinshaw be present, but three other people were added to this number: Arthur Koestler, Jack Sarfatt, and a friend of Ted Bastin, by the name of Mr K.A. Appiah. Thus the fifteen foot by fifteen foot square room was a little crowded, although with discipline we managed to avoid too many difficulties. I had been fending off the press all day; we needed all the peace and quiet we could get. I arranged for the telephone to be disconnected lest it should disturb my observation of Geller. The short periods during which Geller would be available must not be wasted.

When Geller arrived after lunch we showed him the equipment we had set up, and he asked to make a start with the radiation monitor. This was a commercial instrument made by Messrs Mini-Instruments, consisting of a Geiger counter enclosed in a stainless steel sheath, and connected by cable to a control panel which registers the nuclear radiation pulses both on a ratemeter and as audible clicks on a loud-speaker. The counter is sensitive to gamma rays through the metal sheath, but for use with beta-radiation a part of the sheath could be slid open to allow the less penetrating radiation through.

Alpha, beta and gamma rays are emitted by radioactive sources when the nuclei of the atoms decay spontaneously. Although the average number of decays in a given time is well-known for each radio-active source, the precise moment at which each beta or gamma ray is emitted cannot be predicted from physical theory. It is a truly random event. Thus if these moments could be changed by mental concentration, and an unusually large number of beta or gamma rays counted, then we might have a clue to the understanding of this apparent randomness. Of course thêre are ways in which a Geiger counter might be activated normally – for example by concealing a radioactive source about one's person. I used the Geiger counter itself to search Geller for such a source, and none was found.*

When there is no radioactive source near the Geiger counter, only a few counts are registered in each second; under our laboratory conditions, about one every two seconds. Most of this radiation reaches the earth from extra-terrestrial sources and is known as cosmic radiation. Thus the instrument records the time-variation of the background count-rate due to laboratory pollution and cosmic radiation. One must recognize that the weakness of the experiment lies in the fact that it is the actual instrument intended to be influenced by the psychic which is used to search for hidden radioactive sources.

The pulse counts from the control panel of the Geiger counter were taken to a Harwell 2000 series rate-meter whose output was chart-recorded (Figure 15.1). When the time constant is set at 1 second, pulse counts appear as small individual 'noise' peaks on the chart, provided that their rate is sufficiently slow. But when the count rate reaches, say, ten or a hundred per second, and remains there for several seconds, then much larger peaks appear on the chart, as is also shown in the Figure.

The correct operation of this system was checked by exposing the counter close to a radioactive source; readings of the order of 25

---

* A press release made without my knowledge omitted this important fact. It is no difficult matter to detect a radioactive source, concealed about the person, by means of the radiation monitor. I can recall an occasion when a journalist purporting to be from *Time Magazine* visited my office and was shown the monitor, which was clicking away to random cosmic ray and other background counts. When he put his hand to it, a little burst of clicking was heard, and I immediately suspected that the journalist was trying to play a trick on me. But the burst could, of course, have been nothing more than a random increase in cosmic ray events, and I explained this patiently. The journalist, who later turned out to be a famous conjuror, half-heartedly claimed he was producing the effect himself, but I politely declined to comment, and he scuttled away in ignorance of my very strong suspicions of him.

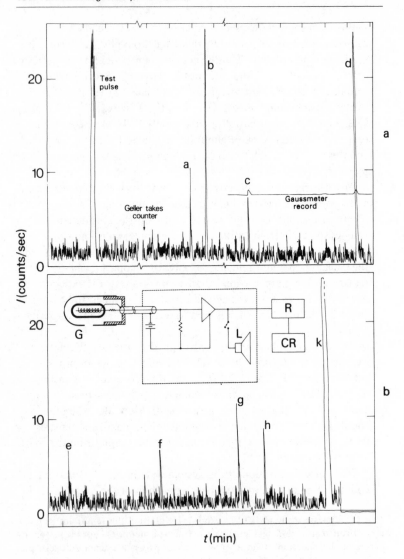

Figure 15.1 Chart-record of ratemeter output from Geiger counter held by Uri Geller. Key to schematic diagram: G, Geiger counter; L, loudspeaker; R, ratemeter; CR, chart-recorder. Insulating parts of the Geiger counter are shown cross-hatched.

Test pulse obtained with beta source. Pulses a–k apparently paranormal; k is the large one witnessed only by A.K., Nick Nicola and myself. Part of the simultaneously running gaussmeter chart record is also shown, and two peaks in the milligauss range appear synchronous with ratemeter output pulses.

counts per second were recorded (Figure 15.1a, Test pulse). Care was taken to check that in the absence of the source the background was not excessive, and that false pulses could not be produced by rough handling of the Geiger counter or its cable. Twenty minutes of constant background were followed by a test pulse from the radioactive source, then by a further ten minutes of constant background.

Then I handed the counter to Geller, who held it in both hands and tried to concentrate. We drew on the blackboard a picture of a mushroom cloud to help him to think of nuclear radiation. All the outward signs were that Geller was concentrating as hard as he could.

Within two minutes, two count rate pulses, one of about 25 counts per second, were recorded (Figure 15.1 a,b). Geller said that he felt some sort of shock, which I thought might have been electrical. But he did not see the chart-record at this stage; we made no attempt to use 'biofeedback', that is, to allow him to learn by watching the chart-recorder. I was attempting to watch both Geller and the chart-recorder. After sixteen minutes there was another pulse (c), and after a further five minutes a large pulse (d), during which Geller reported feeling a prickly sensation. We then allowed the apparatus to run without Geller holding the counter for a further ten minutes. There was only background radiation recorded, and the apparatus was switched off.

During the experiment the gaussmeter and its chart recorder had been kept running, with the probe fixed to a table about two feet away from Geller. Nick Nicola had been supervising the chart-record, but I did not watch it myself. There had been small movements in the gaussmeter chart-record, as there sometimes are when people do not keep quite still. But there were two larger pulses which Nicola told me corresponded exactly in time with the two count rate pulses (c) and (d).

I was already beginning to suspect that the origin of the Geiger counter pulses could be electrical rather than nuclear; we conducted further experiments on the following day. During a twenty-five minute session, four count rate pulses (e–h) were recorded, reaching maximum rates of about 10 per second. A second Geiger counter was also exposed, but it was not touched by Geller, and it did not register either audibly or visibly during these pulses. Only the counter which Geller actually held in his hands registered. A tape-record of the loudspeaker clicks from this counter was also made, and whilst there were clicks corresponding to the first two chart record pulses, there were very few corresponding to the last two. The effects on the Geiger counter were not quite those which bursts of nuclear radiation would have produced.

After twenty-five minutes all the witnesses except A.K. and myself were sent out of the room, and Geller was asked to make an extraordinary effort to produce a large pulse. Within three minutes he produced a count rate pulse (k) which was well off the scale of the chart, and may have been as high as 200 counts per second (Figure 15.1b). What is interesting about this pulse was that it arrived *before* Geller intended it. The transcription of the audio-tape reads as follows:

Geller: I'm gonna shout! . . . All right . . . (knocking) . . . (deep breath out) . . . I'm gonna count to ten and

Geller: on ten it's gonna go, 1,2,3,4,5,6,7,8,9   (Simultaneously)
Hasted: It's going already.

Geller: ten!
                                (both shouting)
A.K.:   -um-ho . . . Did you see that?

Hasted: I saw nothing, but it was ten times harder than anything we've had yet.

The peak on the chart-recorder started when I said, 'It's going already.' No clicks were audible. The pen stayed off-scale until 'Did you see that?', when it returned to zero, and some clicks were audible. Geller felt some sort of shock, and Koestler also experienced a shock. They both were temporarily exhausted.

I verified that the Geiger counter was still operational, and was still proof against mechanical effects such as pulling the cable or knocking the counter. Everyone came back into the room and Geller relaxed. My conviction was growing that the pulses were electrical in origin, but I did not see how electrical pulses could have entered into the circuit. Next day I realized that the shielding was incomplete; I tried the effect of short-circuiting a 90 volt battery along the screening case. Even though its window was closed, so that the case completely surrounded the counter, a count rate pulse was produced every time I passed current through the case.

A Geiger counter is essentially a metal cylinder with a fine wire mounted axially. It contains gas at a pressure of about 5 torr (about 1% of atmospheric pressure), and a steady voltage is maintained between wire and cylinder, just insufficient to cause spontaneous electrical breakdown. The entry of nuclear radiation is sufficient to trigger such breakdown by collisional ionization. The electrical energy of the breakdown is rapidly dissipated, but the counter produces an electrical pulse which is registered at a suitable amplifier. The counter quickly returns to pre-breakdown conditions and awaits the next pulse.

The Geiger counter circuit is shown in the insert to Figure 15.1. The cable connecting the counter to the electronics is screened, but the stainless steel Geiger counter screen is not connected to the screened cable; it is mounted on an insulating bush and is electrically floating. An electric transient in the screen will couple both inductively and capacitatively to the input of the sensitive amplifier and produce a pulse on the count rate record. Such transients are apparently what Geller was producing.

These electrical transients are more than a thousand times stronger than normal; typical potential differences that develop, for example between the left human wrist and the right, are several hundred microvolts, but they vary in time with heartbeat, breathing and muscular work. Local areas of skin hardly show any time-varying potentials; there is usually the equivalent of a high impedance separating these areas from the physiological conduction regions, which show time-varying potentials. But it follows that such a high impedance would protect the source, that is, the interior of the body, against shocks from surface effects. It therefore seems likely that the source of Geller's potentials lies at the surface of the body.

Let us consider the possibility that the effects Geller produced on the Geiger counter were simply due to static electricity at the skin surface. Friction on very good electrical insulators produces a static charge which can sometimes be discharged, producing a spark. But it would have to be a powerful static charge to produce a potential on the stainless steel case sufficient to trigger a low impedance amplifier. Frictional production of static charge acts by the removal of surface electrons from the insulator or their addition to it. Nevertheless, Geller had no cloth to produce the friction, and he was squeezing rather than rubbing the Geiger counter case; he held it quite still in his hands. His feet were not moving on the carpet. Those of us who have tried in my laboratory to produce static on metal surfaces without friction have had no success. There must be some mechanism by which the charge was produced, and since normal subjects cannot produce it one can legitimately call it paranormal. There have been reports from the USSR of subjects who have been able to produce static charge without friction and use it to

apply forces to objects without touching them. Geller's Geiger
counter pulses seem to have been phenomena of the same sort.

Just as the paranormal production of dislocations in the metal lattice
results in metal-bending, so we might look for the origin of these
electromagnetic phenomena in the local movements of charged particles;
but there is at present no evidence to identify the carriers. Interference
on video-tapes is sometimes encountered during recording of metal-
bending and psychokinesis sessions. We have several times suspected
that the origin of this may be paranormal. Following more recent
experiments, described below, it does seem that the paranormal production of electric charge at a certain location might be a possible primary
event.

These experiments came about almost by accident. In chapter 4 we
noted that in no-touch strain gauge sessions precautions should be
taken against touching. We therefore developed an electronic detector,
similar to those in use in manual contact switches. Its circuit is shown
in Figure 15.2. The metal specimens on which strain gauges were
mounted were themselves connected to the input of the amplifier. A
manual touch would produce a sharp signal, arising from a combination of body electrostatic charge, change of input impedance and,
possibly, increased mains pickup. Note that the electrode impedance is
to earth is low (typically 100–300 Ω).

We conducted several sessions with Stephen North, but no touch
signals were recorded at first. One evening David Robertson and I were
watching closely, when suddenly a substantial signal was recorded; but
it was clear to both of us that Stephen's hand was about eight inches

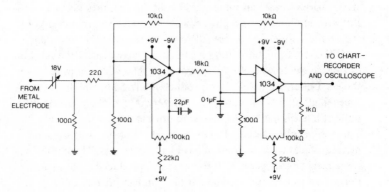

Figure 15.2 Circuit of detector for electrical effects

from the metal, and was quite stationary. There was no question of touch or of dynamic capacitative coupling of manual electrostatic charge during movement of the hand. We made no comment, but subsequent no-touch signals appeared, and one of these, which fluctuated in polarity, evoked a cry of 'Ow' from Stephen. He felt a sharp prick in his thumb, and I was able to squeeze a minuscule amount of blood from a tiny red mark. I can characterize the event only as a paranormal pin-prick, possibly related to the pricking sensations sometimes reported in hauntings, poltergeist cases and in the literature of witchcraft. One of the witches in *Macbeth* was supposed to cry: 'By the pricking of my thumbs, something wicked this way comes.' We repeated this type of experiment several times, concentrating our interest on the question of whether the electrical pulses were synchronized with strain pulses or not. No consistent generalizations could be made; some were synchronous and some were unique to one or the other action; no variables that we changed seemed to make significant differences.

At this point I became aware of the early (1901) experiments[40] in France and elsewhere on the ability of physical mediums, particularly Eusapia Palladino and Stanislava Tomczyk, to discharge gold leaf electroscopes without touch. Physically, this is a more or less identical experiment to the one we had been attempting. The discharge occurred in jerks and the subject felt a tingling sensation. Langevin took part in these experiments, as well as other scientists such as Marie Curie and d'Arsonval. They agreed that the phenomenon was genuine, but could find no explanation, and they were particularly concerned with the question of whether atmospheric ionization was produced; they concluded that there was none. In more recent times, table-lifting experiments[41] also turned up some unexplained electrical signals.

If there were atmospheric ionization between the hand and the electrode (with a potential maintained on the electrode), then the passage of a current would be detectable by magnetic induction. We attempted such detection by interposing a 5-in.-diameter ferrite torus surrounding the direct hand-electrode line. The torus was wound with a caduceal coil connected to an amplifier, and the system was calibrated by applying a current pulse to a wire aligned along the hand–electrode line; such a pulse was recordable on the chart-record output of the amplifier.

In several sessions we obtained signals on the torus system, and sometimes these were synchronous with signals on the electrode system. We were beginning to believe that there was an atmospheric ionization path. Then it occurred to us that the secondary coil was electrically unscreened (although insulated); it might be that paranormal electrical charges were being induced directly on the secondary coil, which was in fact closer to Stephen North's hand than was the electrode.

We then surrounded the secondary coil with a metal screen, constructed with insulation in such a way that the screen did not constitute a single turn around the torus. Immediately, the secondary coil signals ceased, although the electrode signals were unaffected. The conclusion had to be drawn that atmospheric ionization currents had not been detected; direct paranormal electrical charges on the visible secondary coil seemed to be an explanation. These could not be induced when the coil was inside a metal screen; instead, presumably, a charge would be induced on the screen itself. We abandoned experiments with the ferrite torus and continued with the electrode system alone. It seemed that both Stephen North and Julie Knowles spontaneously produced electrical charge, of either sign, at visible metal electrodes. We have not taken this work very far yet, but it appears to be interpretable as a paranormal 'primary phenomenon', comparable with the paranormal movement of atoms in metal crystal lattices or at grain boundaries. Sometimes both occur simultaneously. In our recent experiments, a screened room has been used.

In essentials our experiment on the placement of electric charge on an electrode remote from the body is the same as that conducted by physicist Hans Betz; in his experiments, well known in West Germany, the psychic demonstrated effects in a resistor which was exposed to him.

One caution is necessary to researchers intending to investigate the paranormal production of electric charge at low impedance electrodes. No movement of the hand close to the electrode should be permitted. Rapid movements can induce signals by capacitative coupling when the hand is electrically charged. Since the differences between the skin charges of different people can vary enormously, the psychic can appear to produce dynamic signals (synchronized with his movements), whereas the experimenter fails to do so. But when the hand is held motionless, dynamic signals cannot appear by normal mechanisms. The rapid movement of static charge along a motionless arm would have to be assumed, and this would appear to be a phenomenon itself to be classed as paranormal or at least inexplicable. The precautions against electrical interference to the equipment in the absence of the psychic subject must of course be stringent. As with dynamic strain experiments, many hours of quiet running are mandatory.

Our recent experiments with Stephen North on paranormal electric effects have unexpectedly implied that the primary action is the touchless placement of a burst of ionization in a very small region close to a metal electrode. The experiment is conducted with parallel plate electrodes, each connected individually to its own amplifier but with an applied potential difference between them of 20V, which automatically changes sign every 11 seconds; the electric field is balanced with respect to earth. The polarities of the signals, typically of 0.1 sec duration, almost invariably follow the potentials; signals are sometimes obtained at both electrodes, sometimes at one only. This is consistent with the hypothesis that carriers of either sign are formed simultaneously, and are separated and drift to the electrodes in the applied field. The collection efficiency is reduced by diffusion and recombination processes; the variation of proportion of synchronized signals with inter-electrode distance is consistent with conventional particle swarm analysis.

Since electrodynamics and magnetic fields are inextricably coupled in physical theory, one cannot exclude the production of static or dynamic magnetic fields as a possible primary paranormal phenomenon. The magnetic fields produced in our laboratory by Geller would appear to have arisen from electric currents. The paranormal movements of ships' compasses (chapter 20) seem to take place by some mechanism other than the production of magnetic field. Possibly the same arguments could be applied to the Stanford Research Institute experiments of Dr Puthoff on Geller in which a magnetometer within a superconducting shield was perturbed. And finally, the paranormal wiping of magnetic memory tapes by Geller, which was reported by Dr Hawke of the Lawrence Livermore Laboratory, could be classified as a magnetization effect arising from structural change rather than as the production of an external magnetic field.

Chapter 16

Structural phenomena

The emphasis of my studies of paranormal metal-bending has been on the investigation of dynamic strain effects, and a little has also been said about permanent structural or morphological changes in the metal specimens.

We now have reasonably good evidence for structural changes in the metal after paranormal metal-bending, but it takes a 'strong' subject to produce them in an easily detected form. Perhaps we should search for evidence for structural effects not only in metals, but in other solids and in biomolecular systems.

In chapter 13 we briefly noted a ferrous metal structural change investigated by the French researchers. Stainless steels can exist in two quite different structural forms, of which one is metastable, so that interconversion is possible. They are known as austenite and martensite. Conversion of the former to the latter can be brought about normally by heating to a high temperature (600–700° C) and also by 'shot-peening' – hammering with hard spherical shot. Conversion does not normally take place at room temperature, but Dr Crussard has reported that exposure to 'mental concentration' and gentle manual stroking by Jean-Pierre Girard has produced conversion of quite large areas; these are clearly seen in the scanning electron micrographs reproduced in his publication.[32]

More recently, structural examination of an abnormal plane bend produced by Willie G. has been made by student metallurgist Paul Mycock. Straight strips of alpha-brass (70% Cu, 30% Zn) were annealed in a furnace and offered to Willie, who succeeded in producing sufficient action to form an abnormal plane bend of some 30°. When the surface of the brass was microscopically examined, small regions of beta-brass structure (60% Cu, 40% Zn) were noticed. The brass specimens were polished, etched and then photographed at one hundred times magnification. The regions are easy to recognize as dark areas against the light of the alpha regions. Of course this observation does not imply that the overall stoichometric composition of the alloy had changed; rather, a 'displacive' transformation occurred, in which a different crystal structure was formed. This experiment is as yet unconfirmed, but represents an example of continuing work.

I myself have attempted relatively little in the way of systematic investigations of morphological changes paranormally produced in metals, since I have not the facilities of a metallurgical laboratory; also it seems likely that only the strongest subjects produce appreciable paranormal structural effects. However, there appears to be no reason why metals should be unique in showing such behaviour; they are not unique in being subject to paranormal dynamic strains or bending. Moreover there are other phenomena, such as faith healing (contact healing by the laying on of hands), which might possibly involve similar effects; therefore I felt that the best course open to me was to devise 'exposure' experiments on solid specimens whose physical properties are very sensitive to small changes in atomic structure or to the entry of impurities. Semiconductors are obviously suitable specimens, and so are single bio-organisms. The electrical characteristics of semiconductors are very sensitive to impurities and are readily susceptible to accurate measurement. The growth rates of simple bio-organisms are also sensitive to small structural changes and to impurities, and there are standard techniques for measuring these rates.

The real test of the suitability of specimens for exposure is whether psychic subjects take to them and feel confident of changing them. Some 'healers' are willing to attempt action on bio-organisms under laboratory conditions. But no psychic of my acquaintance seemed confident that he could modify a transistor; I had to introduce my subjects gently to the idea.

There is an interesting reason why it is important to know whether it is possible for a subject to affect the electrical properties of a transistor. Experiments on extra-sensory perception, and especially some modern experiments on psychokinesis,[42] are now conducted with electronic apparatus containing transistors and other components. In such experiments electronic random number generators are affected by psychic subjects, so that they no longer operate randomly; their departure from randomness is suitably displayed on an array of lights which the subject is asked to 'affect'. Often there is a clock-face circle of lights, and under complete randomness the illuminated light does not wander far in either direction from twelve o'clock. But if there is a departure from randomness, the light moves round the circle, either clockwise or anti-clockwise. Strong psychics are able to achieve impressive movements.

The question arises: Do the laws of physics break down in some way that we do not understand, or is some component in the electronic equipment affected by the psychic? Alternatively, is the effect similar to the electric charge production discussed in the last chapter? Effects produced on various electronic components – resistors and capacitors – have been studied elsewhere; in my own experiments I have exposed Zener diodes and field effect transistors to the action of subjects.

The 'characteristic' of a Zener diode is the dependence of current I which it passes upon the voltage V applied to it – the function $I(V)$. In a certain voltage range there is normally a fairly sudden increase in current with increasing voltage. This is sensitive to the level of impurity atoms in the depletion layer of the crystal, so that there is a good physical basis for the electrical detection of crystallographic change. On the other hand, it could be that a change in the $I(V)$ characteristic was attributable to a change in one or the other junction.

A minicomputer (Digico Micro 16) has been used to generate a 1024 bit staircase voltage lasting a period of seconds. This is applied to a Zener diode in series with a stabilized resistor, the voltage across which is monitored and the information stored in the computer. Both digital-to-analogue and analogue-to-digital converters are used. A characteristic (A) is shown on a visual display unit and if necessary recorded on chart or on punched paper tape. A second characteristic (B) is measured after an interval of 4 minutes, without any exposure to the psychic. Within the computer, B is subtracted from A; since they should be identical, the result $B - A$ is a horizontal line, $I = 0$ at all V. However, there is some noise in the measurement system, which is manifested as a series of spikes along this line. The number of these can be made a small fraction of the total bit number 1024. Each spike is 10 mV in magnitude. The number or number density of spikes is measured.

After this preparation a 4-minute exposure of the Zener diode to the psychic is made. Only the Zener diode is shown to the subject; the stabilized resistor is screened from view so that any effect on it should be minimized. The computer is not operating during the exposure. The Zener diode is temperature-stabilized by immersion within a transparent plastic bag in ice water 0° C. In similar experiments on a field effect transistor this was found to be unnecessary, since the sensitivity of the characteristic to temperature variation is apparently smaller.

After the 4-minute exposure a new characteristic (C) is measured and the difference $C - B$ displayed. If the exposure has given rise to any variation of the characteristic, then instead of the horizontal line there will be a step or a series of steps. We do not expect a smooth curve because the instrumentation is incapable of recording any change smaller than 10 mV (except in terms of frequency of spikes); the effects we have found have only been of the order of tens of millivolts. The exposure of Zener diodes and later of field effect transistors to Willie G. and to adult healer Dr Melvin Cann has produced some small but possibly real effects. Table 16.1 summarizes the conclusions of the experiments.

The importance of these experiments lies not in the very small and probably not significant success achieved, but in their potential for the future. Here is something for psychics to perform, with very small possibility of fraud, with maximum simplicity of *exposed* apparatus, and yet very close to the atoms themselves; the characteristic is sensitive to small atomic disturbances. It does not necessarily follow that all these things are advantages, but if they are, then this surely is an experiment with potential. It does not follow that many psychics will find this an easy effect to produce, but if we are entitled to believe that a very small mass transfer is easier to produce than a large mass transfer, this is likely to prove a successful experiment. Our experience with teleportation (chapter 19) suggests that minimizing the mass transfer leads to success. Another advantage of this method of experimentation is its adaptability to standard microprocessor technique. It is good training in modern methods of experimentation.

Possible physical bases for the modification of a junction characteristic by the addition of atoms or molecules are not difficult to find. For example, the experiments of Lambe and Jaklevic[43] led to a new method of deriving molecular absorption spectra from the structures in barrier junctions. Perhaps there is scope for applying these techniques to psychic research.

Biological growth rate experiments are also likely candidates for structural research, because it is possible that they will be popular with psychic healers.

I am not a professional biologist, although my interests have ranged as wide as biomolecular research. I have been impressed by the experiments of Dr Bernard Grad[44] and of Sister Justa Smith[45] on the abilities of healers to alter growth rates of bacteria and enzymes. I think it is important that specialists make as many experimental studies as possible with healers, and it is important for healers to recognize the significance of such studies.

Since I am no specialist I must leave most of this work to more competent people, but I can at least follow the ideas and instructions they give me. In Birkbeck College there is a long-standing tradition of mycology research, at present kept alive by Dr Brian Plunkett. He drew my attention to the simplicity of experiments on the growth rates of fungi. A fungus is a very simple form of life, often without cellular structure; 'strings of linked peptide-containing helices' might describe its form. A previous set of growth-rate experiments has been conducted by parapsychologist Dr Barry[46] in Bordeaux. Mucors such as *Mucor hiemalis* can be grown in Petri dishes containing a layer of nutrient jelly. Under sterile conditions the centre of the jelly is inoculated by placing thereon a small disc of mucor on jelly from a previous strain; a cork-borer of ¼in. is used for this operation; eight such dishes are covered and allowed to grow in a sterile environment (the interior of a glass dome in a selected laboratory). After 24 hours the radial growth is well established and the mean diameters of the fungi are measured. The dishes are randomly divided into two equal groups, of which one is exposed to the action of the subject for a few minutes, under observation, while the other is kept in another room without the knowledge of the psychic. It is unnecessary to remove the plastic covers of the Petri dishes during exposure. After exposure both batches of dishes are replaced together under their dome.

After a further twenty-four hours the mean diameter of all fungi are again measured, and this is repeated at further 24-hour intervals until each entire dish is filled with fungus. The experiment is carried out 'double-blind'; that is, the dishes are marked in code in such a way that the measurer does not know whether he is measuring an exposed or an unexposed fungus.

I carried out a preliminary series of ten such exposure experiments with Melvin Cann and Willie G. It appeared that exposures were sometimes associated with small changes of growth-rate, almost always inhibitions.

I therefore undertook a more extensive series of experiments, with Matthew Manning as subject, and these are in course of publication by the Society for Psychical Research.[47] My conclusions were as follows:

> We may claim that whilst a consistent effect on growth-rate has not been produced by the subject, there has been one exceptional exposure after which an extremely unlikely retardation of growth-rate occurred. We are unable to fault the experimentation for this

Table 16.1

Session no.	Subject	Conclusions
1	Melvin Cann	Inconclusive. Unexposed diodes show 1 positive effect in 4 experiments. Exposed diodes show 4 positive effects in 11 experiments. More stability required.
2	Melvin Cann	Stabilization of resistance greatly improves sensitivity 1 negative experiment 1 strongly positive experiment Total extent of change in characteristic, $\Delta V = 50\,mV$
3	Melvin Cann	Signal averaging installed 1 negative experiment
4	Melvin Cann	2 positive experiments, $\Delta V = 10$ mV, 10 mV
5	Melvin Cann	2 marginally positive experiments, $\Delta V = 4$ mV, 5 mV 2 negative experiments 2 marginally positive experiments, $\Delta V = 5$ mV, 5 mV
6	Willie G.	2 negative experiments
7	Willie G.	2 negative experiments

exposure, but are of course aware that it would be unwise to claim
the capture of an effect on the basis of a single anomalous batch.

Of course we must address ourselves to the question of whether any
generalization can be made about the physical mechanism by which, in
general, structural molecular effects might take place. In metal-bending
I already incline to the view that displacements of atoms are the most
frequently found primary mechanism, and it would seem that such displacements could also bring about changes in growth rate in other
materials. The psychic is, however, not concerned with understanding
mechanisms; his action is goal-oriented.

Chapter 17

Some psychological effects

Induction

In the presence of a 'strong' metal-bender, the 'power' is sometimes transmitted to other people, who temporarily 'produce' deformations of metal objects in their own hands. This I shall term 'induction'.

Typically, at Uri Geller's television performances or press conferences, he would attempt deformation of cutlery or latchkeys and would ask the audience themselves to concentrate on bending something, whether it be an item in their own pockets or hands, or the object which he himself was trying to deform. Several times in my experience someone in the audience came forward with a bent object, reporting that they felt it bend in their own hand, and sometimes that they saw it bend there. The frequency of such events cannot yet be estimated. Scattered around the world are journalists whose latchkeys have bent in their own hands. To some extent, a journalist could be regarded as a sceptical observer.

In sessions with Jean-Pierre Girard, similar induction effects have been reported. Some of the people involved are technologists, some are journalists, some are scientists of distinction; it is unlikely that they are all fooling themselves or being fooled. In Italy and Spain successful attempts at induction have been made on television and radio by charismatic entertainers.

At this stage it is premature to attempt an answer to the question of how far it is the inducer and how far it is the induced person who is 'responsible' for the bend; it might even be someone else entirely. Usually the member of the audience finds that he cannot repeat the performance on his own, but there have been many instances of child metal-benders starting in this way, documented in Britain and Japan.

In the studio of a British Independent Television 'Jimmy Young' show during 1975, I saw Uri Geller and six-year-old Belinda H. bend a spoon together; there were two members of the audience, a house-wife and a cameraman, to whom this induced bending happened. At a press conference for Uri Geller during 1976, I saw it happen to the astronomer Patrick Moore. Privately I smiled, as I thought he made rather a meal of it. But the laugh was on me, since a few days later when Uri fractured a silver fork for the Marquess of Bath at Longleat, it happened to me also, and I too was unable to prevent myself making a meal of it. In my case it was merely a cufflink which snapped, and coincidence is just possible. On three different occasions I have experi-enced the loosening of metal tooth-stoppings after successful sessions with Uri Geller, Girard or Masuaki Kiyota. Maybe these were coinci-dences.

When Girard first came under the scrutiny of Dr Crussard and other French physicists, a particular point was made of practising induction effects, since they are of some sociological value from the point of view of validation. A physicist who has felt a piece of Pechiney aluminium alloy bending in his own hands is unlikely to regard this as fraud. Some of the people to whom this has happened are of great distinction; I will not drop names, because they are embarrassed by the events. It is necessary to understand that an emotional shock can occur, and I have indeed experienced this myself.

A particular observation made by Dr Crussard was the following. When a metal-bender holds a strip of metal in his hand and 'allows' it to bend, there will usually be only a single bend, at one position along the strip (see also chapter 6). But when Girard held one end and a physicist held the other, there were sometimes two quite distinct places along the strip at which bends occurred. Similar effects may possibly have occurred in our distance effect experiments described in chapter 9. When I exposed a long strip of aluminium to Stephen North with three or six resistive strain gauges mounted along its length, the vast majority of the synchronous signal triplets or sextets were strongest in one region of the strip, falling off in strength at each side of it; it will be recalled that their magnitudes were fitted to Gaussian probability curves; the 'centre of action' and 'region of action' both varied some-what with time. But there were occasional signals appearing uniquely on the far sensor, with the strip in a radial horizontal configuration, and of course the usual position of one of the experimenters was at the far end of the strip. Could these signals have been examples of the induc-tion effect?

There are further questions, which we cannot yet answer. Does a fraction of the induction effect last much longer? Do all the child metal-benders owe their ability to an original induction process? How effective is induction at a distance — because many of the child metal-benders, unlike Belinda H., have never been physically near to Uri Geller so far as they know? In the belief that induction may be a real effect, at least at small distance, I have tried to 'activate' children by inviting them to parties with Geller and with Girard. But for most metal-benders watching Geller on television seems to have been sufficient. Thus the effect is probably more psychological than physical.

Some light may be thrown by a report of adult psychokinetic subject Suzanne Padfield, now married to physicist Dr Ted Bastin. Suzanne does not bend metal, but has shown great ability at psychokinesis, moving light mobile objects under glass domes (chapter 20). She claims to have induced the ability in other people, when these were in her presence. But in one instance her pupil was able to reproduce the effect in her absence, on the same afternoon as the original 'lesson'.

I have observed possible induction effect during a psychokinesis demonstration by Dr Julius Krmessky in Bratislava. I almost convinced myself that when asked by Dr Krmessky I could myself will the change of direction of movement of the suspended pointer. However, Dr Krmessky and also Czech physicist Dr Adamec were in the room, and it could well have been that Dr Krmessky was picking up my will and, consciously or unconsciously, producing the changes himself. I have never had any similar psychokinetic success myself, either before or since the session in Bratislava.

Another form of induction has been explored by Uri Geller twice in my presence. He sometimes attempts to call an additional 'power' from an observer, asking him to place his hand over the metal object which is to be affected. Geller then moves his clenched fist over the top of the observer's hand, without touching it. At some position the 'power' is supposed to be strongest; this is sensed physically by the observer, who tells Geller; concentrating in this position, Geller is able to produce an effect. The feeling in the observer's hand is basically a tingling sensation (possibly the pricking of chapter 15). On the first occasion on which I saw this it was physicist Dr Jack Sarfatt who was the active ·observer; Geller succeeded in producing a sudden bend in a pure molybdenum disc which later exhibited ferromagnetism (chapter 11). On the second occasion I myself extended my hand and experienced the sensation quite distinctly in my knuckles; Geller brought about the fracture and partial disappearance of a vanadium carbide electron microscope foil from within a capsule (chapter 19). My knuckles were not entirely free from discomfort for more than an hour. The extent, if any, to which Geller's 'power' was assisted by me is almost impossible to determine, and systematic experiments have not been carried out.

I include mention of a reported instance of remote induction which, if replicated, could have far-reaching consequences. David Nemeth is a young metal-bender who has demonstrated his ability to me on resistive strain gauges, and in other ways, in the presence of various observers. His mother was nursing in a hospital more than ten miles from their home, and she had the keeping of the key of a poisons cupboard, a special responsibility for her. One day at work she searched for her key and found it in her pocket, bent; she was unable to reopen the cupboard lock. Although her first thought was that the paranormal bending was her own, it transpired that David had at that exact time been particularly anxious that his mother should come home to him. Mrs Nemeth wished to discourage this from happening again, but there was a recurrence under similar circumstances. I attempted to stimulate an experiment, giving David and Mrs Nemeth identical sets of different-shaped metal pieces; David was to concentrate on one and see if the similar one in his mother's possession bent in the hospital. No success was achieved with systematic experimentation.

My interest in such induction experiments has been stimulated by the feeling sometimes subscribed to by metal-benders that 'the power comes through them or from outside them'. I do not yet know whether this is true or not, or even whether it is a meaningful statement to make. Certainly there is a 'distance effect' (chapter 8) in that the power demonstrates itself within a slightly mobile 'region of action', removed from the body of the subject. But the metal-benders do not regard this region as a manifestation of an 'external' source of power.

Induction effects are one of the most tantalizing of all the metal-bending phenomena, and their existence is very difficult to prove quantitatively. A great deal more study is necessary. Our understanding is made more difficult by the possible existence of 'post-active effects', discussed below. Metal-bending is sometimes found to continue after the 'conscious' action by the psychic has ceased; but has the action really ceased? And might an induction effect have taken its place?

All attempts I have made to send telepathic messages or communicate by means of signals on resistive strain gauges have failed. It occurred to me that strain gauge signals were similar in many ways to the paranormal raps produced on table-tops and elsewhere by 'sitter groups' when a question is asked of a 'discarnate entity'. This entity can even be imaginary, invented just for the purpose of the experiment.[48] The answer is usually given paranormally by code in raps. During successful resistive strain gauge sessions, the metal-benders and I have occasionally asked questions in order to obtain answering signals, but have been vouchsafed none.

There is one possible type of induction we have not yet considered – induction by inanimate objects rather than by people. There is no experimental proof of such an effect, but the following is worth mentioning. Mrs Lloyd told me that certain items of cutlery bent by her daughter Alison, when placed with other cutlery in the kitchen drawer, would bring about further bends of neighbouring cutlery. These events do not represent a proof of induction by inanimate objects, since the influence of Alison was not eliminated. But it does suggest a profitable line of experiment. Do particular inanimate objects stimulate a subject to bring about signals on resistive strain gauges? One is reminded of the rocks and gemstones sometimes held by water-diviners in their hands during their dowsing activity.

Post-active effects

By a post-active effect we signify the continuance of deformation of a piece of metal for a period of time after the metal-bender has apparently ceased his action.

The evidence for such an effect is difficult to quantify, because it is not easy to know by what criterion we should decide that the metal-bender has in fact 'ceased his action'. Many people, including myself, have observed events with Uri Geller and others in which the bending of a latchkey or spoon was attempted, with some degree of success; the object was then allowed to lie on the table, and Geller regarded the attempt as successful; minutes later someone who was keeping his eye on the spoon reported that in his opinion the bending was continuing; this was confirmed or sometimes contested by those present.

Such an event cannot be cited as a post-active effect, because in the absence of instruments Geller does not know for certain, neither does anyone else, just when he is 'ceasing his action'. He is still close to the object and may still have it in his mind. The only criterion at present available to us is that action at more than 10 m distance has not been reported, except by inductive effects; therefore, if continued deformation was reported after the departure of Geller, either a post-active effect or an inductive effect might be claimed. Anecdotal evidence satisfying this criterion exists, but I am unable to cite anything that I have observed personally.

Since inductive effects seem to be fairly common, I am inclined to ascribe even departure-criterion post-active effects to induction. What is required is a rigid application of the criterion that the subject and all observers should depart, while strain gauges are left running.

There is another complication, purely physical in nature, of which we must take account. Many household metal objects, formed from rolled strip and having at some stage suffered differential cooling, are permanently under residual internal stress; if this is suitably relaxed they will warp or bend slightly. The relaxation might be brought about by heat, by machining a layer off the surface or by paranormal softening. Only annealed specimens — heat-treated to relax the internal stresses — are free from this property. However, the relaxation deformation is usually not large, and would certainly be insufficient to account for paranormal metal-bending effects in general. Many of my deformation experiments, and also those of John Taylor, have been performed with annealed specimens.

In early researches I performed the following experiment (chapter 11) to find whether internal stresses play a role. Identical brass strips, precisely machined, were prepared. One was annealed and the other was left with its internal stresses unrelaxed. The two strips were now mutually attached, side by side, by pinning through one end with two steel pins. The standard of machining was such that the combined pieces had the appearance of being a single strip of brass with a fine line down the middle. The strips were exposed to observed action by Uri Geller and by Belinda H.; on the two successful occasions, it was the internally stressed strip which bent slightly; the bend was in the same direction as those in pieces cut from the same bar and heated. The annealed part remained undeformed. The experiments were stopped by removal of the specimen before further bending occurred, and there did not appear to be any post-active effect.

Although it was demonstrated that internal stress relaxation played a dominant role in this case, there is no proof that normal residual stress is responsible for post-active effects, if indeed there really are such effects. It would be more probable that anomalous internal stress was produced paranormally, as we know it can be; internal stress relaxation might possibly contribute a post-active effect.

Resistive strain gauge experiments are necessary to the study of post-active effects. Suppose that a series of signals is obtained at a metal specimen, without visible deformation occurring. Will the signals continue if the subject departs from the sensor? Several sessions with Nicholas Williams and Stephen North were deliberately interrupted in this way, but no significant signals have been recorded after the boy had accompanied me out of the room. No evidence for post-active signals was afforded.

On the basis of the foregoing discussion, I am unable to claim experimental evidence for a genuine paranormal post-active effect.

If metal-bending is supposed, as we think it is, to be a largely spontaneous phenomenon, then the whole concept of 'post-action' loses its value. There is some evidence to show that when metal-bending is occurring, the subject's electroencephalographic (EEG) signals are predominantly in the low frequency, alpha band, with possibly some delta and theta. But apart from this, there is typically little observable connection between the metal-bending action and the physiological functioning of the subject (see chapter 13).

It is of importance to research also the psychological background to the action of the metal-bender and his companions. This type of work was first carried out by Batcheldor and Brookes-Smith[41] on the psychokinetic contributions to table-lifting sessions. They proposed the hypothesis that the action occurred at moments of sudden change in the psychological state of one or more of the subjects. Such a hypothesis is readily tested in the case of metal-bending by experiments with resistive strain gauges. Julian Isaacs has taken on a programme of such experiments, including audio-recording of conversations during sessions with several subjects; the audio-recording was synchronized to the strain gauge recording.

I have personally observed several occasions on which the sudden relaxation of concentration on the part of the subject has been accompanied by a dynamic strain signal. Sometimes the relaxation was not spontaneous, but was brought about by the initiative of the experimenter – e.g. by saying, 'How about a rest and a cup of tea?' Julian Isaacs has observed similar features, with other changes of mood. With a psychokinetic subject the strain gauge apparatus could possibly be used as a lie detector. In a sense the relaxation-triggered events could be classed as post-active.

Goal orientation and the psychology of experimentation

Although I am no professional psychologist, I shall try to describe some of the psychological features of the experimental sessions which my colleagues and I have mounted.

My policy has been to spend as much experimental time as possible with children, at the expense of time spent with adult subjects. Although some powerful adults undoubtedly produce greater and more frequent effects than do the children, there is currently an atmosphere of dubiety that has been deliberately created around the adults and which I have tried to avoid. The historical reasons for this are obvious.

Hundreds of years of naturally-occurring strange phenomena have had their social repercussions. Society's fear of and distrust for that which is not understood has spilt over into the ranks of the scientists themselves, the majority of whom have refused to regard psychic research as important. The seriously interested minority have been forced onto the defensive, so that they now usually regard the psychic subject as a sort of laboratory animal. This relationship has led inevitably to polarization, distrust and, at worst, fraud. I have therefore tried to develop a pool of psychic subjects from virgin territory, using immature teenagers and younger children. These groups are quite capable of mischief, but their efforts are primitive and easily detected. The mystique that surrounds the conjuror's abilities rests partly upon his patient development and practising the sleight of hand for long daily periods; this is not a profession which produces many child prodigies. I am much more confident of being able to detect fraud when investigating children than when investigating adults. Moreover the motivations of children are as readily understood or misunderstood as those of adults; they are best understood by other members of their family, with whom a close relationship must be maintained during the period of experimentation.

What must be established above all else is some degree of curiosity motivation in the child and family. They are, after all, being asked to spend long boring periods in collaboration, without appreciable material gain. Subject motivation is a problem faced by human psychologists everywhere, and very often the traditional solution is simply one of payment for time spent. I have avoided this, partly so as to conserve research support, but more particularly so as to avoid any motivation of the children to produce results. Of course result-motivation must be present even when there is no payment, but I try to minimize it by working in the family home, by doing experiments in which negative results are an occasion for satisfaction, and by the replacement of the positive result-motivation by other goals.

The curiosity motive must not be confused with logically conceived reasons for co-operation in the research. However simple the social and cultural origins of these reasons may be, the curiosity motive is distinct from them. Although the prime motivation for man's pursuit of science has been the need to control his environment, this environment *includes himself*; the control and development of one's own abilities is itself a powerful motive, closely allied at a subconscious level to curiosity.

The children who have contributed most to this research have on the whole been drawn from families with some academic or educational connections; this is partly by my choice and partly by theirs. I have tried to develop an atmosphere in which the entire family respects and becomes curious about what is being done. Clearly this in itself is insufficient to induce paranormal effects: there must be relaxation, psychological good health and, above all, the learning of the appropriate 'attitude of inattention'. For some practised people such as Jean-Pierre Girard, attention, even concentration, is necessary, but always accompanied by and interspersed with relaxation. We have seen that during metal-bending there is a preponderance of alpha waves in his EEG, combined with a very high pulse rate.

For most children, on the other hand, it is a matter of learning inattention, or avoidance of concentration on concentration. This is a skill rather similar to learning not to stay awake at night. The intention to bend metal, like the intention to sleep, must be firmly maintained, but the subject can allow the conscious thought and the senses at times to wander. I find that while observing I must keep conversation going, so as to induce what by experience I believe to be the correct proportion of inattention on the part of the subject. I also find it useful to play upon motivations that I know by experience to be successful. These include the following: (1) competition: on one occasion I organized a race between children in the rate of production of signals; (2) relaxation: for example, saying that we are now going to break for tea will sometimes induce signals; (3) feedback: for example, drawing the child's attention to special features of the signal just recorded; (4) the need for antagonism to the scientist or parent: the motive to prove him wrong, by producing data which are at variance with preconceived ideas he may be unable to put aside; (5) vindication of the child's belief and confidence in himself; finally, but rarely (6) affection and joy at being close to the wonders of nature.

Part of the observers' learning of inattention is their learning not to glare fixedly at the metal specimen and strain gauges when dynamic strain pulses are being sought. Certainly, one must watch carefully, in case the desire to touch the specimen becomes too strong and the child yields to it. But if possible several people should be present so that the need for constant staring by each one is lessened. We may use indirect viewing through a mirror, or the various methods of touch prevention and touch detection.

My experience is that any feeling on the part of the child that the watching is entirely directed at the detection of cheating can inhibit the action. The desire to touch is not usually strong, but it may be triggered by feedback; when a signal is seen or heard, there can occasionally be an instinctive response to move a hand towards the metal specimen. This should be pointed out and avoided.

With younger children there are good reasons, as there are in education, for making the whole thing into a kind of game. Games demand goals, and displays and rewards when they are achieved. For example, dynamic strain gauge signals can be made to switch on lights, or can be incorporated into the scoring system in a game of chance. The game remains essentially one of chance because the phenomenon remains essentially spontaneous; in researching it we are trying to reduce it to a succession of observations. This process is an unnatural one which cannot be forced, though it may be assisted. Inevitably there are frustrations, since, in the words of the Australian poet John Manifold: 'Nothing is born without screaming and blood'. With very young children, dynamic strain gauge signals can be made to operate puppets with which the child can identify.

The most rewarding result is the production of finished articles, decorative or useful, in bent metal. These have provided the strongest motivation for children such as Andrew G., Stephen North, Julie Knowles and Willie G. An example of Nicholas Williams's work appears in Plate 17.1.

The complicated forms taken on by easily deformed metal strips and wires contain psychological and parapsychological information. Despite the difficulties of validating the events, even unobserved phenomena should not be entirely ignored; we should consider the circumstantial evidence surrounding them.

Andrew G. 'invented' these complicated forms. He was the first to use paperclip wires as a sculptural medium, and thereby to develop both his creative and his metal-bending talents. He found that paperclip wires would become screwed up tight into interesting shapes, which were christened 'scrunches'; he was soon able to control the bending to such an extent that the scrunches had representational forms: little men, animals and so on. But he found that in order to get results it was necessary to work in solitude, in his own bedroom or in the bathroom.

His mother, a sculptress, had her own workshop in the house, and Andrew no doubt wanted to imitate her.

From the point of view of our research, it is very important that the metal-bending operations be observed visually. But from the point of view of the craft of metal sculpture, observation is of little importance. Andrew followed his own motivation and that of his parents, and made small attempt to train himself to work in anything other than solitude. For this reason he did not progress very far under observation in achieving extensive and complicated movements of wires and thin metal. Several other children have produced bending with extensive motion, albeit in the family home and of a spontaneous character; and with these there has been some observation, at least by the family. Julie Knowles, Nicholas Williams, Stephen North and Willie G. have achieved motions and deformations of wires or thin metal strips with family observation; thus the degree of validation is higher than before.

The pattern has been as follows. I have offered strips of aluminium alloy, usually 40 cm × 8 mm × 0.75 mm, to the metal-bender, and at first my only instructions have been: 'Just experiment with these and see what happens; leave them around and see if they will bend.' I was careful not to let it be known what forms I expected; but the forms that were reported and shown to me had usually great similarities.

Some children and families were a little scared when the first no-touch

Plate 17.1 'Conflict', produced by Nicholas Williams; photograph by David Rookes

movements and deformations occurred, and in several cases I received late-night telephone calls which I tried to answer with reassurances. One end of the strip would be held in the hand, and some bending with stroking started. Gradually the strip would 'start to go on its own', either into a coil, a spiral, a twist, a fold, a tangle or a work of art. I would examine the deformed strips and study the similarities and the differences quantitatively — as for example in the work on the pitch of twisted strips described in chapter 7. Occasionally the strips would not be held in the hand, but just laid on a table; one or more would start to move on its own. In chapter 7 I described such an event with Nicholas Williams in which I observed the movement, not visually, but aurally and by dynamic magnetic field measurements. But I have never actually seen complicated bending movements of these thin strips; the only people who have are the children and sometimes members of the families. I have video-tapes of no-touch sudden and gradual bends, and also of some pulling and pushing of thin strips by what might be imagined to be an invisible hand; but although this resulted in bending, the forms produced were not complicated.

I have confidence that in broad outline the extensive spontaneous movement phenomena are in reality as I have described them. The folding rates (chapter 7) have been shown to be as high as three folds per second. At first the control of the phenomenon is very poor, but there are motives for the child to improve it. The game is to make decorative and representational objects and even to produce metal 'strip writing'. There is no hard and fast dividing line between what is consciously intended, and what occurs in an uncontrolled way but is thought to be a felicitous result, and is therefore allowed to stand; in the Jackson Pollock mode of normal graphic and sculptural art this is no doubt equally true. The basic forms of metal-benders' art are coils, spirals, anomalous plane bends, twists and folds. The most popular end-products are flowers, animals, human forms, abstracts, strip-written texts or messages, and jewellery. But only the strongest of the metal-benders reach this point, and many never succeed.

My experiments on paranormal metal-bending are continuing, but I have attempted here to complete my description of what little has been achieved so far; even at this rudimentary stage of investigation I believe it is worth speculating about the manner in which the phenomena fit, or fail to fit, into physical science as we know it. However, metal-bending is not unique as a psychic phenomenon; there are others which could be relevant; some are of great dubiety, some seem much more plausible. During my researches with metal-bending children some of these phenomena have come my way; I have not ignored them, but have tried to observe and investigate as best I can. It may be worthwhile to devote a few chapters to setting down these observations; they could provide a clue to the sorts of excursions into physical theory that are going to be necessary for the interpretation of psychic phenomena as a whole, with metal-bending as perhaps the most amenable part. But I have approached the other phenomena with the same attitude as that proposed in chapter 1: 'Believe nothing that you hear and only half of what you see.' Another important text is: 'The finest memory is inferior to the palest ink.'

Chapter **18**

Poltergeist experiences and teleportation

There is an extensive literature[49] which describes what are known as 'poltergeist phenomena'. Psychic researchers have sifted through first-hand accounts, judging them by the same criteria as those applied to historical, anthropological and forensic source material. Other psychic researchers have themselves been fortunate enough to observe phenomena, and have written careful or less careful accounts. On this basis most scholars have concluded that many strange physical phenomena have really occurred at intervals throughout history. The thinking public is less inclined to be sceptical about these events than it is about other psychic phenomena; there is a sense of 'it doesn't happen to me, but all the same it seems to happen to some people.'

The modern technical term for physical poltergeist phenomena is RSPK (recurrent spontaneous psychokinesis). In a poltergeist 'case', objects sometimes spontaneously fly about the house, apparently in a random way, without discrimination. But it is seldom that anyone is hurt by them. Sometimes their paths of flight are unnaturally crooked, and often the objects are not seen to leave their normal positions; sometimes they just appear in the air and gently drop. Sometimes they arrive warm and sometimes they arrive with spin, or angular momentum. Sometimes they 'appear' in motion, their flight starting from a position different from their normal place. Sometimes the origin of the objects is unknown, as in the cases where showers of stones are reported.

Furniture, heavy and light, can move spontaneously about the room, tip over, and even levitate and crash down again on the floor. Sometimes these movements are observed, sometimes they happen when no one is in the room, for example, during the night. A typical poltergeist case will last only for a period of weeks or months. The spontaneity of the movements has led to the opinion that the phenomena are caused by a 'ghost'. However, the more usually accepted view is that one or more of the personalities involved, usually children, are unconsciously 'responsible' for the phenomena, in that they are physically present when they occur. Such personalities have been called 'epicentres' (although this term is also used to describe the area of the house in which events most frequently happen). When the subject realizes that he or she is 'responsible', and is thereby the centre of attention, he often adds to the effects by normal physical means.

Rarer and stranger events, including many quasi-physical as opposed to physical phenomena, have been reported in poltergeist cases, but the above are the most usual and the most relevant to metal-bending. In this chapter I shall not attempt an accurate generalized description of poltergeist cases, but instead shall concentrate on certain personal observations which have relevance to metal-bending and to physics.

I have had to live with poltergeist phenomena on several occasions, and the experiences are not easily forgotten. I have kept notebook records of nearly a hundred 'movements' of objects which I witnessed. I have records of many more reported to me by other observers of English cases.

It happens that the particular type of event I have observed most frequently is the travelling of an object from one location to another in a most abnormal way. It might best be described as the *disappearance* of the object in its original position, and its *re-appearance* somewhere else. This is the phenomenon known, as I subsequently found, as 'teleportation'. It is likely that this phenomenon is of physical similarity and relevance to metal-bending, and therefore I shall discuss it in detail; I introduce it by way of a description of the poltergeist phenomena (rather atypical) which I had the opportunity to observe in my own home.

In November 1974 my wife Lynn and I had been in our house in Surrey for only two years. Our ten-year-old son John Andrew was away at boarding school. One Saturday afternoon Uri Geller and two friends paid us a visit. I had already met Uri on several occasions and had observed his metal-bending. But Lynn had never spoken to Uri and had never seen anything bend. She was strongly sceptical, and had never had the slightest interest in psychic phenomena; until my first observations of Uri, neither had I.

Lynn served us drinks in the lounge, and our guests commented on the carvings displayed on the piano and bookshelves. Lynn took Uri into her kitchen to get him an apple while the others stayed in the lounge. A plan of the ground floor of the house is shown in Figure 18.1

to indicate just where they were standing in the kitchen (g,l). Lynn had started to tell Geller that she was entirely sceptical about metal-bending, and I was just entering the kitchen (h). I saw clearly a small object appear a few feet in the air and fall to the floor in front of the back door. It was about the size of the lid of our vacuum coffeepot, and at first I thought that this is what it was, and that pressure had blown it out. Geller turned round to face it, and we saw that what had appeared in the air and had fallen was a small Japanese marine ivory statuette of an old peasant. This had been in its normal place on the bookshelf in the lounge, as in Figure 18.1(b).

I was certain that the statuette had not been thrown; it would have described a trajectory instead of dropping more or less straight

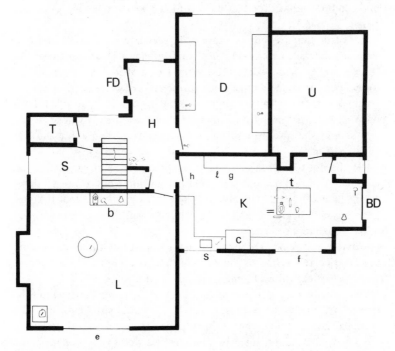

Figure 18.1 Ground-floor plan of the Hasted house showing positions of appearance and disappearance of objects. L, lounge; K, kitchen; U, utility room; D, diningroom; H, hall; T, toilet; S, study; FD, front door; BD, back door; b, bookcase; c, cooker; e and f, windows from which observers watched striking clock; s, kitchen sink; t, kitchen table; h, l, and g, positions of Hasted, Lynn and Geller at moment of appearance of statuette in front of locked back door.

Objects whose changes of location are shown include clock key, diningroom door key and turkey liver.

downwards. Any ball-game player is quick to react to trajectories, and should be able to judge where a ball has come from. This object is rather smaller than a cricket-ball, but not far from spherical. It was probably made in the nineteenth century. If the statuette had been thrown by Geller, it would have bounced into the corner instead of dropping downwards. Moreover Geller had his back to its landing-place, and his hands were in front of him, with an apple in one of them. I was certain that Lynn had no physical part in it. If the statuette had been thrown from the hall by one of Geller's friends, it would have had to pass me, standing in the doorway; I was sure that it had not. The statuette could not have come in through the back door, which was locked from the inside; all the windows were closed, and according to my notebook no visitor had been into the kitchen before Lynn and Geller.

It is true that I might not have been prepared to describe this event as a disappearance followed by a reappearance if I had not heard of strange events having taken place when Geller visited American labora-tories. But the sudden appearance of the statuette was such a clear-cut phenomenon that I had no alternative but to accept it, although I was puzzled and tried in my own mind to explain it away. Lynn's reaction was shock; she also believed it to be an inexplicable event and was frightened.

We did not touch the statuette until it had been photographed. Lynn used her Polaroid camera, and obtained nothing but black pictures, which in itself could possibly have been a paranormal effect (chapter 24), since she operated the camera perfectly well the same evening; but other explanations might also fit.

While we were all standing around looking at the statuette, a second object appeared in the air and dropped. This time we all observed it, and it was clear to us all that it had not been thrown. It was the key of a Buhl clock which stands next to the statuette on the bookshelf in the lounge. Normally the key is hung on the clock, although, since the clock had had no pendulum for thirty years, it was never used. However, I recognized it easily, since it is unique and well proportioned. If the statuette and the key had passed in normal parabolic arcs from the lounge bookcase straight to their destination in the kitchen, the arcs would pass through the wall (see Figure 18.1). Perhaps there could have been more complicated curved paths, passing out of the lounge door into the hall, and thence through the kitchen door and across the kitchen. But the observers would have been very likely to see the object moving in such a path; in particular, I myself was standing in the kitchen doorway when the statuette reappeared, and if it had simply moved all the way in a normal trajectory it must have passed close to me. If the movement of the objects had been in a single normal trajectory, then the objects would have had to pass through a wall to get to the place at which they reappeared.

Lynn and I were to find in the subsequent weeks that objects apparently reappearing on the other side of solid walls was a common feature of these phenomena; sometimes the objects would have had to pass through the wall of a container or wrapping to appear where they did. Our observations continually reinforced the presumption that the events were not to be described as objects flying about, but as objects disappearing and reappearing. We might suppose that the 'ability' had been induced in Lynn.

Uri Geller was due to leave for Italy next morning, which was Sunday. On Monday Lynn watched Geller's (recorded) television appearance during which the statuette and key events were briefly described by me. She invited her friend and neighbour Liz Dobson, who left at 3.30 pm, some time after the viewing. Then Lynn went upstairs to have a bath, and came down about 4 o'clock. She was alone in the house, and the outside doors were locked. Lynn is of a nervous disposition.

At once she saw that the key was not on the clock where it had been half an hour previously. She found it by the back door, almost exactly where it had fallen two days before. Furthermore the objects on the bookcase had been disturbed; the ivory statuette was on its side, and so was its neighbour, a little jade Buddha. A magnetic toy was not in its equilibrium condition but in its metastable condition, and a carved ivory ball was no longer on its stand.

Lynn telephoned my laboratory, and I told her that I would come home as soon as possible, but that she was to leave the key exactly where it had fallen (I measured it to be 8½ in. away from the kitchen wall and 2 in. from the back door (Figure 18.1)).

At 4.30 she telephoned me again, this time more frightened. The Buhl clock had chimed three times, each time striking five, and now the hands were not at their previous position of 5.30, but at 6.10. She had not seen them move. Although the clock had no pendulum and had remained static for many years, there was apparently energy stored in the clockwork mainspring and in the striking spring.

I went home at once, and reassured Lynn; we had supper. At 8.15 Lynn went into the lounge and started to approach the clock. Immediately it chimed three times, five strikes the first time, but then four and then four again. I heard the first one from the kitchen, quickly came into the lounge and observed the two remaining chimes. The sound comes from a small bell, and is both clear and pleasant; between each strike there is an interval of about a second. Lynn was not in a state of mind in which she was likely to have been tampering with the clock mechanism. She remained frightened, and I reassured her by telling her that I would replace the key in its normal position, and that everything would be all right.

But when I reached the back door and stooped down to pick up the key, another chime of five strikes was heard. I returned to find Lynn still standing in the lounge but now even more disturbed. She claimed that she had not touched the clock, and I attempted without success to produce strikes by percussion, tilting, etc., and by unfastening the front glass and adjusting the hands in either direction. But it occurred to me that the chime might take place if I went to get the key again; and so it did; five strikes.

Lynn was standing in front of the clock, so I tried the identical experiment again, and it worked again. Lynn could not see what I was doing in the kitchen, but of course she knew that I was going to fetch the key, and could hear me walking through the kitchen. Lynn and I found we could produce paranormal clock chimes by this ritual for a period of more than eight weeks. The strikes were heard whenever we underwent the curious routine. We invited several groups of observers – from my own physics department, from the Society for Psychical Research and from the editorial staff of the science journal *Nature* – to see and hear the evidence. More than eighty separate chiming events were obtained, and, more important, this was a harmless channel into which the 'poltergeist energies' could be steered. Later, with the assistance of a horologist, I studied the clock mechanism in detail to see just how the chimes and hand movements could have been triggered; it could not have been done manually without fabricating a long wire tool. As long as the chimes continued, no objects flew round the house; but eventually, when I removed the clock for examination, teleportations and other phenomena started up again. I kept detailed notes, but I will describe only one further event out of about forty.

On 23 December, despite the disturbances, preparations for Christmas were going ahead. We had ordered a turkey from our butcher and, in addition, a second one which would be purchased from us and taken away by our friend David Jenkins. David was living on his own and was faced with the prospect of cooking Christmas dinner for his visiting relations. His local butcher was unsatisfactory, whereas we had every confidence that ours would offer a good bird.

He arrived to collect his turkey during the evening, but it was past 11 o'clock when we all went into the kitchen to present it to him. It was wrapped in a plastic bag and was resting on a tray on the bare white plastic table-top. Beside the turkey, on the tray and wrapped in another plastic bag fastened with wires, were the giblets, liver, etc.

Suddenly a brown object appeared on the table in front of us, and I thought for a moment that it might be a leaf that had floated in through a window. But it was in fact a turkey liver, and we checked that one was no longer in the sealed plastic bag with the giblets. It resembled the other turkey liver, which we found to be safely in its own bag in the larder.

Lynn had at that moment told David that he could make the giblets into soup. But what appeared were not the giblets but only their near neighbour, the liver.

There was no smear of blood on the white table, such as the liver would have made if it had moved along the surface. There had been no sound. And there seemed to us no normal explanation of how the event occurred. I did not keep the liver for pathological examination, but I did check with our butcher that it was actually a turkey liver.

This event was one of the most significant I had observed, since the liver in all reasonable certainty started from its situation inside the sealed plastic bag, and finished outside it. All three of us saw first of all an expanse of white table, and immediately afterwards a piece of liver on it. There were no holes in the plastic bag, although it was not vacuum-tight.

Chapter 19

Further detail of teleportation

In this chapter, as in the last, I describe events which I originally observed and categorized as 'disappearance/reappearance phenomena'. Only later did I find that in the literature of psychic research these phenomena are designated 'teleportations'. An object suddenly ceases to be visible at its original location and suddenly reappears at a different location, usually within thirty feet of the original. It seems not to matter whether a solid wall lies in the path the object must take. Sometimes the object passes from one room to another, even through closed doors, without being visible on the way. Sometimes the object does not reappear, but simply vanishes from within a closed capsule; sometimes an object reappears within a capsule, and sometimes an object appears from an unknown previous location; this has been described as an 'apport'.

During July 1975 I was exposed to a short but rapid sequence of teleportations while staying in the New Otani Hotel, Tokyo, in the room next to Uri Geller. About 10.20 pm one evening after a press conference during which there had been a miscalculation that upset Geller, his secretary Trina and photographer Shipi departed to send a Telex message. I left Geller in his room, and unlocked the door of my room and went in. Within a few seconds I saw a small object fall to the floor, not from a great height, but within one foot of the drawn window-curtains. It was a pair of nail-clippers, but it did not belong to me. When I took it next door to Uri, he told me that it belonged to him, and would normally be kept zipped-up in a leather case from which he showed me that it was missing. While we were speaking, a glass tumbler dropped to the carpet behind us, in the centre of the room. I took Uri back to my room to show him where the nail-clippers had fallen, but we got no further than opening my door when there was an explosion and crash. Broken glass was found all over the area by the door, and in the hotel corridor. One glass tumbler from my bathroom was now missing. Hotel guests in the corridor saw the flying glass but could offer no explanation. We cleared up the broken glass; Uri returned to his room and I to mine. Almost immediately I saw the sudden appearance of my magnifying lens in the middle of the floor, on the carpet. By good luck it was reasonably well in my field of view at the time, so that I was able to be certain that it did not just fall to the ground. Previously it had been on the desk, more than six feet away.

All this had taken only three to four minutes. When Trina and Shipi returned, we all went down to the restaurant and Uri lit a cigar, which was, I believe, unusual for him. But he kept complaining that he could not keep it in his mouth, that it 'went away from him'. When he operated the elevator contact switches, all twenty-four switches flashed on simultaneously. During dinner a spoon appeared to curve upwards gradually on the table, untouched by anyone, and in full view of us all.

It was a troublesome evening, and possibly all the disturbances had resulted from Geller's being upset at the press conference. My powers of observation were stretched to the limit, but I did my best to examine each event from the point of view of trickery, and I concluded that most must have been genuine teleportations.

My first laboratory experience of teleportation was the disappearance of a fractured piece of vanadium carbide electron microscope foil from its location in a cellulose capsule. This event was described in my 1974 notebook[39] as follows:

> Geller finds that his powers are improved by working on a large block of metal, and he soon felt sufficiently activated to attempt a bending without touching. We laid out a collection of metal objects on the metal surface plate, and this time there was only one latch-key; the rest were single crystals, of copper, zinc, silicon, germanium, nickel and vanadium carbide.
>
> In addition I laid out three encapsulated electron microscope foils which Tony Lee had provided. When a specimen is viewed under an electron microscope, it must be thinned down to an extent which allows the beam of electrons to pass right through it. The specimen is formed into a disc of about 2 mm diameter, and 0.2 mm thickness; it is thinned down by special techniques until in the centre it is only ten or twenty atoms thick, although its thickness at the edge is unchanged. I had been given three nickel crystal foils, and two crystals of vanadium carbide, each weighing about 30 mg. This

material has the appearance of a metal, but it is harder than glass and rather brittle. The foils had been examined in the electron microscope, and so could easily be identified in a similar instrument. As is customary, each foil was encapsulated in a cellulose pill-case, the sort that dissolves in the stomach and releases the powdered drug inside. These pill-cases were made in two halves, which are a slide fit into each other. Their wall thickness is 0.08 mm, and a scale representation is given [in Plate 19.1]. I had looked at the capsules when Geller had telephoned me about half an hour before and had found the foils in good order, but I only glanced at them and did not actually examine them closely when putting them out on the surface plate. The capsules had remained in their plastic box in a closed drawer of my desk in the meantime, and I had been in the room sitting at the desk all the time. There was a strong presumption that they were unchanged, but in view of what was to happen I now regret this oversight; it detracts from an otherwise perfect experiment.

When all the specimens were laid out on the surface plate, I held my right hand, palm downwards with outstretched fingers, a few inches above them, and Geller passed his right hand slowly above it. He said that the 'power' could well be strongest in one particular place, and that I might be able to sense where this was by a feeling in my hand. On a previous occasion Jack Sarfatt had experienced a sensation in his hand during the no-touch bending of a molybdenum crystal, and Geller himself claims to have experienced sensations in his hands.

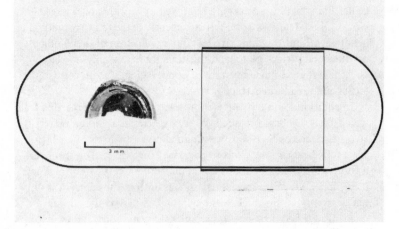

Plate 19.1 Fragment of vanadium carbide foil remaining in cellulose capsule

When Geller's hand was directly above my knuckles, I felt in them a warm sensation, as though I was experiencing strong dia-thermic heating. I wondered if this might be radiant heat from Geller's hand being unusually hot, but a quick touch with my other hand told me that it was as cool as my own. I said to Geller, 'This is the place, try to increase the "power" here.' He concentrated, with his hand still above my knuckles, and the capsule, which was directly below them, gave a little jump, like a jumping bean. I did not see this, since I could not see through my own hand; but Ted Bastin reported it. Then I removed my hand a little to one side, and I myself saw the capsule give a little jump. Geller removed his hand, which had been at least ten inches above the surface plate. Bastin and I examined the capsule, without opening it, and we found to our astonishment that although the capsule was undamaged, only half the foil was inside. A photograph of the fractured foil within a scaled cross-section through the capsule appears [in Plate 19.1]. Bastin immediately took the capsule containing the fractured foil; he did not open it; he was going to Cambridge, and could ask Tony Lee to view it in the electron microscope. Geller had at no time touched the capsule.

I did not know quite how seriously to take my warmed knuckles, or how to answer the question of whether the sensation was of psychokinetic origin or purely psychological. I did experience slight discomfort in the knuckles for about two hours.

We searched the desk, which had been cleared for the session, and as much of the office as we could; but we could not find the other half of the foil; it was a tiny object, after all. We decided to leave the office straight away, and arrange for a thorough vacuum cleaning of the desk and carpet. Fortunately vanadium is fairly rare and small quantities of it can be detected by neutron activation analysis.

We were forced by our observations to the preposterous conclusion that a part of the foil had disappeared from inside the closed capsule, presumably reappearing somewhere else in the laboratory. It could not have passed through the wall of the capsule, since the latter was undamaged.

It is true that we did not see the half-foil reappear; but it did dis-appear under circumstances which led us to think that conjuring was out of the question.

I have observed other events in which the appearance of an object rather than the disappearance is seen. This is why I believe that it is as likely that the half-foil reappeared somewhere as that it vanished altogether. Not all of these 'disappearance/reappearance' events are demonstrably not just flying through the air; but the instances, of which this is one, in which the object passes out of a closed wrapping capsule without breaking it, force me to the conclusion that 'disappearance/reappearance' is the correct description.

Next day Ted Bastin telephoned me from Cambridge, saying that Tony Lee and he had opened the capsule and examined the half-foil under the electron microscope. No substitution had taken place. The foil displayed a brittle fracture in the 100 plane, with a small proportion of conchoidal fracture. This would be typical of the mechanical failure of a brittle crystal such as vanadium carbide. The crystal is face-centred cubic (the same as common salt), with a superlattice of vacancies sufficient to make up the stoichometric formula V_6C_5. Some small facets of ridges about 200 Å across were recognized running along the crystal; these might have arisen from a previous heat treatment, or as remnants of a cleavage in the 110 plane, or from polish damage, or they may have been oxide.

Lee and Bastin also examined the other encapsulated vanadium carbide foil, and tried to fracture it with long-nosed pliers, holding it in tissue paper in a vice. It was a slow and delicate operation, taking almost an hour to perform, and despite great care the broken half of the foil flew in the air and could not be found. The crystals are tough and extremely springy; being under internal stress, they fly apart rather than fall apart.

I had supervised the vacuum-cleaning of the office floor; the sweepings were sent to Professor Henry Wilson at the Scottish Universities Reactor Centre for vanadium analysis by neutron activation. His colleague Dr Whitley[26] reported a high level (29 ± 6 μg vanadium in a 5 g sample), which might possibly indicate that the sweepings contained some of the foil. However, my own shoes might well have deposited this amount after my regular visits to the college workshops. Vanadium is present in small quantities in many types of steel, and therefore in the turnings and filings on a workshop floor. I continued to sample my floor-sweepings to see what the typical vanadium level is; in February 1975 the level was as high as 140 ± 30 μg, but we cannot conclude that we have found any of the fractured foil.

David Bohm pointed out that the vanadium might actually have passed into the steel of the surface plate; I therefore arranged for drillings both from the centre and from the edge of the underside of the surface plate to be analysed. The levels were both 0.270 ± 0.016% of vanadium; this figure is below the maximum of 0.4% which is found in some types of steel. I concluded that there was no evidence that the vanadium had passed the surface plate.

The significant thing about these observations is that part of the vanadium carbide appeared to have passed through the wall of the capsule without leaving a hole.

Since I found myself forced to believe in teleportations, I wished to control them, or at least to induce metal-bending subjects to bring them about. It occurred to me that the first such event I had seen, the fracture and disappearance of the vanadium carbide foil, involved only a very tiny object. Perhaps such events are more common the smaller the object involved and the thinner the wall that is traversed. I therefore prepared molybdenum electron microscope foils inside similar capsules, and determined to expose them to my strongest metal-benders. This time the security against tampering would be greater; some handling might be necessary, even though Geller had not had his hand closer than ten inches from the vanadium carbide capsule.

I wrapped two capsules in several thicknesses of Scotch tape, which would have to be stripped off or cut if the foil was to be extracted by hand. I also placed a single crystal of germanium in a Teflon tube, and bonded the lid with epoxy-resin. Foils and crystals had both been weighed accurately. Capsules and tube were now all placed in a transparent plastic box (50 × 30 × 10 mm), whose lid was bonded with epoxy-resin, for further security. The foils and crystal could be seen through the walls of their containers.

I offered the box to Nicholas Williams after a successful metal-bending session. I first got him to talk about the various similar events he had experienced in his home. He grasped the box in his hand for nearly a minute. I could not see the foils within the box, since his hand enclosed it, but one end of the box was in my field of vision the entire time. When I examined it, there was one foil missing from within its capsule. The capsule was apparently undamaged. The other foil and crystal were still present.

We repeated the 'experiment', and this time the second foil was missing from its capsule, which also appeared undamaged. On the third attempt, a silicon crystal was missing from its capsule. Since all three objects were very small, and the room contained a carpet and much furniture, we did not search for the objects at this stage. But Nicholas said he might 'bring something back', and I again gave him the box, a photograph of which with fresh capsules appears in Plate 19.2. Within seconds the silicon crystal was seen within its tube. The box now contained two capsules without their foils, and one Teflon tube with a silicon crystal inside it. I replaced the box in my inside pocket, and when I returned to the laboratory and examined it thoroughly, I found no damage to the sealing of the box, or to the sealing of the capsules. I opened the Teflon tube and weighed the silicon crystal, finding no change within 1 mg accuracy. There appeared to have been no normal way in which these phenomena could have happened. I have since realized how lucky I was to be at the right place at the right time with the right equipment to observe such rare spontaneous events.

It would of course be an even more convincing demonstration if the object were to appear inside a laboratory glassware sphere. Since such a sphere can be positively identified against reproduction in a number of ways known to physicists and glassblowers, the existence of such a sphere containing an object would be proof positive of *either* teleportation *or* the error or fraud of the glassblower and physicist who prepared the empty sphere and identified it empty and filled.

It happened that I was well supplied with laboratory glass spheres, each with a small hole, for the validation of unwitnessed metal-bending described in chapter 3. I decided to attempt teleportations into these

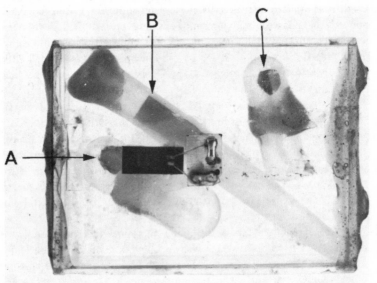

Plate 19.2 Transparent plastic box sealed with epoxy-resin, containing (A) fragment of molybdenum foil within capsule sealed with epoxy-resin; (B) fragment of silicon single crystal within hypodermic needle case sealed with epoxy-resin; (C) fragment of molybdenum foil within capsule sealed with epoxy-resin.

spheres. The object would have to be larger than the hole for its appearance inside to be considered a paranormal event. I told Nicholas Williams, who was still in an active 'poltergeist state', what I imagined might happen: a small object, which he could choose, might be found inside one of the spheres. He used to leave the sphere in what was believed to be a particularly 'active' part of the house, with the chosen object close to it. What happened, several times, was that the object was found inside a shattered glass sphere, the pieces lying underneath and round the object. Possibly a teleportation event is accompanied by an impulse on the capsule, sufficient to fracture it when it is made of glass and the object is large, but insufficient in the case of the foil in the cellulose capsule. It will be recalled that the capsule out of which Uri Geller 'caused' the fractured foil to disappear experienced a force which made it jump. That force could have been associated with the fracture itself, or alternatively could have been electrostatic, since the capsule material has extremely small dielectric loss. I have since arranged that empty identified and weighed sealed spheres should be offered to Indian mystics, but up to the present none has been returned filled.

Encouraged by my experiences on the teleportation of small objects out of capsules by Nicholas Williams, I tried a similar approach on Stephen North. Stephen, then aged thirteen, had experienced a few such events in his own home, but did not know what to make of them. I was therefore careful not to explain too much about the nature of teleportation, but I waited until he was successfully performing metal-bending in my laboratory, and then introduced him to a small plastic box containing three metal single crystals. I told him that if he had sufficient confidence 'something' might happen to the crystals. A series of events followed which surprised me considerably; they exceeded what I had expected, and Stephen's excitement was great.

The box was an opaque plastic egg (2 in. × 1 in.) previously belonging to Andrew G. The halves fitted snugly together, and I carefully wound Scotch tape several times round them to make a good seal; removing the wrapping would normally take about half a minute, unless damage were permitted. At 11.30 am Stephen started to shake the plastic egg, which rattled continuously, the crystals being inside. After a few minutes, all of it in my field of vision, the rattle suddenly ceased; there was a clear inference that the crystals had left the egg. I decided not to open it up at this stage, but to ask Stephen to shake the egg some more to try and get the crystals back. He did this, but there was still no rattle. On opening up the egg I found not crystals, but a £1

Bank of England note, number HN15.686737, which Stephen thought had been in his pocket previously; indeed, this banknote was found to be missing. One crystal, a vanadium carbide ingot, was still in the egg (or had left and returned), and was prevented from rattling by the pound note. In Stephen's back pocket, tightly zip-fastened, were found the zinc and germanium crystals.

I replaced all the crystals in the egg, and nothing happened until 2.15 pm, when we again checked them and found them present. I re-sealed the egg and Stephen continued to handle it in my full view until 2.20 pm, when the rattling stopped, and I opened the egg and found it empty. The banknote was still in Stephen's pocket, but no crystals. However I found an unexpected object in his pocket: a broken cufflink of mine which had been stored away in a polythene bag in a desk drawer, following its fracture during a cutlery-bending session of Uri Geller. Stephen had not been near the drawer, and was puzzled by it all.

After 2.25 pm Stephen suddenly cried out; there was something in his mouth — it turned out to be the germanium crystal. Stephen did not know that other events of this type had been reported, and he was rather scared. In order to get him away from the scene of action, I took him out to another laboratory and locked the office door behind us. When we returned about twenty minutes later I entered the office first and almost immediately saw one of the zinc crystals in a prominent position on a ledge which had been empty when we left. Stephen thought that the paper-chart-roll box might contain a crystal, and I at once found the vanadium carbide ingot inside. We then searched my briefcase, and the other zinc crystal was found inside.

During this period a number of metal objects in the laboratory were found to have bent; I continued at intervals to shake the plastic egg, empty and re-sealed empty at 2.20 pm, to see if there was anything inside it. At 3.30 it was found to rattle, and a small strip of aluminium alloy, an anomalous plane bend by Willie G., was found inside. I took it out and re-sealed the egg; but at 3.45 Stephen's bank note HN15.686737 was again found inside the egg, after he had told me that it was missing from his pocket.

It was time for Stephen to go, so I gave him the egg and also an identified aluminium bar. He handled the bar in the taxi as we drove down Gower Street to Shaftesbury Avenue. But when we reached Trafalgar Square he could not find the aluminium bar in the taxi. I said nothing, but when I had left Stephen on the underground train, home-ward bound, I returned immediately to the laboratory and found the identified bar on a stool. I did not have to have clairvoyant powers to suspect that the laboratory was the obvious place to which it would teleport.

This accounts reads just as though a mischievous boy had been playing tricks all day; but of course I was very careful to watch the sealed plastic egg all the time that I could, and I had deliberately tried to make it difficult for Stephen to misbehave. I have gone carefully over the events of the day, and am unable to fault my observation of Stephen.

On one further occasion Stephen has had success with the plastic egg. We had just completed a metal-bending session on an aluminium crystal complete with six resistive strain gauge sensors. He had been unusually successful at achieving signals, and was excited. He took the egg, which was sealed with Scotch tape and was supposed to contain a small flint arrowhead and a marked electrical spade terminal. I inspected and re-sealed the objects in the egg, and Stephen took a cup from his mother and drank his tea, having placed the egg beside him. But when he reached the bottom of the cup, the spade terminal confronted him; the flint arrowhead remained within the egg. Stephen is still in possession of the egg, and occasional teleportations in and out of it are reported.

I now summarize some important features of the teleportation phenomenon; these are based on my own observations.

1 For obvious reasons, it is much more usual for the appearance than for the disappearance to be observed. Indeed, it would be very difficult to be certain that both things happen at exactly the same moment (say within 0.2 sec) without some instrumentation. On rare occasions the disappearance and reappearance locations are both within the field of vision.

2 The reappearance can take place either in the air or on a surface such as floor or table. The reappearance of an object in liquid was described above, but I have not observed an object actually falling into liquid. Accounts exist of reappearance inside solids, particularly fruit. Teleportations into identified hens' eggs have also been reported.

3 Reappearing objects have often been observed to appear with their own angular momentum. I have seen objects spin rapidly as they fall to, or appear on, the floor. It is difficult to make generalizations about direction of rotation or orientation of the axis of spin.

4 In many poltergeist flyings, linear momentum is reported to be associated with an object at the moment of its reappearance. At first I did not realize that this feature was common, since nearly all the poltergeist flyings in my home had been just appearances and falls. But I heard detailed accounts by Maurice Gross, the Society for Psychical

Research investigator of the Enfield poltergeist, where events became violent in the autumn of 1977. A feature was the glass marbles which flew about the room. There was no question that these marbles were simply teleporting, and did not have flight trajectories; they could be seen in flight; but the problem of where their trajectories started was more difficult. They seemed to start from the closed window, yet there were no marbles on the windowsill. The most likely alternative was that they had teleported to the window and appeared with linear momentum into the room.

This feature might offer a clue to the 'dog-leg' flight-paths which are sometimes observed in poltergeist cases, and were seen at Enfield. In these paths there is a sudden change of direction in mid-flight. We might interpret this as a teleportation in mid-flight, to a position almost identical with the point of disappearance, but with the appearance associated with a new linear momentum vector. All this is somewhat speculative.

5 Occasionally a clicking sound (more of an unnatural 'ping') accompanies an event. I am almost certain about my hearing such a sound on several occasions.

6 Sometimes the object which appears is warm (say about 45°C). On the first occasion on which I noticed such a feature, I assumed that the object might have been in contact with a hot stove; however there was no evidence for this, and similar events have been observed with no hot stove in the house. Reports of the appearance of warm objects have appeared fairly frequently in the literature of poltergeist phenomena, but I did not know of this until after my own observations.

7 On rare occasions the disappearance of an object is observed several minutes or even hours before its reappearance. A disappearance is noticed, and at a later time the reappearance of the object is also observed. There is no question that the object was at the location of the reappearance for all of the interim period; this location remained exposed to the field of view of observers, and was usually an obvious one. When I have been certain of this feature, I have assumed that there were in reality at least two consecutive teleportations, the end-point of the first teleportation being unknown — perhaps in a cupboard or even outside the house. But there is no evidence justifying this assumption; some other interpretation of the observations may be correct.

8 In my experience there is seldom very much vertical separation between the locations of disappearance and reappearance. I have observed no unequivocal events starting on one storey of a house and finishing on another. In few events has the vertical separation been

more than 1 m. In other words, there is very little change of gravitational potential.

9 The sizes and shapes of the objects that undergo teleportation can be the subject of only cautious generalizations. I have never observed object dimensions greater than about six inches; a statistical survey of sizes might only reflect the size distribution of domestic objects. In my experience sharp-edged objects are found less commonly than rounded objects. Indeed the collection of about thirty items which have travelled around Uri Geller's New York apartment contains mostly ellipsoids and spheres.

10 The inconvenience and embarrassment caused by teleportations often leads to the question: How can these things be halted? The literature of poltergeist cases has often stressed the psychological contradictions and frustrations of the 'epicentre' 'responsible' for the phenomena. The psychiatrist may see these angers and frustrations as manifesting themselves physically as teleportation events. When relief is experienced and the tension is relaxed, the phenomena cease. One way of reducing the tension is for the subject to concentrate on the production of a controlled psychokinetic event, a movement rather than a teleportation. Whether there is success or failure in producing movement, the spontaneous phenomena can be halted, at least temporarily, perhaps because of the 'psychical energy' drained from the subject. I have also applied this method to halting bad attacks of spontaneous metal-bending.

11 Very little has been observed which supports the hypothesis of gradual rather than sudden appearance. The gradual appearance and gradual disappearance of apparitions, reported among others by Crookes,[50] would seem to be a different phenomenon, at least as regards the long times of appearance. At the Stanford Research Institute,[51] during Uri Geller's visit, an interesting video-tape was made of a wrist-watch falling through the field of view onto a table. Although it seems that the appearance took place above the field of view, the watch is seen to flicker as it descends; in consecutive frames the light reflected from the watch increases and decreases. One might be tempted to regard this as an 'oscillation in the intensity of the appearance', but a more likely interpretation is that the presence of angular momentum causes the light reflected from the watch to vary periodically. A very interesting claim has been made by Dr Miyauchi that Masuaki Kiyota has materialized (or teleported) a full Coca-Cola bottle in stages; the bottom first, and then the top.

12 An attempt has been made by Roll[52] to assess the dependence of frequency of poltergeist events (appearances) upon their distance

from the subject. He proposes that this is an exponential fall-off. It has been claimed by German researchers[53] that events from their recent cases do not fit this behaviour. Although Roll is a most experienced and skilled investigator, one might question the applicability of such quantitative analysis at this time. Clearly there must be some falling-off with distance, since there are few 'apports' or teleportations with the subject miles away from the event. Nevertheless, both the number and density of household objects and the dimensions of the rooms could affect the statistics. The distance effect, if it were possible to separate with any accuracy, would probably turn out to be psychological rather than physical in nature; the notions of territory and even *Gestalt* could be relevant.

13   After each object reappeared I made a superficial optical examination, sometimes using a low magnification microscope; but no unexplained signs of damage have been detected. On one occasion the neck of a wine-glass snapped on falling, after its reappearance above a steel radiator. The objects seemed all to be physically unaffected by the experience of being teleported. Some accurate weighings of laboratory objects teleported (e.g. the crystals exposed to Nicholas Williams) showed no change.

14   Some teleportations of volumes of liquid have been reported in several poltergeist cases investigated by Professor Bender and other German psychic researchers. In the Schachter case, a 'globe of water' was actually seen to appear in mid-air by the plumber who was summoned. The description included the statement that it was as though an invisible rubber balloon filled with visible water had suddenly come to occupy a position in mid-air, and immediately burst. The globe of water fell immediately to the floor, where splashes and a puddle were made. Many puddles appeared in these cases, although the appearances were not usually observed.

Chemical analyses were made of the water puddles, and the composition was found to correspond with that of the water in the plumbing system of the house. A reasonably likely interpretation of such an event is that a mass of water from a part of the system teleported into the room. Nevertheless it has not yet been possible to show by measurement whether when one of these events occurs the volume of the water in the system is decreased. Did an air-lock appear? No information is yet available about temperature, linear or angular momentum, turbulence, or explosive energy, at the moment of appearance. Water appearances are fairly frequent in the poltergeist literature, one of the most unexpected being at the British Embassy in The Hague.

15 Information is slowly accumulating about teleportations of living creatures, including human beings. I have never witnessed such events myself, but I have received reports from various victims and from their families. What might be conjectured to be teleportations of insects into closed rooms have been described in the literature. Very little information is available about larger creatures, but I once received a detailed report from Matthew Thompson, a poultry farmer in Dorset, which he summarized as follows:

> I have within recent weeks had two separate instances of birds (caged chickens) disappearing and reappearing some hours later. I am talking about birds disappearing literally into thin air and being neither visible nor audible. Any possibility of them being removed by some other persons and then returned can be completely ruled out.

I have had no opportuinity to check in detail on Matthew Thompson's information, but I think it worthy of notice.

Similarly, the teleportation of living humans is something which I have not observed in my own field of view, but about which I have studied a number of reports and have been able to question the observers and teleportees. An account[6] has appeared of an event in which Uri Geller found himself transported in an instant from New York City to the suburb of Ossining, where he fell through the roof of a sun-lounge. The shock experienced was considerable, and the event was never repeated. Nothing inconsistent has appeared in the answers that Uri Geller has given me about the details of this event.

Although Uri Geller did not keep the event a secret, news of it did not at first make an impression in England: one of the metal-bending families knew nothing of it when they reported the strange behaviour of their son. They would continually find him in unnatural places, wedged in between wardrobe-top and ceiling, and so on. They would be running a hot bath for him, and suddenly a scream would announce his 'transportation' from his bedroom into the overheated bath, for which he was totally unprepared. The affliction of this family lasted for several months, but eventually grew less serious.

Nicholas Williams also claims to have been teleported out of a locked room. When his father pointed out that this left them with a problem of the key remaining on the inside, Nicholas teleported back again to unlock the door! He has described the experience as something like being in a blizzard. Mrs Greta Woodrue of New England has reported delayed teleportation, similar to those described for inanimate objects in section 7 above. It was about eight minutes before she was again with her family, who were already frantic with worry. She had no experience of the passage of this time. Recently I have been present at what may have been the delayed teleportation of a boy. The period of delay was three minutes, and there was very little experience of the passage of time. A few similar events, concerning the medium Mrs Guppy, are to be found in the literature of psychic research.

16 It is not yet possible to unravel differences which may exist between 'apports' and orthodox teleportation events. Obviously the validation of such events is almost impossible unless the arrival is actually observed. I outline three incidents from my experience.

In one incident I returned to my locked office to find in the centre of my desk what looked like a silver paperknife. I had just returned from the stately home of Longleat where I had observed Uri Geller soften and bend an item of the family silver; so I immediately contacted the Marquess of Bath to find whether the silver was his, but it was not. Neither had it apparently any connection with my colleagues or with Geller himself; in fact he has not seen it to this day. Experts later identified it as a Mexican hair ornament such as might be used in the ceremonies of the dead – 'Los dios de los muertes'. It was not a mere piece of tourist silver. Neither I nor my colleagues had ever had any connection with Mexico, but it may be significant that Geller's first Mexican visit took place several weeks later. On the other hand, it may not.

The second incident took place in 1977 in the house of Gill Costin, whose attempts to teleport letters to Uri Geller will be mentioned in chapter 23. Although he never received these letters, some letters which appeared 'in reply' – themselves conceivably 'apports' – seemed significant to me. One day a crucifix on a chain appeared in Gill's room; it was a souvenir of Lourdes. Gill is not a Roman Catholic, or indeed strongly religious at all, neither had she nor any of her friends or family any connection with the pilgrimage centre of Lourdes, or with France. It may be significant that my daughter Annie visited Lourdes with a rather spiritual pop group several weeks later; but again, it may not.

In the spring of 1979 I was lecturing on the same platform as Guru Raj Ananda at a meeting whose title was 'Mystics and Scientists'. Answering a question from the audience about teleportations, I tried to arouse the Guru's interest in teleporting some 'vibuthi' or sacred ash for me; reports have been published describing such events brought about by Sai Baba and other mystics.

What I got, deposited into my hand from Guru Raj's apparently empty hand, was a hard black brittle object about the size of a pea. I understand that Guru Raj does not know where these objects come from, but believes they might be sweets teleported from Indian children. I immediately double-wrapped the black object in paper and placed it in my inside pocket inside a smaller wooden box with a tight-fitting lid. For further security two rubber bands were fastened round the box. I intended to analyse the black object, but when the rubber bands were removed and box and wrappings opened four hours later, no black object was there.

Guru Raj gave the opinion that it is very difficult to produce an 'apport' which will not vanish within a matter of hours or days. But this is out of keeping with the permanence of the Mexican silver pin and Lourdes cross. Hopefully the Indian child will enjoy the return of his sweet!

Even as brief an account as this illustrates the sort of difficulties which are faced by investigators of 'apports'. It may be a long haul.

I will return to some theoretical speculation about teleportation later; it should be clear from the foregoing that some serious modification of modern physical theory may be necessary. The reason for devoting so much space to this subject in a book about metal-bending is that sometimes the same people are involved in 'causing' both types of phenomenon; also there are interesting, if speculative, physical similarities, in that a teleportation of atoms within a crystal lattice would cause the propagation of a dislocation; we noted in chapter 13 the importance of loop dislocations in metal-bending, and I am currently researching the density profiles of impurities implanted into single crystals by particle accelerators.

Chapter **20**

The paranormal movement of objects: psychokinesis

We have seen that in poltergeist cases the actual movement of objects can take place by paranormal means; and we have inferred that these movements might be brought about by the action of paranormal quasi-forces; such a phenomenon is termed psychokinesis (PK). It is important to determine whether psychic subjects could produce such movements, or quasi-forces, in a reasonably controlled way. As we shall see, it is possible that in metal-bending there is a psychokinetic, as well as the paranormal softening, component.

Since it is rare for heavy objects (requiring large quasi-forces) to be moved, the approach by experimenters investigating psychokinesis has been to construct simple apparatus in which only a very small quasi-force is necessary to bring about observable motion; they have used as light and mobile objects as possible. The simplest experiment is to suspend a very light horizontal pointer, such as a matchstick or a quill, from a fine thread, silk or man-made fibre; the psychic is required to rotate it, at a distance. Alternatives are to float the pointer on water, or mount it on a needle-point.

The first serious recorded experiments of this sort were those made by Sir William Crookes[50] during the nineteenth century. To avoid pointer movements due to currents of air, he enclosed the apparatus under a sealed glass dome. Being an extremely capable experimental scientist, he quickly realized the magnitudes of the quasi-random movements of pointers due to air currents within the dome, thermal gradients or electrostatic and electromagnetic forces. He decided to evacuate the dome and then observed movements due to visible radiation. These were appreciable only when the pointer was coloured white on one side and dark on the other, and was shaped for maximum effect in the form of a thin vertical pair of discs. Visible or infrared radiation falling on the discs would bring about movement only when the dome was evacuated, and we know now that a very high vacuum also inhibits movement just as efficiently as does atmospheric pressure.

This device is well-known as the 'Crookes Radiometer' and is available commercially as a novelty; when it is exposed to a bright light or to an electric fire the paddles rotate, often rapidly. The physical mechanism is still understood only in outline, but apparently the temperature differential between light and dark surfaces affects the residual gas molecules, whose mean free paths are sufficiently long for the increased speeds of the hotter molecules to impart increased momentum to the surface they subsequently impact; hence the inhibition both by very high vacuum and by atmospheric pressure. Crookes accepted this explanation, although he had at first thought he had actually measured the electromagnetic radiation pressure.

In order to avoid movements of our psychic pointers due to this cause, we must avoid colour differentials betwen the two sides; indeed it is unnecessary to make the pointer in the form of a vertical disc — the vertical area can be made comparatively small. Crookes, using an enclosed dynamometer, reported that the psychic Daniel Dunglass Home was able to exert quasi-force upon it, without touch.

Since the time of Crookes, various investigators have offered similar 'light mobile objects' to psychics, in order to test whether they could move them from a distance.

One reason for the rejection of what may well have been genuine psychokinetic phenomena reported by qualified scientists has been the unfortunate tendency by the authors to dress the effects up with fancy names, and attribute to them properties which could have been those of hallucinatory phenomena, or of real paranormal physical phenomena, but inextricably associated with ritualistic processes necessary to the subject's unconscious; for example, the association of various physical phenomena with large and beautiful single crystals.

Thus history records the apparent success, and later rejection, of such things as animal magnetism, Reichenbach's 'Od', N-rays, X^x-rays, Rigid rays and the Orgone. We shall probably never know just how many, if any, of these physical phenomena really occurred.

One modern British researcher, who has made careful observations with such psychics as Suzanne Padfield, is Benson Herbert.[54] Members of the Toronto Society for Psychic Research have experimented with Jan Merta.[55] Merta chose fairly large feathers as pointers, and was able to produce rotation from distances of several metres. By means of a horizontal capacitor vane of metal foil attached to the suspension, the rotation of the feather pointers could be registered as a varying capacitance between the rotating vane and fixed vane. Records exist of the background fluctuations and of the deflections produced at command; their internal consistency has become available to me for analysis.

A Czechoslovak physicist who has psychokinetic abilities and has successfully experimented on himself is Dr Julius Krmessky. I have visited him at his home in Bratislava and seen him successfully move such pointers under 10-in. diameter domes. I determined to apply the technical experience I had gained to experiments, using the metal-bending children.

I learned to minimize normal movements of the pointers in the following ways. Electrostatic and electromagnetic forces are the easiest to guard against. The dome should be made of glass and not of transparent plastic; the latter more easily accepts and retains localized electric charge, which produces an electrostatic force field. A conductive dome distributes the charge and destroys the horizontal electric field; the surface electrical conductivities of both sodaglass and Pyrex are usually sufficient to distribute charge in a small fraction of a second. An experiment with frictionally induced charge, which on a plastic dome can move the pointer but on a glass dome should not, must be carried out as verification. If there is still movement, then the glass must be coated with antistatic ointment; an alternative is to coat the glass with a silver film of about 20 μ thickness; the transparency is not destroyed, and the dome takes on a beautiful mauve tint. The base on which the dome stands must also have sufficient conductivity for horizontal electrostatic fields to be avoided.

The base should also make an airtight seal with the dome, standard techniques such as a vacuum wax or soft sealing compound being adequate for this purpose. In this way the air currents from the room are excluded from the interior, so that it is necessary to worry only about air currents generated by thermal gradients within the dome itself. These can of course be eliminated by evacuation, but if care is taken to avoid external heat sources (such as the psychic's body or electric fires), this will be necessary only when the paranormal movements to be detected are very small. Experiments should be carried out to see what pointer movements, if any, are produced by artificial heat sources. With sufficient experience it should be possible to avoid evacuation of the dome.

Movements of the pointer arising from instability of the mounting of the dome and its base should also be investigated. Preferably the apparatus should be left stationary for several hours, or overnight, in the absence of the psychic. In an evacuated system no unexplained pointer movements occur. Very slight movements over a period of weeks may be traceable to instability of the mounting, or to mechanical relaxation effects in the suspension fibre. Alternatively, one can actually suspend the entire dome.

Only when we are certain of having a stable piece of equipment should we expose it to the action of the psychic. Since the quasi-force required to rotate in the horizontal plane a pointer suspended from a fine thread can be as small as 10^{-4} N, I imagined at first that the task should not be difficult for paranormal metal-benders. Nevertheless they did not have great success in moving pointers under domes. Andrew and Willie G. both produced very little pointer movement, but Julie Knowles has produced sudden rotations of the pointer through as much as $90°$; evacuation of the dome was not possible, but care was taken to avoid thermal convection. No metal-bender came near the performance of Dr Krmessky, who produced rotations in either direction at will for the Czech physicist Dr Adamec and myself. Dr Krmessky almost (but not quite) induced me to believe that in his presence I was myself having some effect on the pointer. When I asked him if this ability induced in others (see chapter 17) persisted after he had left them, he gave the opinion that as soon as they were completely alone the induced ability left them. Suzanne Padfield, the English girl who has several years' experience of being able to move pointers, told me that she once induced the ability in another person in such a way that it lasted for several hours after she herself had departed.

One feature I have noticed with Dr Krmessky and Uri Geller is that the psychic cannot be certain of the direction in which the pointer will start to move when he begins his concentration. But once the movement has started, in either direction, he is able to change the direction at will; he is uncertain which way it will go in the first place, and there is sometimes a very small oscillation before the movement takes place.

When Jan Merta applied his pointer movement device, which was made of two horizontal chicken feathers, to the interruption of a light beam falling on a photocell and thereby closing an electrical circuit for a remote control 'wish-switch', he was careful to design it bi-directionally so as to allow for this effect. Application for patent rights to the 'wish-switch' was attempted, but abandoned.

Another feature of the ballistic pointer motion produced by psychics is that we cannot be certain how jerky is the quasi-force producing it. With both Julius Krmessky and Julie Knowles I had the impression that the force was produced in bursts or pulses; but it is very difficult to be certain of this because the suspended pointer behaves in a ballistic manner; it moves freely, with a very long period of oscillation (perhaps 15 sec) when it receives just one short pulse of torque. Only with accurate recording of the motion is it possible to make some analysis of the time-dependence of the quasi-forces.

If the pointer were restrained by some normal force field, then it would, if displaced, oscillate with a shorter period (perhaps 1–3 sec). Hence the pointer would be easier to control, and the time-dependence of any quasi-force would be easier to infer. But this would be at the expense of sensitivity of the apparatus. More quasi-force, of the order of 0.01 N, would be necessary to move the pointer.

Such an arrangement is provided by the magnetized pointer of a ship's compass, which is normally constrained in the horizontal component of the earth's magnetic field. It is adequately shielded from air currents and is not prone to electrostatic effects. The commercial liquid-filled variety is particularly stable, but of course can easily be rotated by the movement of a small bar magnet concealed about the person. But the movement of such a magnet is detectable by magnetometer, which can easily be made sensitive to fields as small as a milligauss. It is necessary not only to search the subject with the magnetometer probe, but also to leave the probe in a fixed position near to the compass during the psychokinetic experiment. The movement of the compass will itself cause a variation of magnetic field to be registered at the magnetometer probe, since the compass needle is itself magnetized. The time-varying field must be thoroughly understood, by previous experimentation, before the psychokinetic experiment; if the liquid in the ship's compass is caused to rotate by hydrodynamic action, the needle will rotate with it and the sinusoidal variation of magnetic field can be recorded.

With the assistance of Dr Kobayashi of Tokyo Metropolitan University, I was able to monitor the paranormal movements of a ship's compass brought about by Uri Geller in Tokyo in 1975. There was no anomalous magnetic field present during the paranormal movements of the compass needle. While Geller was in Tokyo, ten compass rotation events were observed by me, and I was satisfied that there was no cheating either by Geller or by anyone else when the magnetometer was used.

Nevertheless I much prefer an unmagnetized suspended pointer to a ship's compass for this type of work. To me it appears that the magnetic properties of the compass needle are an unnecessary complication, an extra factor which can introduce difficulties not present in the simpler experiment. There might be confusion about a possible paranormal production of magnetic field. The Tokyo evidence suggests that there was no magnetic field produced when the compass needle was deflected, other than the change in field due to the movement of the needle; but this may not always turn out to be true. Arrays of small compasses have been used by the French researchers, and the results are even more complicated.

Some well-known experiments on the paranormal deflection of a compass needle were carried out in Leningrad with the psychic Nina Kulagina.[56] A moving picture has been widely shown in the West, in which not only is a compass needle deflected, but the compass case itself is seen to rotate on the table. Movement of a non-magnetic compass case would of course not arise from the variation of magnetic field, whether paranormally or normally produced, unless the needle was locked on its axis in some way.

It requires very much more force to rotate a compass case on a table than it does to rotate a suspended pointer. In order that the required force be minimized, and thereby the task made easier for the subject, a compass case can be mounted so as to be very easily rotatable. I have found that a simple arrangement is to attach a needle-point to the centre of its base, and float the compass case on sufficient liquid mercury to ensure that the rim of the base does not touch the bottom of the mercury trough. The needle-point, however, remains in contact with the bottom. The compass can then be rotated by a very small torque, not very much larger than that required to rotate the needle.

I have offered a liquid-filled ship's compass on a mercury bearing to Uri Geller, and he produced small movements of the compass case; the needle did not move from its alignment with the earth's magnetic field. No video-record was taken of this event, but it was observed by several people. However, no success has been achieved by metal-bending children on either stationary or mobile compasses.

Lest we should be lulled into a complacent attitude to our understanding of this particular psychic phenomenon in terms of a relatively simple 'paranormal quasi-force field', a report by Suzanne Padfield suggests that there is more complication. She reported that she could deflect her compass for comparatively long periods of time (minutes); moreover the compass experienced long periods of deflection only when it was placed in certain areas of the room. Although this sounds exactly like the action of local anomalous magnetic fields, I am assured that this explanation was examined and rejected. The proposed phenomenon opens up interesting new possibilities.

An interesting experiment was observed by an engineer, Dr A.S., when Uri Geller visited Professor Taylor's laboratory at King's College, London. An unevacuated plastic dome had been prepared, in which was a 10-cm pointer made of stout brass wire, suspended from a fine thread. Uri Geller was allowed to touch, but not to move, the dome. Violent rotations of the pointer were observed (?electrostatic). An impressive event ensued: the metal pointer slowly curled into a 45° bend inside the dome, without moving on its suspension. Such events are very rare; they demonstrate clearly the difference between the internal origin of the metal-bending action, which does not greatly disturb the centre of mass of the metal, and the apparent external origin of the quasi-forces which are responsible for the movement of light objects.

Another form of paranormal movement experiment, not usually carried out under a dome, is on the sliding movements of light objects resting on a table. Many people have seen the moving picture of the Russian psychic Nina Kulagina demonstrating these movements, without touching the objects themselves. Since the Russian scientists also claim that electrostatic fields can be produced paranormally, it is important to make certain that the cause of this motion is not electro-static. This can be done by rendering the working surface and the objects themselves slightly conducting. Low-loss polymers should not be used. There is also the important issue of fraud by the use of fine threads, particularly when these are passed round static objects in such a way that a hand movement causes a movement of the object in the opposite direction.

I became interested in the possible ability of metal-benders to produce this effect when I was told by Mrs Nemeth that a plastic cup had moved on the tea-table near where David (then aged eight) was sitting. 'But that is something I don't talk about,' she said.

The opportunity to witness Jean-Pierre Girard attempt such an effect came to me in the summer of 1977, when I was asked to monitor film material being made in Paris for NBC television (in the United States) by Alan Neuman.[30] My task was to view the experiments, which were carried out on a glass table under camera, from a distance of about five feet; I concentrated particularly on the possible use of threads, even though there was a relatively long filming period (more than one hour); but I found no evidence of fraud. I also found it impossible to move objects on the table by frictional electrostatic means. The objects which moved paranormally in camera were a brandy glass (45 g weight) and a lipstick case (20 g weight). The movements recorded, and now widely seen by audiences, were jerky and only of a few inches' distance. I lodged a detailed report with the television company.

I adhere to my general conclusion that some psychics, including some metal-benders, are able to produce temporary quasi-forces which act locally on neighbouring sensitive mobile apparatus.

Since my studies of psychokinesis have concentrated on the physics of the phenomenon, I have avoided conducting the orthodox psycho-kinetic experiments on influencing the throw of dice, or of their placement in certain areas on a working surface. It is quite possible that the success achieved by some subjects in throwing dice is attri-butable to paranormal actions similar to those I have been investigating. Stephen North has been able to produce signals on a pair of strain gauges actually mounted on a die, but of course the die was suspended and not being thrown at the time.

Dice-throwing and placement experiments[57] might be influenced by many physical factors, some or all of which could be open to a 'primary' paranormal action. There could be electrostatic forces induced piezo-electrically, tribologically or paranormally; mechanical forces induced either on the die or in the mechanical thrower by tribological artefacts, air currents, thermal effects, or paranormal changes in elastic properties; as well as the mechanical distortions produced apparently paranormally in dice strain gauge experiments by Stephen North. I find it difficult to assess dice-placement experiments, because the control of these factors is technically difficult and is not usually described in great physical detail.

One result reported by dice experimenters is that the paranormal successes achieved by some subjects are equally great when heavier dice of equal size are used. This is not disturbing to parapsychologists, but is puzzling to physicists; the finding may not be so difficult to understand if it is remembered that it holds only over a certain range of masses, and that the exact extent of this range is not yet known. A really large-scale experiment has recently been reported with a very large lead die weighing ten thousand times heavier than normal – quite an impressive feat of engineering, the motion being achieved with the use of a robust inclined plane. But no paranormal action was achieved. This is in line with our experience that really powerful psychokinesis is exceedingly rare, whereas quasi-forces of small magnitude may not be so uncommon.

These quasi-forces may also play a part in metal-bending, quite distinct from the internal action, softening, deformation, structural change and so on which we have been discussing in earlier chapters. Qualitative evidence for this exists in our video-records of the elastic paranormal bending of a long flexible metal strip held in the hand of

Julie Knowles. Quantitative evidence comes from the published work of Professor Sasaki and his colleagues[58] in Japan on the conduct of mechanical stress-strain experiments in the presence and absence of metal-bending children. A stress-strain graph from his data is shown in Figure 20.1. In the experiment, a metal wire starts from the very small strain corresponding to a very small stress and is taken in stages up the $\sigma(\epsilon)$ curve. At a certain moment the metal-bender is 'introduced' and succeeds without touch in distorting the specimen elastically so that the strain ϵ increases whilst the normal applied stress σ is unchanged. When the normal stress is increased and the metal-bender ceases his action, the metal returns to its original stress-strain graph. Thus the paranormal action was elastic and did not cause yield or, presumably, any change of physical properties. It could be described as the action, without touch, of a quasi-force.

The question of whether a psychokinetic quasi-force is responsible for the movement of the water-diviner's cleft stick is a difficult one to answer. In this method of 'dowsing', one stick is held in each hand, and normally the system is maintained under stress in two different ways. Each of the two sticks is bent into a curve, with the cleft joint forming a cusp. The hands prevent their straightening. In addition, each of the two sticks is slightly twisted, the directions being opposed. Untwisting is prevented by the cleft joint and by the action of the fingers. This combination of stresses, bending and torsional, is maintained by the muscular action of the dowser; if he were to relax the appropriate

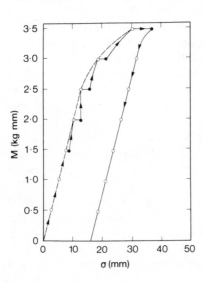

Figure 20.1 Stress-strain history (open circles) measured in Young's modulus experiment by Professor Sasaki. A series of weights, of increasing magnitudes, were suspended from the wire, and its lengths were measured accurately. The introduction of the metal-bending child to the experiment at various times during the measurements results in temporary increased strains (closed circles). Note that after the removal of the child and the addition of an extra weight, the specimen returns to its normal stress-strain curve, until the uppermost point is reached.

muscles suddenly then the system would move. In good adjustment, the cleft stick and dowser's hands are in metastable static equilibrium. A small displacement to this equilibrium causes a rapid movement to a different static equilibrium position. This displacement could be of three types:

(a) a slight unconscious relaxation of certain muscles;

(b) a psychokinetic force applied principally at the cleft joint;

(c) a temporary paranormal modification of the elastic properties of the cleft stick, similar to paranormal metal-bending action.

The second and third possibilities would be impossible to prove by instrumentation, except in the absence of the first; alternatively if the extent of the first contribution could be measured, the magnitudes of the contributions from the second and third possibilities might be estimated. At present this is out of the question, and I must conclude that there is no evidence for psychokinetic contributions; the muscular relaxation hypothesis remains the most plausible. This is also the case for angle-rod dowsing.

Chapter **21**

Human levitation

We have seen that some psychics are able to slide objects about on a surface without the use of touch. I have not seen, but have heard, reliable reports of the occasions on which Jean-Pierre Girard has held small objects levitated above the table surface for a period of several seconds; this was also reported to be without the use of touch or fraud. We might suppose that a paranormal quasi-force field was operating, such as electromagnetic forces operate in the normal levitation of metal objects above current-carrying coils. If a psychic quasi-force field can act on small objects, why can it not also act on the human body and allow it to levitate?

There have been several reported instances of religious mystics levitating themselves slowly off the ground during prayer; the most famous are St James of Compostella and St Joseph of Copertino.[59] The nineteenth-century psychic, Daniel Dunglass Home, was reported by responsible investigators and scientists to have floated about the room and, on 13 December 1868, out of a window and back again.[60] Other reported cases of levitation are those of Sister Maria Vilani, Veronica Giulani, St Bernadino Realino, St Theresa of Avila, St Francis of Assisi, Stainton Moses, Florence Cook, Eusapia Palladino,* Maria Vollhardt, Willi Schneider, Schrenck-Notzing's 1927 anonymous subject[40] and the Eddy children of Chittenden, Vermont. I have seen an interesting short moving picture[61] made by a German journalist

---

* Not all of these in this list are of equal sanctity, and it will be recalled by students of psychical research that Eusapia Palladino enjoys a particularly poor reputation in the matter of fraudulent phenomena. It appears that what especially disenchanted the British researchers with Eusapia was her conviction of being caught cheating on the croquet field!

named Ohlsen portraying the levitation of a West African priest Nana Dwaku above burning coals. Human levitation is one of the 'siddhis' or powers supposed to be available to Hindu mystics, and attempts have been made to teach their development in Europe. Photographs of air-borne meditators have been widely publicized, but of course still photographs provide much less information than moving pictures. It is believed that in the first stage the subject experiences a violent but slow vibration of the entire body — these are almost muscular twitches; a more advanced subject becomes able to make small leaps from a bodily position in which leaping would normally be impossible — the lotus position, seated cross-legged on the ground. In the final stage, the subject becomes able to levitate his body steadily at will.

Probably the nearest thing to levitation encountered by psychic researchers is the throwing about of human bodies in a poltergeist attack. There are accounts of this in the literature, and in 1977 in England witnesses reported this phenomenon in the Enfield poltergeist case, which is in course of documentation by Maurice Gross and Guy Playfair. There have been intances of sleeping child metal-benders being found on top of wardrobes, etc., complete with bedclothes; climbing would have been just possible, but the presumption, not well proven, is that the bodies were levitated up to their new situation. In 1979 the throwing about was again reported in the Midlands. There is also the possibility of teleportation, and of composite processes of successive teleportations and levitations. One witness at Enfield (Mr B.) claimed that he was lifted out of his chair and that the feeling was as though a cushion of air, not a draught, pushed him upwards. There was also a twisting motion, which rotated him almost half a turn in the process. I can only conjecture at this stage, but I think it at least reasonably likely that in some poltergeist cases bodies have been thrown about.

In British schools 'levitation games' are sometimes played by children. A ritual is occasionally followed (e.g. running round and round a seated or lying child and chanting, 'He is ill; he is dead' etc.); after the ritual a number of children attempt to raise the body, each placing one or two fingers underneath it. The game starts with many children, who find the task easy, using only normal forces. The number is reduced one by one, and the continuing ease might suggest a paranormal contribution. The unexpected success has sometimes caused worried teachers to forbid the continuance of the game. I have found many children who insist that the body suddenly seems to lose weight.

But occasionally the lifters press their hands downwards before the lift, and the relaxation of this muscular tension makes the lifting seem easier than it would otherwise be. If we are looking for a paranormal rather than a physiological effect, then obviously this pressing of hands should be avoided.

I have been impressed by taking part myself in the lifting of fifteen-year-old Gill Costin by Kim Griffiths and her schoolfriends. Gill makes her body go rigid, and it certainly takes an effort to get her off the ground. But when she is off the ground she sometimes appears to become lighter. Sometimes her raised body glides forwards or sideways, and the lifters have difficulty in preventing this. Naturally the idea comes to mind that one or more of the lifters are pulling or pushing her horizontally. All the lifters deny this, and changes in arrangement of the lifters make no difference.

This children's game is sufficiently strange to be worth further investigation with the aid of instruments, the lifters standing on a chart-recording weighing machine.

One of the metal-bending children, Willie G., has told me that he was able to levitate himself, but only when quite alone in his bedroom. I asked him to levitate up to his bedroom ceiling and write and put his inked fingerprints on it; he was also able to carry a Polaroid camera up with him, to photograph himself in proximity to the ceiling. All these tasks were done successfully, but of course do not represent good validation. Willie's reported levitation still remained a very private activity, and it would not take place when other members of the family were in the room, let alone myself. Since Willie's home was far away, but his father often visited London, I decided to video-tape Willie in my laboratory.

I attempted to instrument possible apparent weight loss when Willie was lying on his back on a special mattress. If he was unable to reach either the floor or any furniture, then weight could be lost either by jumping up off the instrumented mattress – a rapid loss – or by levitation, which might take place with a more gradual weight loss. The instrumentation, similar to that used earlier by Dr King and myself in experiments with Graham P., consisted of an inflatable rubberized mattress connected to a recording differential capacitance manometer. On the mattress was placed a wooden board, and initially the mattress was connected by rubber and glass tubing to both arms of the differential manometer. After Willie had taken up his position flat on his back or kneeling on the board, a stopcock in one arm of the tubing was closed, so that the reference pressure in that arm of the differential manometer was now fixed. Any change of pressure in the mattress, due to a change in weight compressing it, could be recorded.

Pressure changes also arise from:
(a) differential temperature changes, by transmission of body heat, by cooling after the heating of the gas during inflation, or the heating due to actual compression;
(b) real or virtual leaks in the system;
(c) mechanical relaxation process in the material of the rubber mattress;
(d) shifts in position of the subject on the board.

The first three causes can readily be studied in independent experiments, and the typical instrumental drifts on the chart-recorder analysed. The fourth factor cannot of course yield long-term pressure changes, but provides plenty of noise of short time constant, as the rubber and the air readjust themselves to the movement of the subject on the board. When the subject shifts his position there is no permanent deflection but, rather, a pulse of about one second duration, usually followed by ringing. A continual violent wriggling or writhing yields a chart-record such as that shown in Figure 21.1b.

In experimental sessions with Willie the results were negative; not only did he fail to get off the ground, but even the chart records failed to show really unambiguous weight losses; all the signals which were recorded could possibly have been attributed to other causes. Moreover the absence of videocamera left me unsatisfied.

I have more recently had the opportunity of getting to know how human levitation is approached by parapsychologists in the Soviet Union; it is known as 'partial death', a term which indicates a rather different conceptual approach. In 1977 a young Russian physicist, Auguste Stern, defected to the West and related some of his experiences in parapsychology. He had worked in the Siberian science city of Novosibirsk, at the Institute for Automation and Electrometry. The parapsychology department of the Institute housed about fifty scientists, but Stern was perturbed about the intended use of the hypnotism techniques on which they were working for 'mind control'. In previous years he had himself participated, he claims successfully, in 'partial death' experiments, being himself able to produce effects.

According to Stern, the technique used in the Soviet Union to induce human levitation is to enclose the prone subject within a cube of mirrors. The multiple images, apparently stretching in all directions to infinity, have the effect of disorientating the subject, who then levitates if he has the ability.

During the summer of 1977, mirrors were set up for Stern by film producer Alan Neuman,[30] who wished to record this phenomenon. I placed my mattress equipment inside, with the necessary rubber tubing leading out through a corner. Dr Stern lay on a large wood-backed mirror which completely covered the mattress; thus he could see nothing but images in mirrors, except for one side wall which was covered with black cloth. The moving picture cameras photographed him through holes in this cloth.

Dr Stern was disappointed that he did not leave the mirror completely. He had not attempted 'partial death' for some years and was disturbed by the resilience of my mattress. A film record exists of his

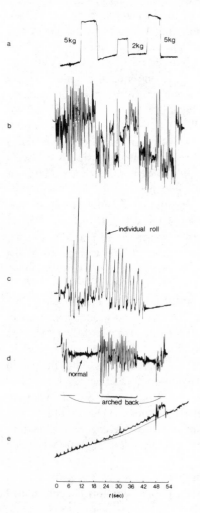

a · 5kg · 2kg · 5kg

b

c · individual roll

d · normal · arched back

e

0 6 12 18 24 30 36 42 48 54
t (sec)

Figure 21.1 Chart-records with instrumented rubber mattress. (a) Mattress calibration pulses of 2- and 5-kg weights. (b) Short-lived pulses produced by sitting upright and violently bouncing up and down. (c) Pulses produced by rolling over from the back to the chest. (d) Pulses produced by strongly arching the back, so that only the head and feet touch the board. (e) Part of levitation experiment record.

squirming motions, which contributed to the noise on the chart records of Figure 21.1e. However, there are inexplicable features in at least two places in the half-hour of recording; these are periods during which a loss of more than a kilogram occurred for several seconds at a time. Such effects could have been produced if the subject had pressed his hands over the edge of his mattress and forced himself up from the floor. But the film record shows that he could not have done this; rather, he squirmed about, shifting his weight to different regions of the mirror. According to Dr Stern, the squirming is not typical of 'partial death' sessions, but was produced because he was unused to the insecurity of my rubber mattress support.

I have made laboratory tests of the 'muscular noise' which is produced by squirming on the mattress. Since rubberized material can expand, the pressure will remain constant only when the areas of contact between mattress and board (and mattress and ground) remain constant. For example, rolling the body over onto one side of the wooden board distorts the mattress, producing pressure changes as shown in Figure 21.1c. Sitting on the wooden board and bouncing up and down produces the artefacts shown in Figure 21.1b, the apparent weight reductions being larger than the 5 kg calibration pulses shown in Figure 21.1a. Arching the back or doing press-ups expends energy in elastic bending of the wooden board, so that a temporary reduction of pressure is found as shown in Figure 21.1d.

My experience of these and similar effects has led to the rejection of nearly all of Dr Stern's chart record as evidence of paranormal weight loss. But there remain two sets of signals, one of which is reproduced in Figure 21.1e, which when taken in conjunction with the film record are difficult to explain in normal terms. My assessment of them is to take them sufficiently seriously to warrant the planning of further research. The cube of mirrors seems to be a powerful psychological support for the subject, but it is difficult to construct with sufficient attention to safety.

Levitation of furniture and humans might be supposed to take place in various ways, of which I mention only two. First, there is the possibility of a continual rapid series of teleportation events, each to a position very slightly removed from its predecessor; this would produce the appearance of continuous movement or suspension. Second, we would hypothesize a tube of quasi-force reaching from the body to the floor, similar to the 'cantilever theory' of table-lifting advanced by Crawford.[24] This careful but little-known experimenter of fifty years ago (Crawford is still remembered by seniors at the Queen's University,

Belfast) found quantitative evidence for the concept of quasi-force in the form of a tube or cantilever stretching from the medium's body to the table which she was lifting. Additional weight was assumed by the medium's body whenever the table was lifted without touch. Imprints of the 'cantilever' were recorded in wet clay, etc.

It is notable that the concept is somewhat similar to the fibres of Carlos Castaneda's (probably fictitious) sorcerer Don Juan.[62] At about the same time as Crawford was researching, the Berlin engineer Fritz Grunewald[63] was performing similar experiments with a platform resting on a system of springs, the displacements of which were transmitted by variations in electrical resistance to a recording galvanometer. His results indicated mainly losses rather than gains in weight.

Chapter **22**

Paranormal optical phenomena

Paranormal optical phenomena are at once the most immediately appealing and the most elusive of all physical effects that we call 'paranormal' – that is, apparently brought about by the proximity of humans, and contrary to the known laws of physical science. Visual perception gives information to the brain at the fastest rate of any of the senses, but the complicated transformation process along the way can give rise to numerous distortions of physical reality – after-images, chromatic distortion, and so on. It is also common to some people to receive 'clear' mental quasi-visual images of people, objects, happenings, both in dreams and in other states of consciousness, some of them very close to full consciousness. The mind-brain mechanism of reception of such hallucinatory images is largely unknown territory, and the possibility of exploring it through the reports of psychic subjects is an exciting one.

The especially confusing feature is that hallucinatory and physical-origin images are sometimes inextricably mixed in the brain or mind. When a psychic says that he sees an 'aura' around a person's head, or a parrot perching on his shoulder, it does not follow that either is a physical thing to which instruments such as cameras or photomultipliers would respond. This does not make them any less real to the psychic, nor does it prevent the psychic from seeing the person himself, and his physical surroundings, at the same time. Thus there is an inextricable mixture. We are led to hypothesize. 'There are two sorts of parrot, physical and hallucinatory.'

And there is a further complication. Apparently genuine photographs exist of scenes which were only imagined as images by the psychic who took the photograph; the scenes were not observed by the witnesses. These are sometimes known as 'thought-photographs', and we shall return to them later in this chapter. So it may be possible to transmit visual information of non-physical origin not only to the eye–brain–mind system, but also to cameras and to other physical detectors of electromagnetic waves. We could possibly extend our hypothesis as follows: 'and there are two sorts of origin of the photographic image.'

I have coined the phrase 'quasi-physical' phenomena to cover channels of perception which behave as though they originated with physical phenomena but which actually do not do so. The mind–brain system is capable of functioning as a mixer, which superposes physical and mental phenomena. Both physical and quasi-physical phenomena claim our attention in this chapter.

The most common report I hear is that the metal-bender has been 'seeing lights': a glow or a ball of light, usually orange or white in colour. Sometimes the light is near by, sometimes it is distant; sometimes it is described as a UFO sighting, and sometimes it is visible to more than one person. In the case of Willie G., a white light was usually seen by him at moments of strong metal-bending 'power'; he claimed to have some control over its appearance and disappearance. At first I thought that all Willie's light was quasi-physical, but this belief was shaken when two reliable observers, watching him from a distance when he thought he was alone, reported seeing lights above his head. Moreover Willie began to obtain curious photographs when using a Polaroid black and white instant camera at moments of light-seeing. Each shows a single smooth sphere illuminated both from the front and from behind. The conditions of Willie's camera operation were controlled not by me but by Dr Cantor,[20] who insists that the Polaroid camera used was functioning correctly on the immediately preceding and immediately following pictures. I did control the conditions under which the photograph in Plate 22.1 was taken, which were within a light-sealed dark-room, using a new Polaroid camera provided by me and the centre section of a freshly purchased film pack; a run of previously black prints had been made with this arrangement immediately beforehand. Willie attempted to concentrate, and produced the curious textured image shown in Plate 22.1. It is true that chemical and electrostatic effects can produce grey fogging and also small patches of light on Polaroid film; but I believe that Willie's textured picture of (possibly) human skin is not to be explained thus.

Willie is convinced that he has seen auras of light around some humans, and especially around himself when looking into a mirror. Sometimes he has claimed to see his own 'chakras', flower-like light sources from within the body; 'chakras' are well known in Indian mysticism (Kundalini yoga).[64] What Willie sees is not physical light, however, since in a darkroom neither my own vision nor a photomultiplier received any signal, even though Willie was claiming to see his aura. It does not appear that Willie's auras are merely after-images, as is often supposed; but they do seem to be mental rather than physical phenomena.

Although I regarded the aura as mental 'quasi-light', I thought it might be worthwhile examining its 'quasi-spectrum'; so I trained Willie to hold a diffraction grating up to his eye and describe in detail the colours he obtained with sources of physical light. He gave careful and repeatable descriptions of both continuum and line spectra, and when he looked at his mirror aura and forehead chakra in the same way, he described to me a continuum spectrum. On the supposition that there might be a contribution from real background light diffracted by something around his head, I varied the background light, using instead of white light, sodium yellow and mercury/cadmium with a

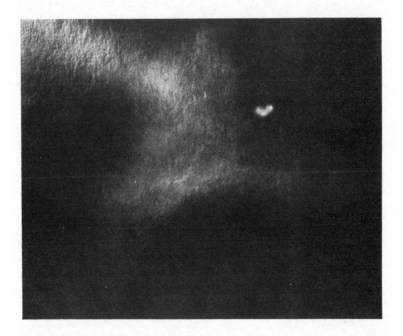

Plate 22.1 Polaroid photograph taken by Willie G. in light-tight room, with camera pointing towards him at a few inches' distance. The small light spots may be chemical (or paranormal chemical) in origin, but it is difficult to explain the well-focused textured effect. Perhaps it represents a forehead in partial shadow.

green filter. But Willie insisted that what he saw through the diffraction grating remained a continuum, even though the relative brightness of the colours was changed.

I also asked Willie to vary the speed of a background stroboscopic light source until the rotation of one of his own chakras, seen in a mirror, appeared to cease. He was able to produce repeatable speeds, which for a 6-petalled chakra work out at a rotation of 7.5 revs/sec. Since it appears very likely that the visions are not of physical visible electro-magnetic radiation but are mental effects which we have termed 'quasi-light', these physical experiments are conceptually meaningless. But Charles Darwin used to describe 'fool's experiments' which he sometimes deliberately conducted; he is supposed to have played the trombone to a group of climbing plants; I am proud to be in his company.

The phenomenon of 'thought-photography', in which photographic images are produced by paranormal means on light-sensitive film in a sealed camera, has claimed attention during the last few years. An English medium by the name of Hope produced paranormal photographic images more than fifty years ago, and was investigated by Crookes and other well-qualified investigators.[65] The best-known example of a 'thought-photographer' is the American Ted Serios, whose efforts have been described in detail by Dr Eisenbud.[66] Serios's thought-photographs have included recognizable pictures of buildings and people, blurred and usually curiously distorted. A record of stills from a movie-camera exists in which the image can be seen to form and focus from one frame to the next. Serios's work is sometimes regarded with suspicion because he insists on having a small black box (which he calls a 'gismo') in front of the camera, but always this box is found to be empty and incapable of playing a physical role. Serios has never been a professional entertainer, and the circumstances surrounding the phenomena he produces are difficult to dismiss as fraudulent.

Another modern subject, Willie Schwanholz, investigated by Professor Uphoff,[67] has the habit of moving his head during the 'taking' of thought-photographs. The instant camera covered with its lens-cap is pointed at his forehead, as is usual in thought-photography; but multiple images are found on the print, just as though a rapid series of mental images was projected.

Since a great deal of normal photography is produced in the dark-room rather than in the camera, suspicion has always accompanied the historical claims of the appearance of spirits and other things on photographs (the so-called 'skotography'). The instant development technique developed by Dr Land and marketed under the name 'Polaroid' has therefore contributed greatly to easing the difficult task of the psychic investigator – to establish the genuineness of the thought-photograph phenomenon.

We can at present rely on the unspoiled character of a freshly purchased instant development film pack; we ensure that the camera is light-tight before we load it, and we can witness that the subject does not tamper with the loaded camera. In particular no pinhole must be allowed anywhere, since a pinhole camera image of the surroundings would ensue. It is my own practice not only to keep the shutter closed but to cover the front with a lens-cap and black tape as a double precaution. After concentration by the psychic, we withdraw the print and observe its instant development. Previously we have withdrawn one or two prints and ensured that they are perfectly black.

Camera cases are opaque to ultraviolet and infrared radiation, but they are transparent to X-rays and gamma-rays. They also possess orifices through which optical fibres could be inserted. We need to preserve security against these possibilities, and also against the methods by which a freshly purchased film pack can be opened up and exposed to optical images. This trick must be carried out in total darkness, by exposing the films in turn to some image source such as a transparency viewer. Signs of tampering can nearly always be detected in the subsequent examination of the film-pack contents, as will be seen from the following details.

The films in an instant pack are (at present) attached at one corner by a black metal staple of fairly precise dimensions. But since each film is required to be pulled out individually without disturbing its neighbours, the staple is divided from the rest of the plate by a continuous corner cut which extends from one edge of the film to the neighbouring edge, and leaves uncut only a gap of about 1 mm. It is this small section of the film-holding material that is broken when a film is pulled out for instant development.

To separate one film from the next, therefore, either the staple must be removed and subsequently replaced, or the film must be folded at the small piece of material which forms the gap in the corner cut. Both these methods leave signs of tampering, either a scratched or substituted staple, or creasing at the fold. It would indeed be difficult to avoid such signs, especially since the operation must be carried out in total darkness. Moreover, if each film is not replaced so that it precisely covers the next, and is not shadowed at the edge by the metal holder, a dark line will appear at one edge of the print.*

I have described these signs of tampering in detail because they were searched for and not found when, in London, the instant photography expert examined the work of Masuaki Kiyota, whose

Plate 22.2 Thought-photograph of London scene (possibly Trafalgar Square, although the details are not correct) produced by Masuaki Kiyota, but not under good observation

---

* One of those present at the Masuaki Kiyota session in London, Mr Hutchinson, has claimed to have found a method by which the pack can be exposed without signs of tampering being left; but this claim has not yet been fully investigated. If investigations are to be carried out using the difficult 'homework' technique, further security precautions with the pack would be advisable – for example with French chalk, or fingerprint examination.

thought-photography came to the notice of British television in 1978. Masuaki did not succeed in producing an image 'to order' in the television protocol, but he was able to produce images (shown in Plates 22.2 and 22.3) when the loaded camera was left with him for a period of hours. Naturally this was not accepted as watertight evidence, but with unnecessary lack of sympathy the trick of producing images on film pack was then dramatically exposed to him on camera. Masuaki has been investigated over a long period by a number of scientists and television producers in Japan; his thought-photographs are considered to be genuine by psychic investigator Professor Walter Uphoff, by film producer Alan Neuman, by journalist David Tharp, as well as by Japanese scientists such as Professor Sasaki and by Nippon Television. An

Plate 22.3 Thought-photograph of marching guardsmen (?) produced by Masuaki Kiyota, but not under good observation

interesting and unique feature of Masuaki's phenomenon is the production of mirror-image photographs, in which the subject of the photograph occupies the upper half of the frame, and an inverted image appears on the lower half.

Sasaki has published an account[68] of his investigations of the light which is detected in the camera when a thought-photograph is produced. Silicon photodiodes (type SPD 111) are mounted within the camera, facing not the shutter but the film itself; their output is continuously chart-recorded, especially during the period when Masuaki believes that the thought-photograph is being produced. A typical light pulse is reprinted in Figure 22.1 from Sasaki's paper. The light intensity behaves in an oscillatory fashion, and perhaps there is here a significant connection with the multiple images of Willie Schwanholz; does the image vary periodically in space, in time or in both?

In Sasaki's more recent investigations, dynamic signals from an array of photodiodes were recorded; it seemed that the most intense spot of

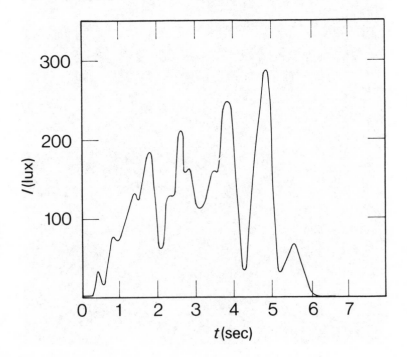

Figure 22.1 Time-dependence of light intensity I measured within camera during thought-photograph produced by Masuaki Kiyota.

light moved around from one photodiode to the next; detailed analyses were made of the data. From this it appeared that a 'light-pen theory' of the formation of thought photographs could be a possibility, but the moving picture data do not support this.

Moving pictures have been reported in several thought-photography sessions, and one example has been produced by Masuaki Kiyota under the protocol of Walter Uphoff and photographer Yutaka Fakuda. The moving picture lasts about three minutes, and consists of a series of views of static scenes, each lasting a period of seconds, interspersed with darkness. The first is the Tokyo Tower, the centre and then the top; next there is a picture of a tall office block, then a block of buildings and after this another block, faced with white; these three may possibly be views of London. Finally there is the Statue of Liberty, first the base and afterwards the top; last, for a short period, a human face appears.

There is considerable unsteadiness in the views, as though a moving picture camera were being held by an extremely wobbly hand. The views appear to form very quickly, but they are in wobbly motion from the moment of their appearance.

It must be recognized that if the paranormal placement of electric charge (chapter 15) is a possibility, then the need for the presence of photons in Polaroid thought-photography is no longer felt. Not only do the film packs respond to electrostatic charge, but so also do photodiodes.

I feel somewhat dissatisfied with my present personal experience of paranormal optical phenomena, and I return to the opening sentence of this chapter, which was that they are 'at once the most immediately appealing and the most elusive of all paranormal physical effects'!

Chapter 23

Informational psychic phenomena

In this chapter we shall touch briefly on those psychic phenomena which involve the transfer of information rather than the movements of matter in space–time. It may be, but is not necessarily, true that information cannot be transferred except by means of photons or through similar channels.

It may on the other hand be that these informational phenomena fall into the category 'quasi-physical' rather than 'physical'. Since the phenomena are sometimes displayed by metal-benders, so that there could be a connection, we cannot ignore them entirely. They may be classified as telepathy, clairvoyance, precognition and psychometric information, and the phenomena are sometimes termed 'extra-sensory perception' (ESP).

'Telepathy' is the transfer of information between humans or other living beings by extra-sensory means. 'Clairvoyance' is the reception by a human of information about physical events. This is said to be 'pre-cognitive' or 'retrocognitive' when the moment of transfer precedes or follows the events. By psychometric information is meant information received from a physical object (e.g. 'This knife once killed Mr X').

Inevitably, since I am a physicist and not a parapsychologist, my approach will be less professional; indeed I have made an effort to avoid involvements with study of the possible telepathic abilities of the metal-benders simply because I have less experience in such studies than I have at observing physical phenomena. But since I found that some of the children had reported plausible telepathic experiences, I will not avoid describing a little of what has happened.

In order to establish in the laboratory the reality of the various forms of ESP, and in particular telepathy, careful protocols are necessary. The subject of parapsychology, in which scientists claim to have proved the reality of ESP in numerous experiments, is often considered to have been established by J.B. Rhine and his collaborators at Duke University in the USA during the early 1930s. There had been experimentation before this, by many investigators, who either found gifted subjects, or found themselves to be gifted. The Oxford classical scholar Gilbert Murray conducted more than five hundred experiments in his home between 1910 and 1915; he was himself required to guess 'events' in the minds of other people in the room, who had previously been asked to agree on an event and to think about it simultaneously. His success seems not to have been explicable in terms of 'hyperaesthesia' or abnormally keen hearing. In the written accounts, we are given some charming examples of events which had been chosen, e.g. 'Mother hitting the purser with a skipping-rope', and we are told that a 33 per cent success rate was achieved, with 28 per cent partial success and 39 per cent failure. This was a similar success rate to that obtained in the well-known Pearce–Pratt card-guessing experiments at Duke, but when these were criticized by psychologists, more elaborate protocols were established; in the subsequent Pratt-Woodruff tests the success rates were lower. Many parapsychologists have conducted telepathy and clairvoyance experiments, and the success rate seems to have been dependent on many factors, *including dependence on the experimenter himself*. The success also declines as the experiment progresses, so that we know that we are dealing not with a repeatable and exactly controllable phenomenon, but with an elusive human faculty. Surprising success rates have been claimed in government-sponsored experiments — 75 per cent in the fictitious transmissions to the US submarine *Nautilus*, and 48 per cent in allegedly real Novosibirsk tests. What is surprising is that this possibly strategically valuable information should have been released by governments; perhaps the public does not yet know which experiments are fictitious and which are real. Nevertheless there is a long tradition of ESP research in the Soviet Union, founded by Professor Vassiliev at the University of Leningrad.

A significant variant of telepathic transmission was first investigated by Abramovski:[69] that of recently forgotten facts. X tells Y a list of words, and Y then writes down as many as he can remember (a high score must be rewarded, for reasons soon to become obvious). X later concentrates sequentially on single words, attempting to transmit them mentally. Y is asked to recall. In the experiments carried out in the Psychological Institute in Warsaw, 154 out of 324 words were successfully recalled. Possibly this specialized kind of telepathy is easier to develop than the more general phenomenon.

When Uri Geller first visited Britain and appeared on television he always included 'mentalism' (demonstration of ESP) in his repertoire. Particularly frequent was the blind 'guessing' of simple drawings. Such 'free response'* exercises are open to the following disadvantages:

1 There are many well-known methods of fraud.
2 It is difficult to determine just how much information there is in each drawing.
3 It is difficult to know how much of the transmission is by geometrical pattern and how much by content. Also failure can occur because of poor drawing ability or ignorance of the subject-matter.
4 Judgment of success is not always straightforward. In particular, it is very difficult to design a control experiment in which the chance of a random guess succeeding can be accurately assessed.[70]

However, there are overriding advantages of playing telepathic drawing games, as follows:

1 They are interesting and provide good motivation.
2 They require very little equipment.
3 The short time taken for an experiment makes it easier to avoid fraud on the part of the psychic than would be the case in a more lengthy experiment.

The 'sender' draws something relatively simple on a writing-pad in such a way that the receiver does not see what is being drawn. The sender should not draw an object visible to the receiver, or otherwise to the forefront of the conversation, and he should not state whether it is a representation or a geometrical pattern. The 'receiver' attempts to imagine and copy this drawing onto his own pad without seeing the original. Comparison is then made, preferably by an independent judge.

Laboratory studies of extra-sensory perception, widely conducted in the USA, Britain and elsewhere, are obviously a good deal more careful and systematic than the above, but there are several reasons why a lower success rate is usually achieved in extended studies. My judgment is that the important thing about telepathy is its spontaneity. The mind of the telepathist at an unpredictable moment receives information, and with experience he can sense that the information has not come to him through normal channels. Not many people regard themselves as reliable telepathists (although at one time it was almost a profession), and it is not very often that the minds of telepathists receive telepathic or clairvoyant information. But when they do receive it, the information is essentially correct. If it is incorrect, the error is

---

* Free response experiments are contrasted with 'forced choice' of targets.

usually in the deduction that the brain makes from incomplete information, since a telepathic link is often fragmentary.

It follows that when a telepathist is tested, for example on guessing the symbols on a parapsychologist's 'Zener cards', there must be many occasions on which no telepathic information comes to him, and he therefore simply guesses at the card. An attempt is made to allow for this by permitting him to 'pass' or refuse the card if he wishes. But we have no way of knowing if he always 'passes' when no information comes. So there is a contribution from the telepathist's inability to distinguish telepathic information from a mere whim or fancy. And the fact that low success rates are usually achieved in such experiments indicates that the ability is small. This has led to the suggestion that there is no difference between telepathy and lucky guesses. To know the difference is the skill of the telepathist – he must know when to keep silent. The existence of the so-called 'decline effect' in telepathy experiments – the failure of a subject to keep up his originally good score – supports this point of view.

The 'sending of drawings' game has something of a built-in protection against decline effect; when one is bored or afraid of failure, one just stops. The most successful telepathy games that I have organized amongst metal-benders were played at a rate of three pictures each day after school. For a few days Richard B. was able to receive about 70 per cent of the pictures sent by my son John Andrew over a distance of ten miles. Some of the pictures are shown in Figure 23.1 In Figure 23.2 I also include some data obtained in casual sessions I have had personally with Uri Geller. Although I am aware of most of the pitfalls encountered in playing drawing games with a television performer, I am reasonably certain that these pictures are not just a load of nonsense.

When the game is played with both sender and receiver in a single room, it is more difficult to guard against cheating by the receiver than it is by the sender or by both in collusion. The sender must be seen to record his drawing under conditions such that he cannot communicate normally with the receiver (this is fairly easy to organize); he must also be unable to tamper with the drawing after it has been made.

However, the receiver's methods of breaking down the security of the sender are more difficult to detect. I have never felt confident of my own security when sending to a professional mentalist, from whom it is difficult to conceal the movements of the pencil; therefore under these conditions I prefer to receive myself, since it is easy for me to know that I have not myself cheated, and that tampering afterwards was impossible, provided that the sender relinquished his drawing to me before I uncovered mine. Under these conditions I have myself successfully received from Uri Geller, although I am usually a poor receiver and sender.

Another form of experiment popular among investigators is known as remote viewing.[15] The receiver is kept in a room and is asked at a predetermined time to guess and record graphically and verbally the visual impressions that the sender is having of the place to which he has travelled. Photographic and other records are kept of this place, for the independent judgment of success rate. Unexpectedly high rates have been obtained not only with recognized psychics but with subjects who had not suspected their ability (including representatives of the government agency sponsoring the research). So far as I know, this type of receiving (or sending) ability has not been tested in metal-benders.

Telepathy is usually regarded as the paranormal transmission of information between two brains or minds, and is thus distinguished from clairvoyance (paranormal knowledge of physical objects) and from pre- or retrocognition (paranormal knowledge of events before or after they happen). Clearly the most advanced form of telepathy is when a two-way mental conversation takes place between two people remote from each other. One of the metal-bending children has had such an experience. I quote his father's report:

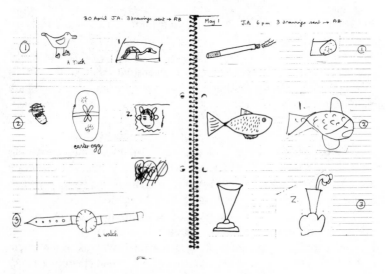

Figure 23.1 Six drawings made by my son John Andrew and 'sent' telepathically over a distance of several miles to Richard B., whose attempts to reproduce them appear on the right side of each one.

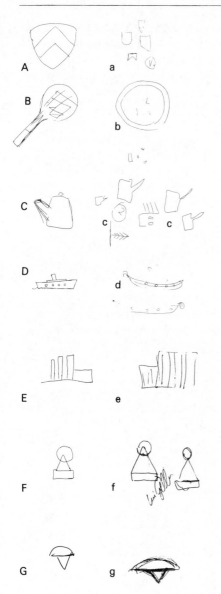

Figure 23.2 Drawings (left) (A–G and 1–10) made by my wife Lynn, Dr Ted Bastin and myself, and guessed (right) by Uri Geller, with reasonable precautions against pencil-watching, surreptitious drawing, etc. Item G was drawn by Geller and guessed in g by me.

In September 1975 my son told me he was receiving a message and I got the details from him by asking him questions and getting him to spell out names. I afterwards checked in an atlas and found a village in Russia with the name he had given and in the geographical situation he had described.

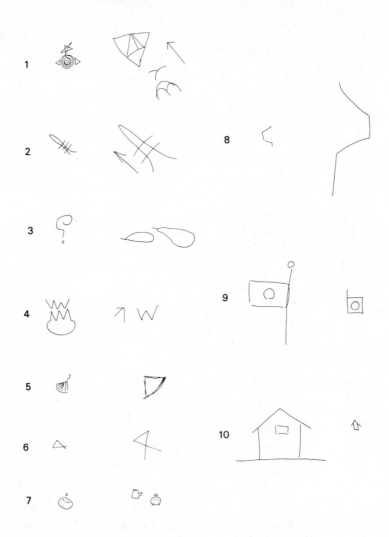

(Figure 23.2)

Q:	From which country?	A:	Russia.
Q:	Boy or girl?	A:	Girl.
Q:	Age?	A:	12.
Q:	Name?	A:	E.P.
Q:	Any brothers?	A:	One.
Q:	Age?	A:	10½.
Q:	Sisters?	A:	Two, ages 2 and 3.
Q:	Father's name?	A:	C.
Q:	Mother's name?	A:	L.
Q:	Where do they live?	A:	S.
Q:	What is it like?	A:	Near water. The wide part of a river where it opens up into a lake, on the outskirts of a village. There is no address — could be a farm. Not very good roads — cart tracks. A community of 3 families.
Q:	How do your family make a living?	A:	Crops (could be potatoes).
Q:	Is the river big or small?	A:	Very wide where she lives; there is a small waterfall where the river widens.
Q:	Do you wear jeans?	A:	No.
Q:	Is she better at telepathy than me? Has she sent out before?	A:	She has received — not sent.
Q:	Has she worked with scientists?	A:	No — but she knows people who have. She knows someone, a great person, who can talk like this. Her name is Madame Kulinga.

The word 'Luneburg' is also in the notes I made, but I have not noted the question to which it applied.

Apart from reference to the atlas, none of the information has since been verified or tested.

Independent unofficial checking of this information is in progress. Real names have been omitted for this reason.

An informational phenomenon with strong physiological overtones is 'automatic writing'. As a form of automatism it is to be classified with automatic speech (cf. de la Tourette's syndrome), sleep-walking, and actions under hypnotic trance. But it is the information that comes out of the unconscious mind rather than the physiology that concerns us here. More than one metal-bender has displayed these talents. The subject's hand moves automatically over the paper, holding pen or pencil; a handwriting and word style quite different from his usual graphic output is produced. Sometimes what is written is information unknown to the conscious mind of the subject; not just forgotten material, but material which the subject is most unlikely to have come across; sometimes it is in foreign, even remote, languages.

In the last century automatic writing was often considered to be a mild form of possession by a discarnate entity or spirit, from whom the information derived. But now the most usual interpretation is that the unconscious mind is responsible for the automatism and is providing the information, having had access to it through an ESP channel. It must be recorded that much of the credit for the provision of an alternative to the spirit hypothesis belongs to Madame H.P. Blavatsky. But it must also be borne in mind that the participation of a discarnate entity is something which cannot be proved or disproved; the unconscious mind may well be capable of producing information having its apparent origin in a spirit; or it may not.

There is also an informational phenomenon, with very strong psychokinetic involvement, known as 'direct writing'. It is supposed that the pencil stands up and writes on its own. I have never observed such an event and, like most people, I find it difficult to accept. But I have complete records and reports of a series of such events from the family of one of the metal-benders: the writing starts by being merely blobs and scratches; then it becomes scrawled curves, then single letters, then short words appear; finally whole sentences are written. But the informational content of this particular case was unremarkable. The father encouraged the writing by leaving paper with written questions, hoping that answers would appear; although their mode of appearance was unobserved, answers did appear. And they were framed in the first person singular, as though what was answering had a personality of its own. The father interpreted this as the participation of a discarnate entity; but the metal-bending child refused to accept this, and believed that he himself was in some way responsible. Thus the unanswerable question of the origin of the words and sentences and indeed the poltergeist events by which they were accompanied directly confronts the observers.

An activity rather similar to direct writing is to induce the reception of information from unknown sources. This activity was first reported in 1880 by the journalist A.P. Sinnett.[71] In 1978 metal-benders Gill Costin and Kim Griffiths tried to teleport letters to Uri Geller, who never received them. But they received 'apports', including some letters, whose origin is completely unknown. The information in them appears to come from sort of 'knowledge store' (or possibly the subliminal memory). The phenomenon is rather like speaking with tongues or automatic writing in remote languages. Here are some quotations from their letters:

1 'θεῖός μοι ἐνύπνιου ἦλθεν ὄνειρος'
2 'οἱ πρεσβύτεροι ὑμων ἐνύπνιου ἐνυπνιασθήσονται'
3 'Die Geisterwelt ist nicht verschlossen'
4 'Radwan'
5 'Nepesh'

The first Greek quotation is from the *Iliad* (2:56), with slight alterations; it means: 'There came to me in the night a divine dream.' The second is from Acts 2:17, and means: 'The older of you will have a dream during the night.' These are of course well known and were traced for me in five minutes by Professor Giangrande. The quotation from Goethe's *Faust* is also well known.

Possibly 'Radwan' refers to the noble Radovan,[72] son of Knight George, nephew of the Venetian premeditor of Zang, and hero of a *Guslerlied* (song with south Slav musical instrument): Radovan simulated death in a yoga-trance in order to escape prison.

Presumably 'Nepesh' is a reference to the ancient Egyptian word for the soul.

It is an interesting collection to be turned up by two teen-age girls, and many people will speculate that they researched the items themselves, possibly with help from school. But if one meets Gill and Kim, one finds this very difficult to believe.

Such communications are sometimes received by psychics, for example Margo Williams, in the form of clairaudience (voices), clairvoyance (pictures), or automatic writing. Sometimes they have been interpreted as information from men and women living as long as two centuries ago. This type of ESP is known as 'drop-in communications'.

It would seem that telepathy is likely to be of very much significance or value only when it is reasonably reliable. Knowledge of when it is reliable is the most difficult thing to achieve, and we have argued that statistical experiments test this knowledge and not the telepathy itself.

Engineers have taken the published success rates of different subjects and calculated that if they were used in parallel – i.e. if we accept a message only when it is confirmed by sufficient subjects – then for 90 per cent reliability we must use more than ten good subjects at each end; we would then be able to transmit information at the rate of 0.04 bits/sec. This is surely the slowest telecommunication system so far designed! But it is largely, although not entirely, independent of distance. Experiments have been conducted over huge distances, and 'firsts' claimed for information received across the Atlantic, etc. Electro-magnetic screening appears to have little effect; in the recent researches of Targ and Puthoff[15] on remote viewing, there have been successes with sending from underground sites, as well as from coast to coast across the United States.

These features, together with the more unusual precognitive and retrocognitive communications, have led to the dissatisfaction of most scientists with the electromagnetic interpretation of telepathy, which is that the brain receives the information carried by some form of modulation of electromagnetic waves. The difficulties of this theory are manifold: first, that the time-varying electric potentials at the surface of the skull (electroencephalographs, or EEG) are many orders of magnitude too weak for transmission and apparently do not carry information anyway; second, that the brain is not of suitable design to receive and unravel purely electromagnetic signals with any efficiency; third, that only extra low frequency and long wavelength radiation (ELF waves) could traverse the long distances and overcome screening, and such waves have an information-carrying ability which is far too small; fourth, telepathy by electromagnetic waves would be expected to show distance and screening effects, and these are not consistently measurable in remote viewing and similar experiments; fifth, no mechanism for precognitive or retrocognitive effects is envisaged in the electromagnetic interpretation.

There have been other physical candidates for a telepathic carrier wave, but all suffer from similar inadequacies. It really appears as though physics must provide new concepts before any physical explanation can be sought.

In this situation we are tempted to postulate simply that telepathy is a mode of behaviour of minds, having such-and-such properties, as elucidated by experiments. Minds apparently have properties which are at present outside the scope of physical science. These properties are best described as 'trans-spatial' and 'trans-temporal', in that both space and time are transcended.

The 'trans-spatial' characteristic would render the question of distance effects in telepathy irrelevant – as indeed it seems to be at present. It also makes the question, 'Where is the mind?' a meaningless one, since the word 'where' implies space. Certainly, minds seem to work in close conjunction with brains situated within the cranium; but their conjunction with other parts of space may also be possible.

A 'trans-temporal' characteristic is necessary for the interpretation of precognition and retrocognition. Possibly it is not the precognition of physical events which is the primary channel, but rather the pre-cognitive contact with other minds which have contact with the physical events via the normal channels of brain and senses. It may further be the case that there is a vast mental store in which the entire spatio-temporal physical sequence of the universe is held; access to this store on the part of a single mind is tenuous, but could be precognitive or retrocognitive in nature. We are tempted to propose that the singularity of individual minds is itself only a concept assumed for convenience, and possibly only with partial truth. Thus we approach the 'collective unconscious', a concept advanced by Jung.[73]

Of all the mental psychic phenomena, precognition is probably the most significant; I have heard it described as the 'senior phenomenon'. But in my experience it is rare amongst metal-benders. Several of the children have had clear visions which they have taken to be precognitive or retrocognitive – visions of supposedly future or past events; but it is difficult to specify details which provide convincing evidence that the visions eventually became reality.

Kim Griffiths, the metal-bender who had received the quotation from the *Iliad*, later told me about further 'messages'; this time there were precognitive elements. I quote them because they are typically fragmentary.

About Radwan. I think there's a Dr E. Jensen. Something about 1934.
(There was in fact a Harley Street physician of this name in the 1930s, and he did become centrally interested in spiritual healing phenomena. But I have as yet been unable to find any connection with Radwan.)

I seem to get ideas all at once about things . . . I saw a signpost to Cam-bridge . . . is there a meeting about these things going on there? . . . One of the people was something to do with chemistry.
(Yes, I had just been to the Society for Psychical Research meeting there, but there was minimal publicity. Several chemists were present.)

The other day I thought about somewhere very cold. I could see it like a film on a screen.
(I had recently returned from a scientific meeting in Iceland.)

Something about a greater power under the snow there. A holy water. Stream or river?
(I was indirectly concerned with an important but confidential issue about dowsing for new hot springs, on which much of the home heating of Iceland depends.)

And something to do with the Russians . . . radiation.
(A talk had been given on Russian high power radio transmissions at the conference.)

A name starting Nanda or Nana — Indian I think.
(Presumably Nana Dwaku, the priest whose levitation above the fire had been filmed.[61] I had recently seen this film for the first time and become interested in it, but it had not been shown in England so far as I know.)

Tell the Professor Hasted that four computers have been told to switch off but have not. This shows how research must go on. These computers are here in G.B. The Manchester people. No. Not right. Moore.
(I did not bother to contact my friends at the new Computer Centre at Daresbury, near Manchester, but I received something of a jolt when I saw the name Moore, which could refer to Laurie Moore, the manager of the computer link in our College. I talked to Laurie, without leading him, about the possible phasing out of computers, and he told me that, of the large London University computers, four and four only were for the chop. But this was news to me, since the University computing services are large and complex.

Two days later I was talking to Professor H., who volunteered the information that one of my research laboratories in another college of London University could be threatened when the IBM 370 (one of these four) came to be phased out. Relocation of services in its old space and elsewhere in the college would trigger off an accommodation squeeze possibly threatening my atomic collisions research.)

If this interpretation of Kim Griffiths's 'message' is correct, there is no doubt that the last part is 'trans-temporal', if not precognitive. There seems to be no normal channel by which the confidential information could have travelled to the Bedfordshire family before it reached me. At the same time, like so many 'psychic stories', it depends very much on interpretation.

Chapter **24**

Physical background

We have claimed in previous chapters that metal-bending contains both structural and quasi-force characteristics. There are at least two types of event on a microscopic scale: the formation of loop dislocations and the destabilization of grain boundaries; one is distinguishable by hardening and the other by softening of the metal.

The action in metal-bending occurs in bursts of strain, which can extend radially around the person of the metal-bender; the unconscious mind of the metal-bender is believed to control the movement of an invisible surface at which the action is concentrated. The recorded strain signals appear to be randomly orientated, and concentrated by 'psychological' or 'observational' factors in a 'region of action'.

Why is paranormal metal-bending such a challenge to scientists? Because it is difficult to be fitted into current physics in any simple way. In order to explain why this is so, we must devote some pages to summarizing the physical background of the material world, as physicists at present understand it. I have space to describe the background only in outline; therefore the level of the description cannot be high, and an apologetic profile must be exhibited at the start!

The basis of human thought is philosophical, and even in philosophy there are strongly polarized viewpoints, described in old-fashioned terms as materialism (reality only of the material world), idealism (reality only of mind, or of God), and dualism (reality both of the material world and of mind). To a non-professional philosopher like myself, it appears that at present materialism is in the ascendant, albeit termed 'central state materialism', in which the reality of both mind and matter are admitted, but in a central material state.

Science is often regarded as the experimental study of the material world; but in reality science must be regarded as a method of study rather than a corpus of knowledge. The method can be summarized as follows: observation and measurements, experiment and confirmation of experiment, formulation of hypothesis, data analysis, rejection or acceptance of hypothesis and its conversion to theory, prediction and verification of prediction of events and quantitative observables, dissemination of findings and acceptance of part responsibility for their application.

It is maintained that the scientific method can be applied to the study of non-material things, if such exist. The psychological sciences use the method in the study of such things as consciousness or human emotions. The method can also be applied to psychic phenomena, which are apparently a mixture of material and non-material things. I take the view that the material side of psychic phenomena must conform at least in part to causality and to the laws of physics. In the physical or temporal absence of an active psychic subject, material phenomena reduce to the laws of physics; but in his presence they may be modified in certain ways. These modifications are themselves subject to study by the scientific method, and that is what I am trying to do.

Newton spoke of physics as the 'study of the causes of sensible effects'. Physics is, classically, based on Newtonian mechanics in Euclidean space, in which velocity, or change of distance with time, is linked by simple algebra to mass, force and time, and the concepts of energy and momentum are derived. Energy, momentum and mass are conserved; they cannot be destroyed or created from nothing, although in Einstein's developments they can be interchanged. Matter possesses mass, and can be split up into a variety of different particles, electrons, protons, and so on, each with its own mass. The structural arrangements of these particles are by now well known, but each particle is in continual motion; the motions, which are according to Newtonian mechanics, define temperature and can give rise to electromagnetic radiation; their collisional interactions define heat transfer.

The forces by which particles interact with each other are four-fold; first, the *electromagnetic interaction*, which is responsible for holding atoms together into molecules, whether they are ordinary inorganic or organic chemical compounds, or biomolecular: second, the very much more powerful *strong interaction*, which is responsible for holding the particles within the atomic nucleus together, and which can be released as nuclear energy; it is only the outside layer of the atoms, the electrons, and not the nuclei which are involved in forming and re-forming chemical compounds.

The third interaction is the *gravitational*, which is unbelievably weak compared with the first two; but since it is stronger for larger masses, and can work over very large distances, it is the interaction which ultimately dominates on an astronomical scale. The fourth is the so-called *weak interaction*, which is responsible for certain types of nuclear process, and which, since the discovery of 'neutral currents', turns out only to be a particularly weak type of electromagnetic interaction.

Immediately we see that if we were to claim a new force to be involved in paranormal physical phenomena, this would be inconsistent with the observations of physics.

However, it is not only atomic particles which have their existence in the physical world; there are also force fields and wave motion. The concept of interactive force carries with it the concept of interactive vector fields of force permeating space. A particle subject to these interactive forces, finding itself in such a region of space, experiences a force whose magnitude and direction are appropriate to the field in that space. The most obvious examples of this concept are electrostatic or electric fields, magnetic fields and gravitational fields. Great philosophical difficulty was once experienced in trying to find an answer to the question of why this should be so. The physicist long ago got used to acceptance of the observational fact that it is a convenient and realistic concept; we shall see that in quantum field theory it is these fields which are fundamentally uniquely real.

Pairs of these fields, for example the electric and the magnetic, are coupled together in such a way that the temporal change of one produces the other, and vice versa. This gives rise to the movement of the fields in space, together with their time-variation at any point in space; this type of movement is that of a wave; it is the fields which move, not the matter through which the wave passes (as with the waves on the surface of water, which appear to travel while a cork on the water surface mostly goes up and down).

A movement of electrically charged particles gives rise to a wave which travels in space at a very high speed: $c = 3 \times 10^8$ m/sec, and is known as a light wave. Light shows all the properties of waves, such as interference, diffraction, standing waves and heterodyning. The frequency of electromagnetic radiation determines its nature; the lowest frequencies are radio waves, then come infrared radiations which we know as radiant heat; then there are visible light, ultraviolet radiation, X-rays and gamma-rays. Since the fields due to these waves can cause the movement of particles very remote from the source of the wave, it is clear that the wave carries energy with it, and the particle whose movement originally generated the wave must lose energy. The temporal variation of the magnitude or the frequency of the waves (modulation) can carry information as well as energy.

One approach to the explanation of paranormal phenomena, both ESP and physical, has been the proposal that the brain is capable of emitting radiation, presumably of a hitherto unknown type, which carries the necessary energy with it. Since spherical waves attenuate with increasing distance and are scattered by obstacles, obvious experiments to test this hypothesis suggest themselves. But if the psychic quasi-force is of an unknown type, it will not necessarily be transmitted as a wave; none of the usual characteristics of wave motion has in fact been found. Perhaps the radiation could simply be electromagnetic waves, but in a frequency band as yet undiscovered. As each new frequency band is opened up and its properties understood, the probability of this being so becomes less and less. I recall that in 1947, when I was a research student, 'thought waves' were supposed by some to be the very microwaves with which I was experimenting daily.

Submillimetre radiation, very soft X-rays (XUV) and now very low frequency radio waves (ELF) were thought by some to be possible candidates. After all, the minute electric potentials produced by the brain (EEGs) do show time-variation in precisely the ELF frequency region. Unfortunately ELF waves can carry information only at a very low rate (cycles per second must exceed bits per second) and occasionally telepathic reception is known to be very much faster than this rate — although of course it is not reliably so. There are precise distance effects for ELF wave transmission, but apparently none for telepathy. Certainly, ELF waves will not bend metal, and indeed electromagnetic waves in general can bend metal only by melting it diathermically. So it is fairly clear to the majority of physicists that if there are such things as psychokinetic phenomena their explanation must be sought outside conventional electromagnetic theory and classical physics.

At the beginning of the present century there were reported a whole series of physical experiments which led to the introduction of entirely new concepts, and which showed classical physics to be only a limited and inadequate way of regarding material reality. It was shown by Planck that energy E exists only in packets, known as quanta, whose magnitude are proportional to the frequency ν of the radiation ($E = h\nu$) where h is the Planck constant. Not only is energy possessed by each packet but also momentum $p = h\nu/c$.

At that time it was also found, as had been predicted by Einstein in his special relativity theory, that the mass m of a particle increases with its velocity v, being given by:

$$m = m_0 / \sqrt{(1 - v^2/c^2)}$$

where $c = 3 \times 10^8$ m/sec is the speed of electromagnetic radiation, m_0 is the mass of the particle when it is at rest; if it could travel at exactly the speed of light, its mass would be infinite. Electromagnetic radiation, being unable to travel except at speed c, and having no rest-mass, nevertheless possesses momentum $p = h/\lambda$ (since c is the product of frequency and wavelength, $c = \lambda v$). Thus radiation has the properties of a particle, as well as those of a wave; radiation is now also a shower of 'photons'. The photons can, as it were, all occupy the same space at the same time, whereas massive particles such as protons cannot do so. There exist two classes of particle, 'bosons' and 'fermions'.

In another series of experiments, material particles were shown to have properties similar to those of wave radiation; and it was also shown that mass m could be converted into radiative energy E, according to the Einstein relation $E = mc^2$. Thus material particles ceased to be conceptualized as very small billiard-balls and could with greater accuracy be regarded as waves confined by the constraints of the inter-actions to certain regions of space. Against this background, modern quantum theory, which is the cornerstone of twentieth-century physics, was formulated by Schrödinger, Heisenberg and others. A 'wave equation' is used in this theory to calculate with precision the probabilities of occurrence of atomic physical events. Many thousands of experimental findings conform to these probabilities, but individual events cannot be predicted; they are regarded as random, but within the framework of the probabilities, which can be precisely calculated. Thus the complete mathematical description of the event is impossible unless a large number of such events are considered. The individual event ceases to be precisely predictable. Such an event can be precisely measured, even if it is unpredictable, but there are also limitations on what can be measured. If the momentum p is accurately measured, then the position s is indeterminate, and vice versa; the product of uncertainties is the Planck constant: $\hbar = \Delta p \cdot \Delta s$. Similarly, energy E and time t are mutually indeterminate: $\hbar = \Delta E \cdot \Delta t$, with $\hbar = h/2\pi$.

Material reality is described in terms of electronic and other 'wave functions', which extend through space, even though the probabilities of finding any electrons outside the usual small atomic dimensions (10^{-8} cm) become very small. Nevertheless, these wave functions are 'non-local' — they are not bounded in the way that particles are; and as far as photons are concerned, they are hugely non-local. Yet at any moment the wave function can collapse and give all its energy into a tiny region whose position is not only unpredictable, but is controlled by the experimenter himself, in that he has controlled the environment of the photons. This collapse, the so-called 'collapse of the state vector', raises great conceptual difficulties in the quantum theory of measurement.

Consider a weak isotropic electromagnetic radiation source emitting one photon per second. The radiation will travel, in all directions, a distance of 3×10^8 m (many earth diameters) in this time. A huge sphere is filled with weak radiation during this period. Now suppose that around the entire surface of this sphere an experimenter arranges an array of photomultiplier detectors; only one detector will be activated by this radiation; and there is no way of knowing which one. Dramatically, the sphere of radiation collapses to a tiny point at an unpredictable part of the universe. The same behaviour could be anticipated for the emission of an isotropic electron wave, or pure 's-wave' electron. Thus it can be claimed that as quantum theory stands at present, the universe is in principle indescribable by causal laws.

However, there is worse to come! Not only are there whole arrays of strange particles in modern physics, including the neutrino, with zero charge and zero rest-mass (therefore not limited in speed by c), but there is also a complete duplication of these particles in the realm of anti-matter. As a result of quantum electrodynamical theory, Dirac postulated that space was entirely and uniformly populated by a sea of electrons of negative mass, and therefore negative energy. When sufficient positive energy is contributed to one of these by a collision, it can become a real electron with positive energy. Thereby a hole is left in space, with positive energy and positive charge – the so-called 'positron', or 'anti-electron'. When this hole attracts or collides with an electron, the two mutually annihilate, releasing their energy as photons. The same applies to other anti-particles, many of which have been observed in experiments. A different approach to anti-matter was proposed by Feynman, who held that the positron was an electron moving backward in time. He represented these conversion processes in the form of diagrams (Feynman diagrams) in which one axis represents time, the other space.

Quantum electrodynamics, or quantum field theory, differs from quantum mechanics in assigning reality not only to the particles of finite mass and to photons and other bosons, but to the fields themselves. The interaction between two particles is considered to arise from the exchange of large numbers of 'virtual' photons between them. The field, consisting of these virtual photons, is quantized – that is, canonical commutation relations are assigned between the position operators and their conjugate momenta. The particles, previously considered to be independently real and giving rise only to fields, are now reduced to the role merely of acting as sources of the real fields. Their particle-like quality, once taken as irreconcilable with their wave-like quality, is now considered to be only a relatively unimportant part of it. Such things as the electromagnetic radiation which accompanies the movement of charged particles can be understood only with the aid of quantum electrodynamics. Procedures such as gauge transformations can be applied to electrodynamical equations; these lead to very powerful results, such as the necessity of charge conservation, the unification of the electromagnetic and weak interactions, and the classification and understanding of the new quantum numbers, isospin, baryon number and, more recently, charm, in the new strange particles which form the subject of high energy physics.

Up to the present it has not been proved possible to unify the gravitational field with the other fields – an ambition which occupied the later part of Einstein's life. However, the gravitational field becomes centrally important in astrophysics, in stellar objects where the density of matter is so great that ultimately no escape from the gravitational fields is possible, even for photons. Nothing can emerge from within the critical radius of such a 'black hole'.

But the existence of anti-matter does make it possible for black holes to emit radiation. The black hole is a gravitational collapse of matter, which according to the theory of general relativity eventually produces a singularity of space–time, where the concept of space–time as a continuum, together with the laws of physics, break down altogether; since the inward motion of the matter exceeds the velocity of light, no communication with the interior of the black hole was believed to be possible and, as far as we outside are concerned, the interior is physically unknowable.

However, according to the Dirac theory, empty space is filled with pairs of virtual particles which come into existence at some point in space–time; these particles move apart, return and annihilate each other. But at the edge of a black hole one particle may fall into it, leaving the other to escape and appear as radiation apparently emitted from the black hole.[74] The in-falling particle, if an anti-particle, would appear to be a particle travelling backwards in time from the singularity. It appears at the edge to have been scattered by the gravitational field, forming a particle travelling forwards in time. One can regard the radiation from a black hole as having come from singularity and quantum-mechanical tunnelling out of the black hole. Since black holes continually radiate by the annihilation mechanism, they continually decrease in mass, reaching eventually the Planck mass $c^{1/2}$ $G^{-1/2}$ $\hbar^{1/2}$ $\simeq$ 10^{-5} g, where G is the gravitational constant. Finally they explode.

The 'tunnelling' process is well known in atomic and nuclear physics; a particle located within a potential barrier and bounded by a certain region of space has a calculable probability of appearing outside the barrier and escaping; no energy is required for tunnelling.

One might regard the tunnelling phenomenon, which is a very well known consequence of quantum theory (and is not necessarily associated with black holes), as a sort of electronic or atomic teleportation. Indeed, the speculation might be made that tunnelling is of primary significance in metal-bending. However, the probability of tunnelling decreases exponentially with increasing height and width of energy barrier as well as with mass of the particle, so that it would indeed be small for the transport of an atom through the crystal lattice, unless some 'mental intervention' were postulated.

Some brief discussion of space–time will be of relevance to our ideas about telepathy and precognition. A diagram somewhat similar to the Feynman diagram is used to represent what is known in relativity theory as the 'light-cone'. We have seen that mass increases as the velocity of light is approached, and since the infinite mass cannot be reached the velocity of light can never be exceeded. This is equivalent to the statement that a diagram can be drawn in the manner of Figure 24.1a in which material reality must lie within the shaded region; this region is known as the light-cone. Nothing material outside the light cone can be known to us. The origin of the graph is here and now: this point in space, at the present moment. Light proceeds along the surface of the cone, but matter can proceed only within it, along single straight or curved lines. Lines drawn within the shaded area of Figure 24.1a represent reality as physics knows it at present. There can be discontinuities in lines if we seek to represent certain types of transition of a particle on this diagram. All lines are broadened due to quantum mechanical uncertainty.

Some parapsychological phenomena might demand that the diagram have a waist, as in Figure 24.1b. This representation would allow a multiplicity of happenings now to lead to the same situation in the future. If existence is continuous in time, then logic does not permit of closed loops, which would represent such situations as a man killing his own mother and thereby preventing his own birth. Another possibility within this diagram is that of superluminal signals travelling faster than the velocity of light. These are represented by lines less steeply sloping than the surface on the cone in Figure 24.1a.

Figures 24.1c and d represent worlds in which discontinuities in time and space play a large part. Existence is possible simultaneously only in the future and in the past in Figure 24.1c; and in 24.1d a parallel universe system merges into a single universe in the future. About the parallel-universe interpretation of quantum theory we shall have more to say in the next chapter.

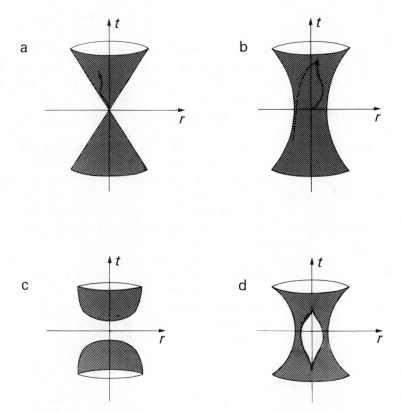

Figure 24.1 Possible light-cones: (a) The normal light-cone of Minkowski 4-space. (b) A waisted light-cone allowing superluminal signals (e.g. non-locality in the Einstein–Rosen–Podolsky experiment). (c) and (d) Possible light-cones allowing parallel universe, quantum-mechanical tunnelling etc.

Chapter **25**

The many-universes interpretation of quantum theory and its implications

It is true that only a minority of physicists are dissatisfied with the usual interpretation (by Niels Bohr of Copenhagen) of the quantum theory of measurement, but at least it can be said that members of this minority have made various proposals aimed at overcoming our mental distaste for a completely random universe that is comprehensible only through statistical laws.

Let us consider a stream of electrons being diffracted by a pair of slits. The familiar wave diffraction pattern will appear on a fluorescent screen. If one of the slits were blocked up, there would be no interference between the two waves, and only a single smudge would appear on the screen. If instead the other slit were blocked up, again only one smudge would appear. But if both slits were opened again, a complete set of fringes would build up as more and more electrons reached the screen.

What about the first electron to pass through the pair of slits? To which fringe does it contribute? Can quantum theory tell us where it will go? At present it cannot, and most physicists would give the opinion that we can never know the answer. The point of arrival of the first electron is random and that of the second electron is still random, and so on. But as an increasing number pass through, the fringe pattern gradually appears. This experiment could in principle be carried out very slowly, maybe one electron per year; the same principle would apply, each electron path being unpredictable. In this extreme example, quantum theory does not seem to be very powerful. The system also seems to have non-locality in time. But for predicting the most probable results of a large number of electrons, quantum theory is extremely powerful; it has developed to the extent when it can be included as part of engineering. With the aid of solutions of the Schrödinger wave equation, the probabilities of events happening can be calculated with precision. These are expressed as the square of 'probability amplitudes', which are represented by means of the bra–ket notation:

<electron arrives at *y* |electron leaves *x*>

or $<y|x>$. Within the limits of uncertainty determined by the Heisenberg Principle, and within the limits imposed by sheer mathematical difficulty, the most probable behaviour of a system can be calculated. One can extend the calculation to that of the probability amplitude of the electron leaving *x* for *y*, and leaving *y* for *x* (two slits one after the other); this would be represented as the product $<x|y> <y|x>$.

Now consider again the question of which of two interference slits a single electron passes through. Since the electron has the properties of a particle, the question is not meaningless; but quantum theory gives no answer, unless there is some method of detecting the passage of the electron. For example, a photon might be arranged to pass behind one of the slits; when it is scattered by the passing electron, detection of the electron is possible. But this introduces an *observer* or *apparatus* into the system, and the probability $|A>$ of the apparatus being in a certain state *A* must be taken into account, as well as the probability $|s>$ of the system being in a state *s*. The combined probability is

$$|s, A> = |s>|A>$$

The observer is an integral part of the description of the event, and without the observer there can be no description and no complete understanding of reality.

A similar difficulty about unpredictability is encountered in the phenomenon of radioactive decay. Most people will be familiar with the behaviour of a 'radioactive source', which is a sample consisting of a species of radioactive atom. When these atoms decay, each one emits (often by a tunnelling process) a highly penetrating particle, which is a form of nuclear radiation. These particles can be detected by a suitable type of detector such as the Geiger counter used in the Uri Geller experiment of chapter 15. The average time taken for a radioactive atom to decay can be measured if sufficient atoms are available. But the exact moment of decay of an individual atom can in no way be predicted by quantum theory. The moments at which the Geiger counter clicks are random within the bounds set by a probability distribution. The quantum mechanical description of the system is a linear combination of the wave functions not only of the undecayed atom but also of the decayed atom. The wave function is the mathematical expression of the form of the wave for the system, and it must satisfy the wave equation.

Schrödinger went further than demanding this inclusion of both wave functions; he insisted that the consequential wave functions must also be included.

He illustrated this requirement with a dramatic example of a cat enclosed in a chamber with a sealed flask of cyanide poison, which can be broken by a hammer which is released by a relay activated only by the radiation pulses from a radioactive source. This source is very weak, so that there is a chance that there will be a pulse within the natural lifetime of the cat, and a chance that there will be none. Since the cat is provided with adequate food, drink and air, the question of whether the cat will live out its natural life or be prematurely poisoned by cyanide vapour cannot be answered with any certainty; only the probability could be calculated. Schrödinger insisted that a complete description of the system must include both the wave function of the living cat and that of the dead cat.

Since no physical condition exists to determine causally the state of a particular system at the moment of measurement, it follows that until a measurement is carried out, a system is properly described by what is known as a state vector, which is the linear combination of all possible states of the system. Only after a measurement is performed can we affirm with confidence that the system, let us say an atom, is in a certain state. Before the measurement, the atom is collectively in all the states.

The problem of the quantum theory of measurement was formulated mathematically by von Neumann[75] and the short account given by de Witt[76] will be repeated here. The world is considered to be composed of two dynamical variables, a system s and an apparatus A. A combined state vector is expanded in terms of an orthonormal set of basis vectors:

$$|s, A> = |s>|A>$$

where s is an eigenvalue of some system observable and A is an eigenvalue of some apparatus observable. The state of the world at an initial moment is represented by:

$$|\Psi_0> = |\psi>|\Phi>,$$

which is a combined state vector with $|\psi>$ referring to the system and $|\Phi>$ to the apparatus. The learning of the apparatus about the system requires a coupling between the two; the result of this is described by a unitary operator U:

$$|\Psi> = U|\Phi_0>$$

U acts as follows:

$$U|s, A> = |s, A + gs> = |s>|A + gs>$$

where g is an adjustable coupling constant, which is said to result in an observation, the information from which is stored in the apparatus memory by virtue of its irreversible change from $|A>$ to $|A + gs>$. Using the orthonormality and assumed completeness of the basis vectors, the initial state vector is found to become:

$$|\Psi_1> = \sum_s c_s |s>|\Phi[s]>$$

where

$$c_s = <s|\psi>$$
$$|\Phi[s]> = \int |A + gs> \Phi(A)dA$$
$$\Phi(A) = <A|\Phi>$$

This final state vector is a linear superposition of vectors $|s>|\Phi[s]>$, each of which represents a possible value assumed by the system observable, the value which has been observed by the apparatus. The observation is capable of distinguishing adjacent values of s (spaced by Δs) provided that $A \ll g\Delta s$ where ΔA is the variance in A about its mean value relative to the distribution function $|\Phi(A)|^2$. Under these conditions,

$$<\Phi[s]|\Phi[s']> = \delta_{s,s'}$$

where δ is the Dirac delta function. The wave function of the apparatus is initially single, but splits into a great number of mutually orthogonal packets, one for each value of s (i.e. s, s', s'' etc).

The apparatus cannot decide which is the correct value of the system observable, and would have to be supplemented by a second apparatus to observe the first one; but the second one also cannot decide, and so must be supplemented by a third; and so on. This 'catastrophe of infinite regression' requires resolution by a fresh approach, otherwise the whole quantum theory of measurement remains inadequate. One cannot make predictions about the whole universe, because the universe must contain all the observers. This infinite regression has an affinity with Russell's paradox and with Gödel's theorem in mathematics.

To recapitulate; in the absence of any observation, matter is in continual fluctuation. When an observation is made, a single value of the energy is observed, and the physical observables instantaneously take on certain single values. Until the observation is made, at a time which is determined by a mental decision of the observer, no certainty about the physical reality is possible. To a second observer this system of 'wave function and first observer' appears to be in continual fluctuation, even when the first observer makes his observation. The second observer believes that the first observer is in continual fluctuation, and is split into many copies of himself, even though he is making an observation. But he must again become singular when the second observer performs.

The conventional escape from infinite regression is that proposed by the Copenhagen school,[77] which states that as soon as the state vector attains the form of the equation above it collapses into a single wave packet, so that the vector $|\Psi>$ is reduced to an element $|s>|\Phi[s]>$ of the superposition. We cannot predict which element will be formed, but there is a probability distribution of possible outcomes. This assumption is not a corollary of the Schrödinger equation, and it leaves the world in an essentially unpredictable state.

A different proposal was made by David Bohm[78] with his introduction into quantum theory of 'hidden variables', which determine the indeterminable quantities but at the same time conform to the probability distribution. For many years the search for these hidden variables has continued, but up to the present none has been found. We are now coming increasingly to believe that the mind is the only remaining undiscovered hidden variable.

A proposal was in fact made by the theoretical physicist, Eugene Wigner,[79] that the infinite regression could be arrested by the intervention of mind. This was almost the first appearance of mind in modern physics; it was accompanied by a mathematical description of the conversion from a pure to a mixed state arising from possible non-linear departures from the Schrödinger equation when consciousness intervenes. Wigner also proposed that an experimental search be made for unusual effects of consciousness acting on matter. It is my own conviction that the clue to paranormal phenomena lies embedded in quantum theory.

An important formulation was made nearly twenty years ago by Everett, Wheeler and Graham.[80] They attempted to deny the collapse of the state vector, and take the full mathematical formalism of quantum mechanics as it was originally presented. The world could be represented by a vector in Hilbert space, a set of dynamical equations for a set of operators that act on the Hilbert space, and a set of commutation relations for the operators; always provided that it were possible to decompose the world into systems and apparatus. Hilbert space is the complex analogue of Euclidean space, namely a space in which a system of orthogonal straight line coordinates is possible. Complex vectors $\epsilon_{(i)}$ satisfying orthogonality relations $(\epsilon_{(i)}, \epsilon_{(k)}) = \delta_{ik}$ are employed. Every vector ψ is a linear function of the unit vectors:

$$\psi = \sum_k \psi_k \epsilon_{(k)}$$

and

$$\psi_k = (\psi, \epsilon_{(k)})$$

This proposal forces us to believe in the reality of all the simultaneous universes represented in the superposition described by the above equations. These universes cannot communicate physically with each other, because the vectors are mutually orthogonal. In three-dimensional space it would be possible to have only three mutually orthogonal sets of vectors, but in a many-dimensional Hilbert space many such vectors could simultaneously exist, so that there is here the basis for simultaneously existing universes which cannot communicate physically with each other. Simultaneous universes have always been a subject which has fired the highest flights of human imagination. One has only to think of Milton, Dante, or in recent times of Jean Cocteau's *Orphée*.

It is not the existence of many simultaneous universes that is the most difficult concept to believe, but the continual splitting of one universe into an infinite (or very large) number each time an observed quantum transition occurs. We can hardly conceive of how many simultaneous universes there must be if this can really happen. For this reason Schrödinger refused to accept the consequences of the fully formal quantum mechanics.

I will repeat the proposal in the words of de Witt:[81]

> The universe is constantly splitting into a stupendous number of branches, all resulting from the measurement-like interactions between its myriads of components. Moreover, every quantum transition taking place on every star, in every galaxy, in every remote corner of the universe is splitting our local world on earth into myriads of copies of itself.

What is really uncomfortable about this formulation is the invasion of our privacy. We do not like the idea of countless ($>10^{100}$) doppelgängers of ourselves, increasing in number all the time, even if they can never communicate physically. Perhaps they could communicate telepathically. But at least a proof can be given, in quantum mechanical terms, of the fact that we cannot feel the splits in physical terms.

Some comfort can be taken from the experience of physics, that it is only in microscopic, atomic, terms that quantum theory gives different results from classical mechanics. In the limit of large numbers of energy quanta within one system — that is in the limit of large quantum numbers — there is correspondence between quantum and classical mechanics. In classical, macroscopic, surroundings the universes all look the same, and this is surely less uncomfortable. Nevertheless there are quantum-determined events, such as the mysterious death of Schrödinger's cat in the chamber, which differ from one universe to another.

If macroscopic objects were able to make quantum transitions, then the situation would be very much more precarious. There is a whole field of physics in which macroscopic quantum effects occur — namely the physics of very low temperatures, close to absolute zero, where superfluids and superconductors exhibit their extraordinary properties. Theorists who have worked in that field, such as Fröhlich,[82] are alive to the possibility that quantum theory may apply macroscopically even at room temperature. If we can describe a macroscopic object by a single mathematical expression, a wave function, when its temperature is close to absolute zero, then for very short periods of time macroscopic wave functions might have significance at higher temperatures, where the movements of the atoms obscure the regularity of the system.

David Bohm and his colleagues[83] have proposed that there is a characteristic time $t \simeq h/kT$ for which a macroscopic wave function has reality. Here h is the Planck constant, k the Boltzmann constant, and T the temperature. This time will be appreciable at very low temperatures, but very short, 2×10^{-13} sec, at room temperature. Only certain types of atomic and nuclear transition can take place in such a short time, but the remote possibility of macroscopic quantum phenomena in solids at room temperature remains. Normally within a solid object the localized wave functions may not be considered as assembling coherently into a single macroscopic wave function; but local coherence domains might develop, the boundaries changing with time and with the characteristic time t determining the rate of the process. This concept has as yet no experimental basis in solid state physics, but it opens up many possibilities. What is proposed is a continual fission–fusion process; the fission of macroscopic wave functions into microscopic ones, and their subsequent fusion into other macroscopic ones. But it is not clear that the temperature T is the thermodynamic temperature.

What has prompted such interest in macroscopic wave functions has been the realization by many physicists of the non-locality of quantum theory, of both photons and particles possessing rest-mass. The Einstein–Rosen–Podolsky paradox is at last coming to receive the attention due to it. The situation envisaged, and now confirmed experimentally, is that in the dissociation of a two-particle system into single particles, with the latter travelling in space, the relative polarizations of the particles become determined and related only at the instant of measurement at two remote locations. This instant can be made sufficiently short for no communication between the two particles by (virtual) photons to be possible; therefore the quantum description of the situation is non-local over the space of the experiment.

The extreme position which it would be possible to adopt is that of considering the whole universe to be described by one single wave function; there would be myriads of stationary states, and until an observation was made, the universe could be written as a linear combination of all of them. This is equivalent to the statement that the universe contains only a single electron, and it provides some justification for the experimentally observed constancy of electronic charge and rest-mass.

In Copenhagen quantum theory, using the wave equation, we can predict the passage of a system of unique energy E_0 into a mixture of states, each with its own unique energy $E_{a,b,c}$, but each possessing a certain calculable probability of being the state to which the first state has been changed; at any instant the energy is equal to $E_0 = aE_b + bE_b + \ldots$ But at the instant of observation a discontinuous change occurs in the system by which it collapses from a mixture of states into one state only.

But in the many-universe formulation, the wave function does not collapse at the moment of an atomic transition; rather, it splits into an infinite number of wave functions, each in its own set of Hilbert space co-ordinates, and each differing from the others in its energy, E_a, E_b, etc. The observer, in his particular universe, is capable of measuring this energy, but another observer, in a different but physically incommunicable universe, would measure a different energy. Since it is purely a matter of chance which universe the observer is in, the particular result he obtains appears to him random. But if he repeats a similar observation a sufficient number of times, then his result is predictable by the wave-equation (from which the forementioned a, b, c, etc. are derived), because all sets of co-ordinates are equally probable. The collapse of the state vector is avoided by postulating that within a single universe only the initial and final states are real, the mixture having no reality unless an infinity of universes is taken into account.

The proposal inherent in the many-universe theory, that each atomic transition in our own insignificant bodies causes the remotest galaxies to split into an infinite number, has resulted in the theory having only a very limited acceptance among physicists. Perhaps it would be more satisfactory if bounds were placed upon the local universes. But such bounds would introduce physical effects akin to surface phenomena, and normal effects of this type are as yet unknown to physics. The original Everett–Wheeler–Graham theory assumed that there was one observer in one universe, the same universe which contains the observed phenomenon.

But if we were to allow ourselves the luxury of a dualistic system, with non-material, or at least trans-spatial minds, then there would be power-ful possibilities for the interpretation of physical psychic phenomena.

For example, we might speculate that the unconscious mind possesses the facility of receiving 'trans-spatial' information from the correspond-ing minds in other 'universes'. Since, because of the orthogonality, physical signals cannot pass from one universe to another, we would be forced to assume that the unconscious mind has trans-spatial properties and is able to communicate with physical reality in other universes only through other unconscious minds.

On the parallel universe model, millions of copies of each individual have parallel existences, but are entirely isolated physically from each other by the orthogonality, which prevents the passage of physical signals between universes. Let us propose that each one of these indi-viduals possesses his own mind, and that communication between these corresponding minds is sometimes possible. No individual knows of the existence of his many *alter egos*. But if he were able to adopt the mind of one of these *alter egos*, he would then take the other universe to be his reality, without knowing that any change had occurred. Moreover, at the moment he successfully does this, one might suppose that his neighbours' minds (the observers' minds) could also come to be domi-nated by those of their own *alter egos*, so that they would also take the other universe to be their reality. All observers could now notice what-ever physical differences there might be between the two universes. The differences could be that psychic phenomena, metal-bending, psycho-kinesis or teleportations have taken place.

This principle could be extended in complication in two ways. First, there is no reason to limit the number of universes to two only, one before the mental change and one after. The only situation in which we know the universe to be singular (locally) is at the moment at which datum of an atomic physics experiment is recorded. This is a comparatively rare moment, so why should we not propose that we all pass through life in a continual state of subtending many universes at the same moment of time? Since these universes are in nearly all respects identical, we have hitherto imagined them to be a single universe. Sometimes a unique universe forces us to notice it, and it is then that we say that an atomic physical phenomenon has occurred.

Second, it might be that some of the universes are partially incomplete in the sense that the mind only knows of their existence locally; the mind might actually impose spatial boundaries on some or all of its local universes. These boundaries could be the 'surfaces of action' at which we have observed metal-bending action to take place. Outside the boundaries, that universe would not exist. If the boundary were made to move through space by the action of the psychic's unconscious mind, with which the observers' minds concur, then one universe will actually grow, contract or change shape; and the surface effects continually resulting from such changes would make up the metal-bending structural and quasi-force action. The change of shape is not noticed in other ways, because so many universes are superposed that no mind regards any one of them as incomplete. If the observers' minds do not concur, then no physical changes can be measured, and the event is hallucinatory. The fusion and fission of wave functions[83] into macroscopic size would also be necessary to this interpretation of physical psychic phenomena.

I include these speculations in order to show the extent to which it would be necessary to go in order to explain physical psychic phenomena with the aid of quantum physics.[84] I have in fact carried the speculations a good deal further, but I will not indulge myself at this stage, other than in a summary:

1 Teleportations could be interpreted using the hyperdimensional character of the many-universes model. It may be that such hyperdimensionality is strongly indicated by the discovery in the 1960s of the non-conservation of parity.

2 Metal-bending and structural change could be interpreted in terms of the reorganization forces which must occur in the creation or annihilation of atoms at the inter-universe boundaries or 'surfaces of action'. The configurations of these surfaces would have to be very complicated, showing turbulence perhaps down to atomic dimensions.

3 Quasi-forces would have to be interpreted in terms of a rapid series of local transformations into universes, each one with its own individual momentum, each slightly greater than the last. The rate of

change of momentum would then have the appearance of a force acting on the transformed object.

4 For psychic acoustic phenomena,[85] psychometry, optical and electromagnetic phenomena and even the insensitivity of the human body to great heat, similar interpretations could be considered.

But if we allow ourselves the luxury of such speculations, then we must be prepared to accept the nightmare universes that could have evolved in continually increasing numbers since the 'big bang'. Precisely how many degrees of orthogonality different from our own these would have to be is difficult even to conjecture.

Since most people (including, probably, the proponents of the original many-universe quantum theory) would stop short of this, they find themselves drawn inevitably to the denial that physical psychic phenomena exist at all. That is why the spearhead of research must be not in theoretical formulations but in physical observations. My purpose in including this chapter has been to show just how difficult it is for a physicist to incorporate physical psychic phenomena within existing physical theory. Once the difficulties are faced, however, a wide variety of alternative hypotheses about the nature of what we have called 'primary events' can readily be envisaged.

Chapter **26**

Some general questions of philosophical interest

We should perhaps address ourselves to the question of how far it is possible to contribute to the problems of philosophy by making observations of psychic phenomena. It is a question without unique answer. Physics is still officially termed 'Natural Philosophy' in some older universities, and there are those who hold that there is no philosophy other than that which derives from physics, mathematical logic and language.

Some prefer the idea that there are two contrasting ways of learning about reality: the intuitive or mystical, and the logical; the latter is an appropriate blend of logic or mathematics with observations and scientific method. The two methods are applied together more frequently than is often supposed.

Within the scientific method, it became fashionable early in this century to make everything subservient to physics. The rest of science was 'mere stamp-collecting'. Not only is our experience in the second half of the century complementary to this view, but also there is a formal mathematical argument which casts doubt upon whether mechanical materialism is actually valid. The argument has arisen from what is known as indicate calculus, a branch of mathematics formulated by Gödel.[86] His theorem states: 'A proposition which includes in its substance a statement of the truth of that class of propositions of which this one is itself a member cannot be shown (proved) to be true.' It follows that there are levels of complication in structure at which entirely new laws and modes of behaviour come into being, laws which are unprovable by the mere extension in complication of the laws of physics themselves. Thus the science of psychology, and even parts of biomolecular science, are based on concepts which are not provable by physics, although in the working out of these concepts there must be no contradiction of physical laws.

In the dualistic approach which we favour, a mind is capable of operating according to its own laws, without these being determined mechanically by the laws of physics. Only the interface must conform to physical laws, and it is this interface which we are investigating in parapsychology and psychic research.

Possibly the most interesting question that is posed by the whole phenomenon of psychokinesis is the relationship between mental time and physical time (real time, local time, etc.). Psychokinetic action is, in part, goal-oriented and observational. On the first occasion the action occurred, perhaps, by chance. The psychic then learned to expect the same result, provided that it was displayed visually, or at least reached his senses in some way, when his consciousness was in a certain state. In a pointer-movement experiment, for example, the psychic does not know which direction the first movement of the pointer will take. Once a movement has taken place, in either direction, he is able to influence the ballistic swing, and reverse its motion, eventually more or less at will. Only the first movement remains something of a lottery, and Dr Krmessky claims that very small oscillations precede it.

Goal-orientation is also important in the electronic psychokinetic experiments pioneered by Helmut Schmidt.[42] The subject is asked to influence an electronic random number generator whose output is displayed as a suitable pattern of lights which he can see. Success is strongly linked to goal-orientation, although the components are subject to influence at the structural or even at the nuclear level. Perhaps the psychic perceives the particular universe in which the lights have taken on a certain pattern, and transports the minds of the observers thither. But at a detailed level he is bringing about structural changes in an atomic nucleus, a Zener diode, or similar component; such detailed effects have been demonstrated and discussed in chapter 16.

One feature that emerges is that the goal is in the future, but the moment of willing the action is in the present. Often the time difference is very small, but the fact that it is there at all raises an important difficulty. Consider the influencing of an electronic device connected to a display which is viewed by the subject. A finite time is taken for the display light signal to reach the subject, and for it to reach his brain and mind. The moment of cognizance of the achievement of the goal is after the moment of will of the action. Goal-orientation on a parallel universe model and indeed on other models implies precognition, and this could imply some modification to physical theory such as the advanced waves of Costa de Beauregard.[87] Precognition is far from unknown as a psychic phenomenon, and on the observational model of psychokinesis it must be invoked in this context.

The model for psychokinesis discussed in the last chapter is based on a particular view of the mind–matter relationship -- the ability of mind to transcend the many-co-ordinate system of Hilbert space which is required for the formulation of the behaviour of material phenomena. Perhaps such a model could also be applied to the mind–brain relationship. If we admit the trans-spatial and trans-temporal character of mind, then its interaction with material brain presents problems; the clues to their solution could lie in the quantum theory of measurement. The proposal has been made[88] that the mind–brain interaction need not be dissimilar to the model proposed for psychokinesis.

Philosophy is concerned not only with questions of reality but also with questions of absolute value in motivation, that is, with ethical problems. The relevance of psychic phenomena is more indirect here. The value of human motivations can be judged only from a standpoint of substantial knowledge about these motivations. Therefore the achievement of such knowledge is the minimum necessary motivation. This knowledge includes a knowledge of the complete human potential, of which psychic ability is surely a part. Therefore the motivation to experiment upon psychokinesis is good. I mention what might appear to be obvious simply because numbers of people attack this sort of research on the grounds that it is immoral, forbidden, or unscientific.

It is important to look with foresight on any social dangers that might come upon us as a result of our new-found knowledge of metal-bending, primitive as it is. Dangers might arise from a lack of control of the phenomenon. It is often maintained, but we do not yet know whether it is true, that there is a built-in safety-catch on psychokinetic phenomena, ensuring that we cannot bring about anything which will hurt ourselves or our friends. Such a concept, for which I have found no experimental evidence, is surely related to the idea of 'white magic'. But I have come across very few reports of even so much as a skin abrasion by metal-bending in several hundreds of events. Some playful misdemeanours have come to my attention, for example, Graham P.'s bending of his granny's knitting-needles when she was at a critical stage of purl and plain! However, the Japanese metal-bender Masuaki Kiyota is troubled by his 'powers' and affirms that he always takes care not to 'think ill' of people, even when provoked, in case there should be dangerous events.

Nevertheless, anything not understood is uncontrollable, and should be investigated until it is understood. It would be dangerous if the increase in magnitude or frequency of occurrence of metal-bending events were to exceed the speed with which we come to understand them.

An obvious danger is that in the presence of a metal-bender 'spontaneous' faults or artefacts could happen in mechanical or electronic control equipment, thereby causing accidents. But if electronic equipment can be affected, and there is a case for taking such a claim seriously, then why do not the television sets of the metal-bending families break down when the children dislike the programmes? We just do not know enough to say, and on environmental grounds alone the sooner we get sufficient knowledge the better.

A programme of screening large numbers of the adult English population has already been started by Julian Isaacs. Of course only the weakest effects on a strain gauge sensor are searched for or found. Sometimes members of an audience at a lecture queue for a 2-minute individual session; sometimes customers take their turn at a booth in an exhibition. No one seriously suspects that he is personally responsible for paranormal dynamic strain gauge effects, and at this stage it is indeed not possible to be certain that it is the one person being screened who is responsible for the effects observed. Nevertheless nearly a thousand people have had their sessions and the data show that perhaps one or two people in a hundred may be producing very weak effects.

We can expect metal-benders to produce paranormal effects on the running of delicate machinery. Most metal-benders cannot wear watches; the continual breakdowns are usually attributed to banging or to chemical action; but in my opinion paranormal action is just as likely. There could be trouble from metal-benders in instrument workshops where the engineering demands very high tolerances. As to other areas where 'psychokinetic noise' could be detectable, the medical area is obviously the most serious; the borderline between psychic and psychosomatic effects is unclear, and indeed may not exist at all.

The usual reaction of scientifically educated people to psychic healing phenomena is one of great caution. No one doubts the common occurrence of psychologically-induced illness, and it also seems that hypnotically-induced anaesthesia, and even hypnotically-induced wounding and healing, are well established.

The so-called 'spirit healing' or 'faith healing' is widely practised, but is perhaps less universally accepted, largely because it is difficult although not impossible[89] to assess its value accurately. Temporary relief and sometimes permanent cure of arthritis and similar conditions are claimed to have been produced by many healers on their friends and others. In Britain this activity is legal, although in many countries it is not. Some hospital nurses are supposed to possess the ability, and medical tests have been made in United States hospitals on quite a large scale. The question of whether the activity might be described as 'paranormal action on molecular structure' or as 'entering parallel universes' has been raised but not answered.

The more extreme techniques of 'psychic surgery' are not at all well understood and are largely rejected by medical scientists. The connections between the Filipino, Brazilian and Mexican psychic surgery and psychic phenomena seem to be close. Genuine Filipino psychic surgeons (some of the more prominent are Tony Agpaoa, Alex Orbito, Josephine Sison and David Elizalde)[90] perform their 'operations' with their bare hands, passing them over the skin and flesh of the patient, who feels very little. There is sometimes what might be termed an 'entering' of the body, without any surgical cut being made. The hands feel 'inside'; there is blood and even flesh to be seen; often, something is removed. Since there is no cut, no healing is necessary; after he has been wiped up, the patient is allowed to get up and walk away. Sometimes, perhaps often, there is some cure.

All manner of things have been 'taken out': tissue, but not always human tissue; sometimes sheep tissue, although the nearest sheep to the Philippines are in Australia. Sometimes the things which are taken out are not animal tissue but pieces of paper, metal, wood, etc. Naturally, conjurors have learned to imitate these curious happenings; I have as yet had no personal opportunity to make first-hand assessments.

Similar curious items appeared in the psychic surgery of the late José Arigo of Brazil; the difference was that he used a knife – not a surgeon's knife but any handy sharp instrument, such as a penknife borrowed from a spectator; there was no attempt to obtain aseptic conditions, and Arigo felt compelled to act in the way he did, being in something of a trance. The operations were little more than crude, rapid probes of the affected organs (especially the eyes) and often some real flesh was cut out. When Dr Andrija Puharich was with Arigo, the psychic surgeon thrust a knife into Puharich's hand and pointed to where he was to cut. But Puharich claims that when he cut he did not feel the flesh under the knife; rather, the flesh appeared to part while the air resisted the knife.

The best-authenticated feature of psychic surgery appears to be the 'psychic injection', by which the surgeon can cause a local pricking pain in the patient merely by pointing his finger at, or sometimes lightly stroking, the area of skin to be injected. I have suffered this being carried out on myself, and several investigators have found that one or more thicknesses of mylar or other plastic sheet are punctured by the psychic injection; sometimes blood is drawn.

We are now familiar with such phenomena as 'apports' and tele-portations. We are not so familiar with paranormal 'entering' of the body, but some years ago two of the metal-bending children reported being able to 'feel inside' the neck and limbs of their bodies; so far as I know, these two children had not heard of psychic surgery, although it is impossible to be certain. Might it be that there are several 'parallel universes' involved, and that a surface of action covers the psychic's fingers, and moves inside the patient's body? The 'apports' are in the nature of symbols of success; the role they play would seem to be psychological — to give confidence to both the healer and patient that psychic events are taking place. The patient is taken mentally into a new universe, one in which he has become healed.

Probably such speculations about healing do not represent a real advance in our knowledge, but they contain a seed by the cultivation of which medicine could extend its branches.

There is one question which all the physical experimentation we have described has not answered, and indeed to which no amount of physical experimentation could obtain a certain answer. That is whether there is for each metal-bender a separate mental entity, apart from the unconscious mind of the metal-bender himself, but able to play a part in the metal-bending. Let us, if only for the purposes of discussion, call such an entity a 'spirit'. Do such spirits exist, and are metal-benders in touch, mentally, with them?

Our starting-point for answering such a question is to ask the metal-bender himself. But this must be done in such a way that there is no suspicion that we are putting such an idea into his head. I never ask such a question outright, but I do, by asking related questions, encourage such statements to be made.

Most child metal-benders mentioned in these chapters have no belief in any spirit controlling or advising them. Some reject the idea strongly. But some of the powerful psychics and metal-benders have such beliefs, and surely we must pay attention to them. Sometimes these beliefs are engendered by the 'external' nature of the physical pheno-mena themselves. For example, Andrija Puharich relates that he hyp-notized Uri Geller and was astonished to hear and tape-record a powerful voice giving dramatic precognitive information. Geller's reaction to hearing the tapes after return from hypnosis was to believe that the voice came from outside himself. But an alternative interpretation is that

Geller was paranormally 'producing' the effect. If one cannot decide between the two interpretations, then the distinction is an unreal one.

The Mexican psychic surgeon Pachita believed that she was guided throughout her work by a spirit with an Indian-sounding name. Masuaki Kiyota believes that he is in touch with a spirit too advanced in its nature to have a name; but for the purposes of communication it is known as 'Zenofu'.

I take the view that the question of reality of discarnate entities is meaningless, because it is a subjective question, incapable of physical proof or logical answer, and therefore in the philosophical sense not a question at all. How can one determine by experiment whether independent spirits are real but non-physical, or whether they are simply a mode of behaviour of the human mind, both conscious and unconscious? The spirits have a subjective existence, and sometimes the breadth of this subjectivity increases, covering dozens, hundreds or even millions of subjects. But there remain other subjects who regard the spirits simply as modes of behaviour. It would seem appropriate to conceive of a term 'partial existence' to cover this state of affairs. Spirits have partial existence. It is possible that the depth of human understanding will so increase that all will treat these matters with the seriousness they deserve; and then it might be more appropriate to speak of 'quasi-existence'. *'Quasi'*, the Latin 'as if', well reflects the situation that it is necessary to treat spirits 'as if' they existed, while at the same time recognizing the objectively true state of affairs. Psychic subjects are seriously affected if they are told that their spirit does not exist; for them this is an obvious untruth, irreconcilable with their own experience. In the last analysis, we can believe only in the existence of what we experience. Which of us can ourselves claim more than a partial or quasi-existence on this basis? How are we to prove to an intelligent creature of, let us say, a quite different size or environment, that we exist? I can well imagine the arguments in progress amongst the possible denizens of UFOs about whether those soft, spindly creatures walking about on the surface of the planet, and glimpsed only for brief moments, are in fact real, or just products of the humanologist's imagination. (I should explain that a 'humanologist' is their equivalent of Ufologist.)

Elsewhere I have drawn attention to the interesting experiments of the Canadian researchers[91] who invented a ghost, whom they called 'Philip', and then succeeded in obtaining paranormal physical phenomena only by invoking the reactions of the all-too-human Philip. An earlier example of fictitious communication experimentation was conducted by investigator P. Stanley Hall,[92] using the medium Mrs Piper, whom he succeeded in making receive spoken communications from a fictitious relative named 'Bessie Beals'.

But this achievement does not prove objectively that other paranormal physical phenomena are entirely the product of human ingenuity, any more than Uri Geller's claim that metal-bending is produced by God is an objective proof of His existence.

Many scientists are far too cautious to have any time for such things. Perhaps the origin of their attitude lies in the social antagonism between the religious, mystic and occult establishments on the one hand, and the new technological establishment on the other. The interests of these groups have always been socially opposed, and traditionally it has been science which replaced magic. Some physical phenomena have remained within the sphere of the mystic and have therefore been rejected by those scientists who, like most of us, are prisoners of their social background. We recall that one of the pillars of nineteenth-century science, the physicist Helmholtz, wrote: 'Neither the testimony of all the Fellows of the Royal Society, nor even the evidence of my own senses, would lead me to believe in the transmission of thought from one person to another independently of the recognized channels of sense.' Today there are many scientists who feel the same, but lack the opportunity or the wish to say so in print.

Since the writings of Bernal[93] and, later, those of Thomas Kuhn,[94] there is an increasing realization that scientific advance does not proceed at an even pace, without impact of social and human forces; these forces play a large part in determining what is accepted and what is rejected at any time. So true is this about our state of knowledge of the nature of psychic and metal-bending phenomena that already science sociologists regard this as a fruitful field of study; they are constantly on our tails!

There is a lot to be said for the argument that, on balance, the success that the mystics have had in capturing the minds of many young people has been harmful to human society; however, it may often have been beneficial to the individuals. On the whole, humanists have much to gain by the advance of psychic and metal-bending research. It might even be claimed that the unification of our system of space is essentially a progressive activity. In science it is necessary to pursue false trails in order that the true trail may be found.

Pseudo-science is certainly not a healthy influence in society; I can claim that although what I have been doing may turn out to be incorrect science, at least it is not pseudo-science. Some physicists claim to have a consistent view of material reality, but if of a religious turn of mind, they close their minds to the questions of the physical reality of miracles; thus they admit the incompleteness of their outlook. But perhaps miracles are not only physically real but understandable within the terms of future physics.

The object of scientific research is in great part to control the material universe. If we take the view that psychic phenomena can never be brought under control, even in very small part, then there is little point in researching on them. Further, what can never be brought under control could be dangerous and therefore should be eliminated (although this is itself a form of control). This line of unconscious reasoning is more common than most people realize; and indeed, it has internal consistency. However, not only is elimination more difficult than control, but also the phenomena are already under some sort of slender control – perhaps the same degree as exists on the future of some of our endangered species of wild life. Metal-bending is itself an endangered talent, at risk of dying out in the world. The supply of new metal-benders is not keeping abreast of the weakening of powers of the old ones. How long will the metal-bending phenomenon remain alive? This is a question rather like those which I posed on the first page of chapter 1; in my final chapter it should not remain entirely unanswered. I can at least make one important point, namely that metal-bending requires, above all, confidence, and if this confidence can be maintained and increased, metal-bending will also be maintained and increased, and thereby controlled and developed.

This is why I have somewhat changed my attitude to the public image of metal-bending. I believe that it is necessary that the reality and detail of the phenomena be given publicity, since only in this way will an atmosphere of confidence be engendered. Of course we do not yet know precisely what the reality and the detail are, but we must work within our limitations. The ridicule of sceptics induces uncertainty and could ultimately bring about the demise of metal-bending. In the event of this happening, let us at least remember that it was once a reality.

Of course the control of such spontaneous phenomena, for public entertainment, is not yet possible for most metal-benders. The television 'performances' have a fairly low success rate. But metal-benders have a duty to practise and develop their powers, and eventually public demonstrations might become a simple matter. The difficulties of professionalism have to be encountered, but these could possibly turn out to be less serious than has been the case with mediumship.

Perhaps the best way to encourage reliable and controlled success is by treating metal-bending as a competitive game. All sorts of possibilities await the arrival of fertile minds. Through this channel the world of education might be reached. Whatever else may be said of educationists, they cannot in general be accused of closing their minds against new ideas. The key to planning the extension of psychic activity is to keep the goal always in mind: to develop a new human faculty; an extension of the stature of man. There must arise organizations dedicated to the development of the faculty; always on a scientific basis, but always hand in hand with imaginative and creative approach and with a faith to extend the abilities of mankind.

Above all, let the faculty be developed by and for the community at large, and not for some section – for a nation, for a class, for a religious or social group. Let the research be not secret, military, or narrowly competitive, but public, co-operative and subject to scrutiny. Let the scientists live up to the responsibility for their findings that all too often they have evaded.

Valedictory verses

Now, Reader, that our tale is told,
Canst thou the riddle guess?
Such things, in simpler days of old,
Were heard with faithfulness.

But we, it seems, are wiser grown;
Less willing to believe;
And till we see their causes shown
Can scarce effects receive.

But if these pages serve to show
A truth their moral brings:
How much imperfectly we know
Even in trivial things.

If you our sense of wonder call
From where it's idle lain,
Why then, good metal-benders all,
You'll not have bent in vain!

References

1   *Bealings Bells*, Major Edward Moor, FRS, John Lader, Woodbridge, 1841.

2   C.P. Snow, *The Search*, Penguin Books, 1965; *The Affair*, Penguin Books, 1962.

3   H.M. Collins and T.J. Pinch, in *On the Margins of Science*, ed. Roy Wallis, Keele University Press, 1979; see also *Nature*, 1976.

4   J.B. Hasted, communication to be published by Francis Hitching.

5   J.B. Hasted, D.J. Bohm, E.W. Bastin and B. O'Regan, *Nature*, **254**, 1975, 470.

6   Uri Geller, *My Story*, Praeger, New York, 1975.

7   J.A. Taylor, *Superminds*, Macmillan, 1975.

8   James Randi, WMCA radio performance, USA, 16 May 1975.

9   Sir Thomas Malory, *Le Morte d'Arthur*, Dent, Everyman's Library, 1906, vol. 2, p. 263.

10   M.H. Coleman, *J. Soc. Psych. Res.*, **49**, 1977, 622.

11   Cotta, *Triall of Witch-craft*, 1616, p. 76.

12   P.G. Quevedo, quoting *Vanidas Continental*, 15 November 1971, p. 80.

13   D.S. Rogo, *J. Parapsychology*, **40**, 1976, 314.

14   A. Jaffé, 'C.G. Jung and parapsychology', in *Science and ESP*, ed. J.R. Smythies, Routledge & Kegan Paul, 1967, p. 264.

15   R. Targ and H.E. Puthoff, *Mind-Reach*, Delacorte, New York, 1977.

16   J.B. Hasted, *J. Soc. Psych. Res.*, **48**, 1976, 365.

17   P. Barnes, J.W. Jeffery, O. Bateman, T. Gare and T. Sothern, Birkbeck College, University of London, MSc dissertations and private communications, 1974; B. Wälti, *Zeit. für Parapsychologie*, **20**, 1978, 1.

18   M. Desvaux, Electrical Research Association, Leatherhead, Private communication, 1975.

19   Wilbur Franklin, *New Horizons*, **2** (1), 1975, 9.

20   R. Cantor, *Tomorrow's Children Today* (Human Dimensions Institute, Canandaigna, N.Y.), 6 (3 and 4), 1978.

21   Z.W. Wolkowski, *Research in Parapsychology*, Scarecrow Press, Metuchen, N.J., 1977, p. 207.

22   E.J. Hearn, *Strain Gauges*, Merrow, Newcastle, 1971; G.S. Holister, *Experimental Stress Analysis*, Cambridge University Press, 1967.

23 J.B. Hasted, *J. Soc. Psych. Res.*, **49**, 1977, 583.

24 W.J. Crawford, *The Psychic Structures at the Goligher Circle*, Watkins, London, and Dutton, New York, 1921.

25 R.D. Mattuck and Scott Hill, H.C. Oersted Institute, Copenhagen, private communication, 1979.

26 J.E. Whitley, Scottish Universities Research and Reactor Centre, private communication, 1975.

27 P. Barnes, MSc dissertation, 1974.

28 E. Rauscher, Theoretical Physics Department, University of California, Berkeley, Report, 1977.

29 J. Hanlon, *New Scientist*, 14 July 1977, p. 80.

30 Alan Neuman Productions, Hollywood, NBC television programme, October 1977.

31 J.C. Dierkens, Psychology Department, University of Mons, Belgium, Report on J.-P. Girard, 'Psychophysiological approach to PK states', 1977.

32 C. Crussard and J. Bouvaist, *Mémoires scientifiques Revue Metallurgie*, February 1978, p. 117.

33 G.R. Booker, A.M. Shaw, M.J. Whelan and P.B. Hirsch, *Phil. Mag.*, **16**, 1967, 1185; E.M. Schulson, *Phys. Stat. Sol.* (B), **46**, 1971, 95; P. Guyot and J.N. Gjurasevic, *J. de Microscopie*, **18**, 1973, 1.

34 S.Sasaki, Y. Ochi, K. Maruta and A. Takaoka, *J. PS Inst. of Japan*, **3** (1), 1979, 3.

35 Ronald Hawke, Lawrence Livermore Radiation Laboratory, California, private communication, 1977.

36 G.R. Schmeidler, *J. Am. Soc. Psych. Res.*, **67**, 1973, 325.

37 R. Mattuck, H.C. Oersted Institute, Copenhagen, report at 1977 Parascience Conference, London.

38 R. Tocquet, *Psi International*, **1**, 1977, 20.

39 J.B. Hasted, in *The Geller Papers*, ed. C. Panati, Houghton Mifflin, Boston, 1976.

40 René Sudre, *Treatise on Parapsychology*, Allen & Unwin, 1960, pp. 218–24.

41 K.J. Batcheldor, *J. Soc. Psych. Res.*, **43**, 1966, 339; C. Brookes-Smith and D.W. Hunt, *J. Soc. Psych. Res.*, **45**, 1970, 265; C. Brookes-Smith, *J. Soc. Psych. Res.*, **48**, 1975, 73–86.

42 H. Schmidt, *J. Parapsychology*, **34**, 1970, 219, 175, 255; **36**, 1972, 222; **37**, 1973, 105; **38**, 1974, 47.

43 J. Lambe and R.C. Jaklevic, *Phys. Rev. Letters*, **17**, 1966, 1138.

44 B. Grad, *J. Am. Soc. Psych. Res.*, **59**, 1965, 95; **61**, 1967, 287; *Int. J. Parapsychology*, **3** (2), 1961, 5; **5**, 1963, 117; **6**, 1964, 473.

45 M.J. Smith, 'The influence of enzyme growth by the laying on of hands', in The Dimensions of Healing: a symposium, Academy of Psychology and Medicine, Los Altos, Calif., 1973.

46 J. Barry, *J. Parapsychology*, **32**, 1968, 237.

47 J.B. Hasted, *J. Proc. Soc. Psych. Res.*, in press, 1980.

48 Iris M. Owen and Margaret H. Sparrow, *Philip, the Imaginary Ghost*, Fitzhenry & Whiteside, Toronto, 1976.

49 W.G. Roll, *The Poltergeist*, Scarecrow Press, Metuchen, N.J., 1976; A.R.G. Owen, *Can We Explain the Poltergeist?*, Garrett, New York, 1964; Alan Gauld and A.D. Cornell, *Poltergeists*, Routledge & Kegan Paul, 1979; H.

Bender, 'Modern poltergeist research', in *New Directions in Parapsychology*, ed. J. Beloff, Elek Science, 1974.

50 Sir William Crookes, *Researches into the Phenomena of Spiritualism*, J. Burns, 1875.

51 R. Targ and H.E. Puthoff, Stanford Research Institute, Calif., private commmunication, 1975.

52 Roll, *The Poltergeist*.

53 H.E.R. Gruber, University of Vienna, communication to 1st Congreso Mundial de Parapsicologia, Barcelona, 1977; H. Bender, Institut für Parapsychologie, Freiburg im Breisgau, private communication.

54 Benson Herbert, *J. Paraphysics*, 7, supplement no. 5, 1973, p. 9.

55 A.R.G. Owen, *Psychic Mysteries of Canada*, Fitzhenry & Whiteside, Toronto, 1975.

56 H.G.J. Keil, B. Herbert, M. Ullman and J.G. Pratt, *Proc. Soc. Psych. Res.*, **56**, 1976, 197.

57 H. Forwald, *J. Parapsychology*, **16**, 1952, 59; **18**, 1954, 219; W.E. Cox, *J. Parapsychology*, **15**, 1951, 40; **35**, 1971, 108.

58 S. Sasaki and Y. Ochi, *J. PS Inst. of Japan*, **1** (2), 1976, 8.

59 An interesting account of the Christian hagiography is to be found in *Psi. International*, **4**, 1978, 44, by José Lorenzetto.

60 Mrs D.D. Home, *D.D. Home, his Life and Mission*, Arno Press, New York, 1876; F.W.H. Myers, *Human Personality and its Survival after Bodily Death*, Longmans Green, 1903.

61 H. Bender, private communication.

62 Carlos Castaneda, *The Teachings of Don Juan, A Separate Reality, Journey to Ixtlan, Tales of Power*, Penguin, 1976.

63 F. Grunewald, *Physikalisch-mediumistiche Untersuchen*, Baum, Pfülligen, 1920.

64 Rt Rev. C.W. Leadbetter, *The Chakras*, Theosophical Publishing House, Adyar, Madras, India, 1927.

65 H. Carrington, *J. Amer. Soc. Psych. Res.*, **5**, 1925.

66 J. Eisenbud, *The World of Ted Serios*, William Morrow, New York, 1967.

67 W. and M.J. Uphoff, *New Psychic Frontiers*, Colin Smythe, Gerrards Cross, 1975.

68 S. Sasaki and Y. Ogawa, *J. PS Inst. of Japan*, **2**(2), 1977, 7.

69 Abramowski, *The Subconscious Normal*, Alcan, Paris, 1918.

70 A. Hardy, R. Harvie and A. Koestler, *The Challenge of Chance*, Vintage Books, New York, 1975; M.A. Thalbourne, *J. Soc. Psych. Res.*, **30**, 1979, 84.

71 A.T. Barker, *The Mahatma Letters to A.P. Sinnett*, Rider, [*ca.* 1890].

72 'F.N.H.', *J. Soc. Psych. Res.*, 9, 1899, 6.

73 C.G. Jung, Collected Works, vol. 9 (1), *The Archetypes and the Collective Unconscious*, Routledge & Kegan Paul, 1968.

74 S.W. Hawking, *Ann. N.Y. Acad. Sci.*, 1977; Eighth Texas Symposium on Relativistic Astrophysics, *Phys. Bulletin*, **29** (1), 1978, 23.

75 J. von Neumann, *Mathematical Foundations of Quantum Mechanics*, Princeton University Press, 1955.

76 B.S. de Witt, *Physics Today*, **23** (9), 1970; B. de Witt and N. Graham, eds, *The Many-Worlds Interpretation of Quantum Mechanics*, Princeton University Press, 1973.

77   N. Bohr and L. Rosenfeld, *Kgl. Danske Videnskab Selskab, Mat.-Fys. Medd.*, **12** (8), 1933.

78   D. Bohm, *Phys. Rev.*, **85**, 1952, 166, 180; **87**, 1952, 389; **89**, 1953, 319, 458.

79   E.P. Wigner, 'Remarks on the mind-body question', in *The Scientist Speculates*, ed. I.J. Good, Heinemann, 1961; *Symmetries and Reflections*, Indiana University Press, 1967.

80   H. Everett III, *Rev. Mod. Phys.*, **29**, 1957, 454; J.A. Wheeler, *Rev. Mod. Phys.*, **29**, 1957, 463; R.N. Graham, Ph.D. thesis, University of North Carolina, 1971.

81   B.S. de Witt, *Physics Today*, **23** (9), 1970.

82   H. Fröhlich, 'The connection between macro- and microphysics', *Rivista del Nuovo Cimento*, **3**, 1973, 490.

83   A. Baracca, D.J. Bohm, B.J. Hiley and A.E.G. Stuart, 'On some new notions concerning locality and nonlocality in the quantum theory', *Il Nuovo Cimento*, **28** B (2), 1975, 454.

84   E.H. Walker, *J. Research in Psi Phenomena*, **1** (1), 1976; 38; **1** (2), 1976, 44; *Math. Biosci.*, **7** (131), 1970; *Research in Parapsychology*, Scarecrow Press, 1973, p. 51.

85   J.L. Whitton, *New Horizons*, **2** (2), 1976, 7.

86   K. Gödel, *Dialectica*, **12**, 1958, 280; *Monatshäfte für Mathematik und Physik*, **38**, 1931, 173; *From Frege to Gödel*, trans. J. van Heijenoort, Harvard University Press, 1967.

87   O. Costa de Beauregard, *Foundations of Physics*, **6**, 1976, 539.

88   Sir John Eccles, 'The human person in its two-way relationship to brain', *Research in Parapsychology*, 1977, pp. 251–62.

89   Simonetta Cassoli, M.D. thesis (available from Via L. Valeriani 39, 40134 Bologna, Italy).

90   A. Stelter, *Psi Healing*, Bantam, 1976.

91   Owen and Sparrow, *Philip, the Imaginary Ghost*.

92   Stanley Hall, *Studies in Spiritism*, London, 1909, p. 254.

93   J.D. Bernal, *The Social Function of Science*, London, 1939.

94   T. Kuhn, *The Structure of Scientific Revolutions*, University of Chicago Press, 1970.

Index

abnormal plane bends, 100, 113, 146;
  see also anomalous plane bends
Abrahams, Roy, 5
Abramowski, 260
abstract, *see* sculptures
accidents, 250
acoustic emission, 131
acoustic phenomena, psychic, 246
acoustic recording, 60
Acts of the Apostles, 223
acupuncture points, 75
Adamec, Dr, 154, 191
adhesives, 57, 62, 102
adult subjects, 159
affection, 160
after-images, 205
Agpaoa, Tony, 251
air currents, 195
air-lock, 184
Alabone, Richard, 46
Allegretti, Lucia, 30
alpha band, 122, 158, 160
alpha-brass, 48, 111, 146
alter ego, 244
aluminium, 60
aluminium alloy bars, 19, 114, 121, 130, 180
aluminium alloys, 34, 123
aluminium crystals, 128
aluminium strips, 17, 20, 58, 78, 86, 88–90, 95, 100, 112, 113, 120, 153, 162, 180, 195
ambidextrous, 75
amplifiers, 64
anaesthesia, 250
analogue signals, 50
analysis, gravitational, 8

Andrade's law, 41
animal magnetism, 189
animals, 18, 163; laboratory, 159
annealing, 17, 48, 111, 146, 157
annihilation, 234, 245
anomalous plane bends, 163, 180; *see also* abnormal plane bends
antagonism, 160
anti-matter, 232, 233
apparatus, 237, 238, 239, 240; memory, 239
apparitions, 183
Appiah, K. A., 136
apples, 166, 168
apports, 172, 184, 186, 187, 223, 252
Araldite, 42, 44; AV1523, 44; AV1566, 44
Archimedean spiral, 109
Arigo, José, 251
arm extension, 71, 76, 84
armpit, 73
art exhibitions, 91
artefacts, 59, 66; electromagnetic, 54, 58; electrostatic, 51, 52, 58
arthritis, 250
astronomical scale, 229
astrophysics, 233
ATI powder, 44
atomic collisions, 226
atomic physics, 244
atomic processes, 7
audio-recording, 158
Aufdermauer, Edith, 30
aura, 205, 206, 207
austenite, 131, 146

molybdenum, 18, 116, 174, 177, 178, crystal, 154
moment, 19, 32, 43, 50, 111, 114, 118, 121, 122
momentum, 184, 228, 230, 231; angular, 91, 165, 181, 183; conjugate, 233; linear, 181, 182; rate of change, 246
Moor, Major Edward, 26, 258
Moore, Laurie, 226
Moore, Patrick, 153
morphological change, 147
Morte d'Arthur, 24, 258
Moses, Stainton, 198
moti, 20
motivation, 249
moving target, 56
Mucor hiemalis, 150
Murata, K., 128
Murray, Gilbert, 215
Musasawa, Yasushi, 30
muscular work, 141
mushroom cloud, 139
Mycock, Paul, 146
mycology, 150
Myers, F. W. H., 198, 260
mylar, 252
mystics, Hindu, 199

N., Graham, 176, 238
nail-clippers, 172
National Bureau of Standards, 7
Nature, 170
Nautilus transmissions, 215
NBC, 19, 20, 194, 259
neck, at metal fracture, 16, 118
needle point, 188
Nemeth, David, 30, 52, 100, 155, 194
Nemeth, Mrs, 155, 194
Nemeth, Steven, 30, 52
Nepesh, 223
Neuman, Alan, 19, 122, 194, 201, 211, 259
neutral currents, 229
neutral plane, 78, 78, 126
neutrino, 232
neutron activation analysis, 175, 176
New Horizons Research Foundation, 5, 27, 30
New Otani Hotel, Tokyo, 172
New Scientist, 121
Newtonian mechanics, 228
Newton, Isaac, 9, 228

nibbling, 60
nickel, 116, 173; filament, 133
nickel-titanium alloys, 38
nicking of spoon bowl, 21
Nicola, Nick, 5, 50, 136, 138, 139
Nippon Television, 23, 121
nitinols, 38
no touch, 52, 54, 56, 60, 62, 123, 125, 142, 143, 162, 188
noise: electrical, 52; muscular, 203; psychokinetic, 250
non-locality, 231, 235, 236, 243
North family, 78
North, Sarah, 78
North, Stephen, 17, 20, 30, 39, 54, 56, 58, 62, 63, 71, 76–133 *passim*, 142–5, 153, 158, 161, 162, 179, 180, 181, 195
Novosibirsk, 201, 215
N-rays, 189
nucleus, atomic, 136, 248
nutrient jelly, 150

observable, 238
observation, 228, 239; regression of, 4
observer, 237, 239, 240
occult phenomena, 5
Ochi, Y., 128, 196, 259, 260
Od, 189
Office of Naval Research Laboratories, 27
Ogawa, Y., 260
Ohlsen, 199
ointment, antistatic, 191
Okada, Sachiro, 12
operators, 240
opinion, polarization of, 1, 3, 4
optical fibres, 209; lever, 136
optical phenomena, 20, 246; paranormal 205
Orbito, Alex, 251
O'Regan, Brendan, 9, 12, 18, 136, 258
organisms, living, 4
orgasm, 123
orgone, 189
Orphée, 241
orthogonality, 241, 244; degrees of, 246
orthonormality, 239
Osaki, Toro, 30
Osborne, Charles, 27, 43
oscilloscope, 142
Ossining, 185

151; phenomena, 146; properties, 36, 38, 43
Stuart, A. E. G., 261
Sudre, René, 198, 259
superconductors, 242
superfluids, 242
superlatttice, 176
superluminal signals, 235
Superminds, 28, 258
superposition, 241
surface effects, 5
surface of action, 64, 70, 73, 76, 77, 83, 84, 86, 90, 100, 101, 227, 245, 252; configuration, 71; movement, 71, 73, 77, 85, 86; rotation, 86, 88, 89, 90, 91
surfaces, 129
susceptibility, magnetic, 115, 116
Swann, Ingo, 132
S-wave electron, 232
sweets, 187
swords, 24
syndrome, de la Tourette's, 222
systems, 238, 239, 240

table, glass, 20
table-lifting, 24, 158, 203
tails, 102, 103
Takaoka, A., 128, 259
Tanaka, Seiyuri, 30
Targ, Russell, 14, 27, 28, 183, 218, 224, 258, 260
Tarrytown conference, 14
Taylor, John, 14, 28, 30, 43, 157, 194, 258
technologists, 152
Teflon tube, 177, 178
telecommunication systems, 224
telepathic drawing games, 216, 217
telepathy, 7, 10, 28, 155, 214, 215, 217, 218, 223, 225, 230, 234, 241, 254; electromagnetic interpretation, 224
telephone, 136
teleportation, 3, 25, 27, 129, 149, 165–86 *passim*, 199, 203, 234, 245, 252; delayed, 186; insects, 185; living creatures, 185
television, 14, 15, 19, 20, 28, 56, 152–4, 194, 211, 216, 250, 255
temperature, 228; change, 59, 132; compensation, 132; melting, 41; thermodynamic, 242
templates, 34

terrestrial effect, 64
territory, 75, 184
texts, 163
Thalbourne, M. A., 260
Tharp, David, 211
thermal phenomena, 131, 132; sensor, 133
thermistors, 132,
thermodynamic equilibrium, 134
thermometer, 132
theta-band, 158
thickness decrease, 127
thigh, 73
Thompson, K. F., 42
Thompson, Matthew, 185
thought-photography, 205, 208, 209, 211, 213
threads, 194
thumb, 6, 7, 119, 143
time, 228, 248
time constant, thermal, 103
Time Magazine, 137
tin, 41, 42
tingling, 143, 154
tinned steel strip, 88
tissue, human and sheep, 251
Tocquet, R., 132, 259
toes, 74
Tokofoyu, Melanie, 38
Tokyo Metropolitan University, 192
Tokyo Tower, 213
Tokyo University, 12
Tomczyk, Stanislava, 143
tooth-stoppings, 153
Toronto Society for Psychic Research, 190
torque, 33, 77, 89, 90
torsional stress, 115
torus, 143, 144
touch detection, 161
touch of metal with fingers, 6, 7, 31, 54, 56
touch prevention, 161
training, athletic, 32
trajectories, 168
transducer, 131
transients, electrical, 141
transistor, 147
transition temperature, 38
tribological electrostatic force, 195
trick, *see* conjuring
trombone, 208
tumbler, glass, 172, 173
tungsten, 60